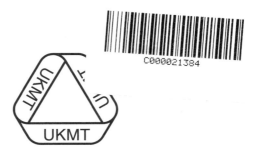

The UK Mathematics Trust

Yearbook

2015 – 2016

This book contains an account of UKMT activities from 1st September 2015 to 31st August 2016. It contains all question papers, solutions and results as well as a variety of other information.

Published by the United Kingdom Mathematics Trust.
School of Mathematics, The University of Leeds, Leeds LS2 9JT
Telephone: 0113 343 2339
E-mail: enquiry@ukmt.org.uk
Website: http://www.ukmt.org.uk

Cover design: – The backdrop is a Penrose tiling whose complexity reflects the activities of the UKMT.

The photographs are

Front Cover:

Certificate winners from Belle Vue Girls' School, Bradford

Back Cover:

UK team at 2016 Balkan Mathematical Olympiad

Team Maths Challenge National Final

ISBN 978-1-906001-32-2

Printed and bound in Great Britain by
H. Charlesworth & Co. Ltd, Wakefield

Contents

This is my first introduction to the UKMT Yearbook as Chairman of the Trust. I am very honoured to be appointed as chair to this wonderful organisation. I was fortunate to attend a school which took the Mathematics Olympiad very seriously, and indeed it supplied several of the UK team members in the 1970s. Sadly I was not one of them! But I gained immeasurably from taking part in these activities and from the enthusiasm of my teachers in promoting them. Thus I was delighted (as well as somewhat overawed) to become part of the UKMT and to be in a position to support its amazing team in their mission to challenge, encourage and support so many of the next generation of UK mathematicians.

This year the trust celebrates its 20th anniversary. It can look back on an extraordinary history of achievement as well as looking forward to playing a central role in the future of UK mathematics. It was a huge pleasure to attend and introduce the Volunteers meeting in October, which celebrated all that the trust has done in these 20 years, and I would personally like to thank all of the volunteers and staff who give their time so generously, and without whom the work of the Trust would not be possible.

The Trust's main activity is of course running the Mathematical Challenges. I am very pleased to report that this year saw our highest ever entry figures across all three challenges, and we are grateful for your support in running these. The number of entries to the Junior Challenge rose from 293,940 to 303,020. For the Intermediate Challenge, the number of entries rose from 259,480 to 262,040. Entries for the Senior Challenge rose from 109,660 to 110,500. In addition the number of participating centres have also risen to record levels, with the Junior rising from 3970 to 4002; Intermediate from 3199 to 3240; and Senior from 2206 to 2223. Both the IMC and the JMC have featured twice in Alex Bellos's puzzle column in the Guardian. Fame indeed! We were pleased to be able to invite more students to participate in the second year of the Junior Kangaroo (5431 students from 1662 schools this year, compared to 5025 from 1636 last year). There was also an increase in the number of teams entering the Team Maths Challenge, with 1770 teams registered to take part in 70 regional heats held between February and April. Of these 88 teams were invited to the TMC National Final held in London in June. I was present at this and can testify to the huge energy and excitement shown by the team members and I especially liked the origami theme for the posters. Congratulations to the winners Westminster Under School.

The UK teams have had an excellent year at international competitions throughout the whole of 2016. The UK team gave an outstanding performance at the Hong Kong IMO, coming joint 7th out of 109 participating nations, returning with two gold and four silver medals. The UK team also came 7th out of 39 participating teams (6th out of 31 official European teams) in the fifth European Girls' Mathematical Olympiad, with one gold, one silver and two bronze medals; and the UK team returned from the Balkan Mathematical Olympiad with two silver and four bronze medals. Let me take this opportunity to hugely congratulate both the team members and also their trainers and supporters for this exceptional performance.

I greatly look forward to my first full year as chair and confidently expect to see even greater successes for the UKMT in 2017 with the prospect of even more competitions ahead!

Prof Chris Budd OBE
University of Bath

Introduction

Foundation of the Trust

National mathematics competitions have existed in the UK for several decades. Up until 1987 the total annual participation was something like 8,000. Then there was an enormous growth, from 24,000 in 1988 to around a quarter of a million in 1995 – without doubt due to the drive, energy and leadership of Dr Tony Gardiner. By the end of this period there were some nine or ten competitions for United Kingdom schools and their students organised by three different bodies: the British Mathematical Olympiad Committee, the National Committee for Mathematical Contests and the UK Mathematics Foundation. During 1995 discussions took place between interested parties which led to agreement to seek a way of setting up a single body to continue and develop these competitions and related activities. This led to the formation of the United Kingdom Mathematics Trust, which was incorporated as a company limited by guarantee in October 1996 and registered with the Charity Commission.

Throughout its existence, the UKMT has continued to nurture and expand the number of competitions. As a result, over six hundred thousand students throughout the UK now participate in the challenges alone, and their teachers (as well as others) not only provide much valued help and encouragement, but also take advantage of the support offered to them by the Trust.

The Royal Institution of Great Britain is the Trust's Patron, and it and the Mathematical Association are Participating Bodies. The Association of Teachers of Mathematics, the Edinburgh Mathematical Society, the Institute of Mathematics and Its Applications, the London Mathematical Society and the Royal Society are all Supporting Bodies.

Aims and Activities of the Trust

According to its constitution, the Trust has a very wide brief, namely "to advance the education of children and young people in mathematics". To attain this, it is empowered to engage in activities ranging from teaching to publishing and lobbying. But its focal point is the organisation of mathematical competitions, from popular mass "challenges" to the selection and training of the British team for the annual International Mathematical Olympiad (IMO).

There are three main challenges, the UK Junior, Intermediate and Senior Mathematical Challenges. The number of challenge entries in 2015-2016 totalled 675,560: once again, a pleasing increase in entry numbers year on year. The challenges were organised by the Challenges Subtrust (CS).

The Challenges are open to all pupils of the appropriate age. Certificates are awarded for the best performances and the most successful participants are encouraged to enter follow-up competitions.

At the junior and intermediate levels, we increased the number of pupils entering follow-up competitions from a total of around 16,600 to a total of around 18,400. The follow-up rounds now consist of the Junior Olympiad and Kangaroo, and a suite of papers forming the Intermediate Olympiad and Kangaroo under the auspices of the Challenges Subtrust.

The British Mathematical Olympiad Committee Subtrust (BMOS) organises two rounds of the British Mathematical Olympiad. Usually about 800 students who have distinguished themselves in the Senior Mathematical Challenge are invited to enter Round 1, leading to about 100 in Round 2. From the latter, around twenty are invited to a training weekend at Trinity College, Cambridge. Additionally, an elite squad, identified largely by performances in the UKMT competitions, is trained at camps and by correspondence courses throughout the year. The UK team is then selected for the annual International Mathematical Olympiad (IMO) which usually takes place in July. Recent IMOs were held as follows: Japan (2003), Athens (2004), Mexico (2005), Slovenia (2006), Vietnam (2007), Madrid (2008), Bremen (2009), Kazakhstan (2010), Amsterdam (2011), Argentina (2012), Colombia (2013), South Africa (2014), Thailand (2015) and Hong Kong (2016). The BMOS also runs a mentoring scheme for high achievers at senior, intermediate and junior levels.

There is a Kangaroo follow-on round at the senior level as well, and over 4,000 pupils are invited to participate each year.

Structure and Membership of the Trust

The governing body of the Trust is its Council. The events have been organised by four Subtrusts who report directly to the Council. The work of the Trust in setting question papers, marking scripts, monitoring competitions, mentoring students and helping in many other ways depends critically on a host of volunteers. A complete list of members of the Trust, its Subtrusts and other volunteers appears at the end of this publication.

Challenges Office Staff

Rachel Greenhalgh continues in her role as Director of the Trust and was joined by the Deputy Director, Steven O'Hagan. They were ably supported by the Maths Challenges Office staff of Nicky Bray, Janet Clark, Gerard Cummings, Sara Liptrot, Heather Macklin, Shona Raffle-Edwards and Jo Williams. Beverley Detoeuf continues as Packing Office Manager and leads the packing and processing team of Aurelija Maciuniene, Rachael Raby-Cox, Stewart Ramsay, Alison Steggall and Tabitha Taylor, ably assisted by Mary Roberts, Packing Office Supervisor.

An outline of the events

This is a brief description of the challenges, their follow-up competitions and other activities. Much fuller information can be found later in the book.

Junior competitions

The UK Junior Mathematical Challenge, typically held on the last Thursday in April, is a one hour, 25 question, multiple choice paper for pupils up to and including:

Y8 in England and Wales; S2 in Scotland, and Y9 in Northern Ireland.

Pupils enter their personal details and answers on a special answer sheet for machine reading. The questions are set so that the first 15 should be accessible to all participants whereas the remaining 10 are more testing.

Five marks are awarded for each correct answer to the first 15 questions and six marks are awarded for each correct answer to the rest. Each incorrect answer to questions 16–20 loses 1 mark and each incorrect answer to questions 21–25 loses 2 marks. Penalty marking is used to discourage guessing.

Certificates are awarded on a proportional basis:– Gold about 6%, Silver about 14% and Bronze about 20% of all entrants. Each centre also receives one 'Best in School Certificate'. A 'Best in Year Certificate' is awarded to the highest scoring candidate in each year group, in each school. There is now a downloadable Certificate of Participation which may be given to all candidates.

The follow-on rounds are the Junior Mathematical Olympiad and Kangaroo (JMOK) which are held around 6 weeks after the JMC. Between 1,000-1,200 high scorers in the JMC are invited to take part in the Olympiad; the next 5,500 or so are invited to take part in the Kangaroo.

The Olympiad is a two-hour paper with two sections. Section A contains ten questions and pupils are required to give the answer only. Section B contains six questions for which full written answers are required. It is made clear to candidates that they are not expected to complete all of Section B and that little credit will be given to fragmentary answers. Gold, silver and bronze medals are awarded to very good candidates. In 2016, a total of 220 medals was awarded. The top 25% candidates got Certificates of Distinction. Most of the rest receive a Merit and of the rest, those who had qualified for the Olympiad automatically via the JMC received a Certificate of Qualification. In addition, the top 50 students were given book prizes.

The Junior Mathematical Kangaroo is a one-hour multiple-choice paper, with 25 questions (like the JMC, but more challenging!). Certificates of Merit are awarded to the top 25% and certificates of Qualification to everyone else who takes part.

Intermediate competitions

The UK Intermediate Mathematical Challenge is organised in a very similar way to the Junior Challenge. One difference is that the age range goes up to Y11 in England and Wales, to S4 in Scotland and Y12 in Northern Ireland. The other difference is the timing; the IMC is held on the first Thursday in February. All other arrangements are as in the JMC.

There are five follow-up competitions under the overall title 'Intermediate Mathematical Olympiad and Kangaroo' (IMOK). Between 400 and 550 in each of Years 9, 10 and 11 (English style) sit an Olympiad paper (Cayley, Hamilton and Maclaurin respectively). In 2016, each of these was a two-hour paper and contained six questions all requiring full written solutions. A total of around 10,400 pupils from the three year groups took part in a Kangaroo paper. In the Intermediate Kangaroo papers, which last an hour, there are 25 multiple-choice questions. The last ten questions are more testing than the first fifteen and correct answers gain six marks as opposed to five. Penalty marking is not applied. The same Kangaroo paper (designated 'Pink') was taken by pupils in Years 10 and 11 and a different one, 'Grey', by pupils in Year 9. In 2016, the Olympiads and Kangaroos were sat on Thursday 10th March and Thursday 17th March respectively. In the Olympiads, the top 25% of candidates got Certificates of Distinction. Most of the rest receive a Merit and of the rest, those who had qualified for the Olympiad automatically via the IMC received a Certificate of Qualification. In the Kangaroos, the top 25% got a Merit and the rest a Certificate of Qualification. All Olympiad and Kangaroo candidates received a 'Kangaroo gift'; a specially designed UKMT key fob. In addition, the top 50 students in each year group in the Olympiad papers were given a book. Performance in the Olympiad papers and the IMC was a major factor in determining pupils to be invited to one of the UKMT summer schools early in July.

Senior competitions

In 2015, the UK Senior Mathematical Challenge was held on Thursday 5th November. Like the other Challenges, it is a 25 question, multiple choice paper marked in the same way as the Junior and Intermediate Challenges. However, it lasts 1½ hours. Certificates (including Best in School) are awarded as with the other Challenges except that we award Gold to 10%, Silver to 20% and Bronze to 30%. The follow-up competitions are the British Mathematical Olympiads 1 and 2 (organised by the British Mathematical Olympiad Subtrust) and the Senior Kangaroo.

6

The first Olympiad stage, BMO1, was held on Friday 27th November 2015. About 800 are usually invited to take part. The paper lasted 3½ hours and contained six questions to which full written solutions are required.

About 100 high scorers are then invited to sit BMO2, which was held on Thursday 28th January 2016. It also lasted 3½ hours but contained four, very demanding, questions.

The results of BMO2 are used to select a group of students to attend a Training Session at Trinity College, Cambridge in March or April. As well as being taught more mathematics and trying numerous challenging problems, this group sits a 4½ hour 'mock' Olympiad paper. On the basis of this and all other relevant information, a group of about eight is selected to take part in correspondence courses and assignments which eventually produce the UK Olympiad Team of six to go forward to the International Mathematical Olympiad in July.

In 2015, the Senior Kangaroo paper, for pupils who were close to being eligible for BMO1, was held on the same day, with the number of participants rising to 4,000.

The growth of the Challenges

In the 2005 UKMT Yearbook, we showed the growth of the Challenges since UKMT was established and this has now been updated. The graphs below show two easily identifiable quantities, the number of schools and the number of entries. In each case, the lines, from top to bottom, represent the Junior, Intermediate and Senior Challenges. As those involved in the UKMT firmly believe that the Challenges are a very worthwhile endeavour, we hope that the upward trends are continued.

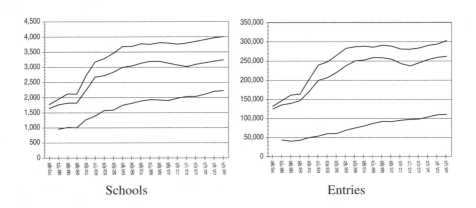

Schools   Entries

Team Maths Challenge and Senior Team Maths Challenge

This event is the successor of the Enterprising Mathematics UK which was run in conjunction with the IMO in 2002. A team consists of four pupils who are in Year 9 (English style) or below with at most two members being in Year 9. In 2016, over 1650 teams took part in Regional Finals and 88 schools competed in the National Final held in the grand surroundings of the Lindley Hall, part of the prestigious Royal Horticultural Halls in Westminster, London, on Monday 20th June.

In addition, over 1200 schools took part in the Senior Team Maths Challenge which is aimed at students studying maths beyond GCSE. The final, which involved 86 teams, was held at the Lindley Hall, part of the Royal Horticultural Halls, London, on Tuesday 2nd February 2016. Each team is made up of four student from years 11, 12 and 13 (S5 and S6 in Scotland, years 12, 13 and 14 in Northern Ireland) with a maximum of two older students per team.

Report from the Director

Thank you for all your help and support in making 2015/16 a successful year for the Trust. It is particularly pleasing to see so many students were able to participate in the Mathematical Challenges, and we are grateful for your work in organising these activities within school.

I hope you enjoy reading about the work of the Trust and sharing the rich mathematical problems contained in the book with those around you. Whilst the Yearbook provides a fantastic overview of our activities, it perhaps is difficult to convey how the Challenges and our other activities can impact on individual lives. We really value feedback from teachers, and enjoy hearing about the impact of our work, such as:

- The teacher from a girls' comprehensive school who took the time to tell us that through our Challenges, the profile of maths has been raised within the school, and students' confidence has increased;
- Sixth-form college students from the north of England who after a team challenge talked non-stop on the way home about the problems, and reflected on how they could improve the way they worked as a group and in pairs;
- The student from a school in Dorset whose experience at a UKMT summer school completely changed the way he thought about maths, and has inspired him to want to do a maths degree at university;

- The girl who is really enjoying the mentoring scheme and the opportunity to explore mathematics way off syllabus, and who tells us our activities have made such a positive and long lasting impact on her life in school and her confidence outside;
- The Headteacher who wrote to us to tell us they believe the Challenges are of significant benefit in encouraging and enthusing their pupils;
- The recognition of the work of the Trust in the 2016 education White Paper.

Please do continue to let us know how we can and do help, or if you feel there are areas of our work you think we can improve.

Our thanks go to our key supporters and donors, in particular to the Institute and Faculty of Actuaries which continues to support the Challenges, and to Oxford Asset Management which supports our mentoring schemes and IMO team. We were also fortunate and grateful to receive donations large and small via www.donate.ukmt.org.uk.

As we approach our 20th birthday, my final thanks are saved for our wonderful group of volunteers and staff who I work with throughout the year and without whom we could not run any of our activities or events. Our volunteers do so much on our behalf, and I would like to publicly thank them all for their commitment and enthusiasm throughout the year. If you would like to join this remarkable group, please contact us via enquiry@ukmt.org.uk. We would love to have you on board!

Rachel Greenhalgh
director@ukmt.org.uk

 Institute
and Faculty
of Actuaries

Profile

The Institute and Faculty of Actuaries (IFoA) is the UK's only chartered professional body dedicated to educating, developing and regulating actuaries based both in the UK and internationally.

What is an actuary?

Actuaries are experts in risk management. They use their mathematical skills to help measure the probability and risk of future events. They can work in lots of different industries like healthcare, pensions, insurance, banking and investments. The decisions that actuaries make in their roles can have a major financial impact on a company or a client, so it's important and very valuable work.

It is a global profession with internationally-recognised qualifications. It is also very highly regarded, in the way that medicine and law are. It is one of the most diverse, exciting and rewarding jobs in the world. In fact, due to the difficult exams and the expertise required, being an actuary carries quite a reputation.

How do I become an actuary?

To qualify as an actuary you need to complete the IFoA's exams. Most actuarial trainees take the exams whilst working for an actuarial employer once they have finished school or university. Exemptions from some of the exams may be awarded to students who have studied to an appropriate standard in a relevant degree, or have studied at Postgraduate level. The Fellowship qualification typically takes three to six years. Those on a graduate actuarial trainee programme can expect to earn around £35,000 a year. This will increase to well over £100,000 as you gain more experience and seniority.

Have you considered the CAA qualification?

The Certified Actuarial Analyst (CAA) qualification is a new qualification that we have launched. Do you love maths and problem solving? It's available to anyone with an aptitude for maths and problem solving and wants to use their great skills in the financial sector. Student and qualified CAAs will provide support in teams where the technical application of maths and risk modelling is essential to business success. It's not targeted at, nor does it specialise in, any particular business sector. What it does provide you with is a strong relevant, mathematical base and the tools and techniques which will open job opportunities for you as you progress in your career. It will take you two to three years to complete the six exams and one year of professional skills.

Do you not want to go to university?

Well, we have relationships with employers who offer apprenticeship opportunities, both at CAA and Fellowship level. You will leave school and enter straight into the work place, learning how to work in an office, learning actuarial techniques, taking exams and best of all... earning a salary! To find out more, see our Directory of Actuarial Employers or our website.

International outlook

The IFoA qualification is already highly valued throughout the world, with 42% of its members based outside the UK. Mutual recognition agreements with other international actuarial bodies facilitate the ability for actuaries to move and work in other parts of the world and create a truly global profession.

For more information on the qualifications and career path visit our website - http://www.actuaries.org.uk/becoming-actuary or join us on Facebook – www.be-an-actuary.co.uk

O*x*FORD
ASSET MANAGEMENT

√ HIGH LEVEL
COMPLE*x*ITY

We are looking for people who can get to the root of high level challenges using innovative mathematical solutions.
Could this be you?

OxFORD ASSET MANAGEMENT is an investment management company with a quantitative focus, based in central Oxford. We invest and trade world-wide, applying computational models to financial markets, analysing a range of data and information.

Our team of over 80 includes researchers, who identify opportunities and build our quantitative models and strategies, software engineers, who design the software that drives our investment strategies, and IT infrastructure specialists, who design and support our infrastructure.

We have a number of opportunities for talented mathematicians, logicians and computer scientists to join our team in the following roles:

- Researchers
- Data Analysts
- Systems Engineers
- Software Engineers
- Logic (Prolog) Programmers

We offer graduate and post-graduate roles, as well as internships for gifted students. For more information, please get in touch at recruitment@oxam.com.

O*x*FORD
ASSET MANAGEMENT

The Junior Mathematical Challenge and its follow-up events

The Junior Mathematical Challenge was held on Thursday 28th April 2016 and over 263,000 pupils took part. Approximately 1000 pupils were invited to take part in the Junior Mathematical Olympiad, and a further 5500 to take part in the Junior Mathematical Kangaroo, both of which were held on Tuesday 14th June. In the following pages, we shall show the question paper and solutions leaflet for all of these.

We start with the JMC paper, the front of which is shown below in a slightly reduced format.

UK JUNIOR MATHEMATICAL CHALLENGE

THURSDAY 28th APRIL 2016

Organised by the **United Kingdom Mathematics Trust**
from the School of Mathematics, University of Leeds

Institute
and Faculty
of Actuaries

RULES AND GUIDELINES (to be read before starting)

1. Do not open the paper until the Invigilator tells you to do so.

2. Time allowed: **1 hour**.
   No answers, or personal details, may be entered after the allowed hour is over.

3. The use of rough paper is allowed; **calculators** and measuring instruments are **forbidden**.

4. Candidates in England and Wales must be in School Year 8 or below.
   Candidates in Scotland must be in S2 or below.
   Candidates in Northern Ireland must be in School Year 9 or below.

5. **Use B or HB non-propelling pencil only**. Mark *at most one* of the options A, B, C, D, E on the Answer Sheet for each question. Do not mark more than one option.

6. *Do not expect to finish the whole paper in 1 hour.* Concentrate first on Questions 1-15. When you have checked your answers to these, have a go at some of the later questions.

7. Five marks are awarded for each correct answer to Questions 1-15.
   Six marks are awarded for each correct answer to Questions 16-25.
   Each incorrect answer to Questions 16-20 loses 1 mark.
   Each incorrect answer to Questions 21-25 loses 2 marks.

8. Your Answer Sheet will be read only by a *dumb machine*. **Do not write or doodle on the sheet except to mark your chosen options**. The machine 'sees' all black pencil markings even if they are in the wrong places. If you mark the sheet in the wrong place, or leave bits of rubber stuck to the page, the machine will 'see' a mark and interpret this mark in its own way.

9. The questions on this paper challenge you to **think**, not to guess. You get more marks, and more satisfaction, by doing one question carefully than by guessing lots of answers. The UK JMC is about solving interesting problems, not about lucky guessing.

The UKMT is a registered charity
http://www.ukmt.org.uk

1. Which of the following is closest to zero?

   A $6 + 5 + 4$ B $6 + 5 - 4$ C $6 + 5 \times 4$ D $6 - 5 \times 4$ E $6 \times 5 \div 4$

2. What number is twenty-one less than sixty thousand?

   A 59 979   B 59 981   C 57 900   D 40 001   E 39 000

3. One lap of a standard running track is 400 m.
   How many laps does each athlete run in a 5000 m race?

   A 4   B 5   C 8   D 10   E $12\frac{1}{2}$

4. In January 1859, an eight-year-old boy dropped a newly-hatched eel into a well in Sweden (apparently in order to keep the water free of insects). The eel, named Åle, finally died in August 2014.
   How many years old was Åle when it died?

   A 135   B 145   C 155   D 165   E 175

5. What is the value of $\frac{1}{25} + 0.25$?

   A 0.29   B 0.3   C 0.35   D 0.50   E 0.65

6. Gill is now 28 years old and is a teacher of Mathematics at a school which has 600 pupils. There are 30 more girls than boys at the school.
   How many girls are at Gill's school?

   A 270   B 300   C 315   D 330   E 345

7. A distance of 8 km is approximately 5 miles.
   Which of the following is closest to 1.2 km?

   A 0.75 miles   B 1 mile   C 1.2 miles   D 1.6 miles   E 1.9 miles

8. What is the value of $\dfrac{2 + 4 + 6 + 8 + 10 + 12 + 14 + 16 + 18 + 20}{1 + 2 + 3 + 4 + 5 + 6 + 7 + 8 + 9 + 10}$?

   A 2   B 10   C 20   D 40   E 1024

9. One of the three symbols $+$, $-$, $\times$ is inserted somewhere between the digits of 2016 to give a new number. For example, $20 - 16$ gives 4.
   How many of the following four numbers can be obtained in this way?

   36   195   207   320

   A 0   B 1   C 2   D 3   E 4

10. A square is folded exactly in half and then in half again.
    Which of the following could not be the resulting shape?

    A   B   C   D   E

11. Which of the following statements is false?

   A 12 is a multiple of 2   B 123 is a multiple of 3   C 1234 is a multiple of 4
   D 12 345 is a multiple of 5   E 123 456 is a multiple of 6

12. The musical *Rent* contains a song that starts 'Five hundred and twenty five thousand six hundred minutes'.

   Which of the following is closest to this length of time?

   A a week   B a year   C a decade   D a century   E a millennium

13. The diagram shows five circles placed at the corners of a pentagon. The numbers 1, 2, 3, 4, 5 are placed in the circles shown, one in each, so that the numbers in adjacent circles always differ by more than 1.

   What is the sum of the numbers in the two circles adjacent to the circle which contains the number 5?

   A 3   B 4   C 5   D 6   E 7

14. In the diagram, $AB = AC$ and D is a point on AC such that $BD = BC$. Angle BAC is $40°$.

   What is angle ABD ?

   A $15°$ B $20°$ C $25°$ D $30°$ E $35°$

15. How many of these four expressions are perfect squares?

   $$1^3 + 2^3 \qquad 1^3 + 2^3 + 3^3 \qquad 1^3 + 2^3 + 3^3 + 4^3 \qquad 1^3 + 2^3 + 3^3 + 4^3 + 5^3$$

   A 0   B 1   C 2   D 3   E 4

16. Each of the nine small squares in this grid can be coloured completely black or completely white.

   What is the largest number of squares that can be coloured black so that the design created has rotational symmetry of order 2, but no lines of symmetry?

   A 4   B 5   C 6   D 7   E 8

17. In a group of 48 children, the ratio of boys to girls is 3 : 5.

   How many boys must join the group to make the ratio of boys to girls 5 : 3?

   A 48   B 40   C 32   D 24   E 8

18. In the addition sum shown, each letter represents a different non-zero digit. What digit does X represent?

   A 1   B 3   C 5   D 7   E 9

   $$\begin{array}{r} S \ E \ E \\ + \ S \ E \ E \\ \hline A \ X \ E \ S \end{array}$$

19. Three boxes under my stairs contain apples or pears or both. Each box contains the same number of pieces of fruit. The first box contains all twelve of the apples and one-ninth of the pears.

   How many pieces of fruit are there in each box?

   A 14   B 16   C 18   D 20   E 36

20. A cyclic quadrilateral has all four vertices on the circumference of a circle. Brahmagupta (598–670AD) gave the following formula for the area, A, of a cyclic quadrilateral whose edges have lengths a, b, c, d : $A = \sqrt{(s - a)(s - b)(s - c)(s - d)}$, where s is half of the perimeter of the quadrilateral.

What is the area of the cyclic quadrilateral with sides of length 4 cm, 5 cm, 7 cm and 10 cm?

A $6 \,\text{cm}^2$ B $13 \,\text{cm}^2$ C $26 \,\text{cm}^2$ D $30 \,\text{cm}^2$ E $36 \,\text{cm}^2$

---

21. The diagram shows a pentagon drawn on a square grid. All vertices of the pentagon and triangle are grid points.

What fraction of the area of the pentagon is shaded?

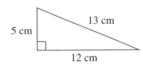

A $\dfrac{2}{7}$ B $\dfrac{1}{3}$ C $\dfrac{2}{5}$ D $\dfrac{1}{4}$ E $\dfrac{2}{9}$

22. Four copies of the triangle shown are joined together, without gaps or overlaps, to make a parallelogram.

What is the largest possible perimeter of the parallelogram?

A 46 cm   B 52 cm   C 58 cm   D 62 cm   E 76 cm

23. The diagram shows the first few squares of a 'spiral' sequence of squares. All but the first three squares have been numbered. After the first six squares, the sequence is continued by placing the next square alongside three existing squares – the largest existing square and two others.

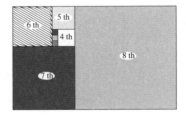

The three smallest squares have sides of length 1. What is the side length of the 12th square?

A 153   B 123   C 83   D 53   E 13

24. Part of a wall is to be decorated with a row of four square tiles. Three different colours of tiles are available and there are at least two tiles of each colour available. Tiles of all three colours must be used.

In how many ways can the row of four tiles be chosen?

A 12   B 18   C 24   D 36   E 48

25. Beatrix places dominoes on a 5 × 5 board, either horizontally or vertically, so that each domino covers two small squares. She stops when she cannot place another domino, as in the example shown in the diagram.

When Beatrix stops, what is the largest possible number of squares that may still be uncovered?

A 4   B 5   C 6   D 7   E 8

The JMC solutions

The usual solutions leaflet was issued.

UK JUNIOR MATHEMATICAL CHALLENGE

THURSDAY 28th APRIL 2016

Organised by the **United Kingdom Mathematics Trust**
from the School of Mathematics, University of Leeds

http://www.ukmt.org.uk

Institute
and Faculty
of Actuaries

SOLUTIONS LEAFLET

This solutions leaflet for the JMC is sent in the hope that it might provide all concerned with some alternative solutions to the ones they have obtained. It is not intended to be definitive. The organisers would be very pleased to receive alternatives created by candidates.

For reasons of space, these solutions are necessarily brief. There are more in-depth, extended solutions available on the UKMT website, which include some exercises for further investigation:

http://www.ukmt.org.uk/

The UKMT is a registered charity

1. **B** The values of the expressions are: A 15, B 7, C 26, D −14, E $7\frac{1}{2}$. Of these, 7 is closest to 0.

2. **A** $60\,000 - 21 = 60\,000 - 20 - 1 = 59\,980 - 1 = 59\,979$.

3. **E** The number of laps is $5000 \div 400 = 50 \div 4 = 12\frac{1}{2}$.

4. **C** There are 41 years from January 1859 to January 1900 and a further 114 years to January 2014. So, since Åle died in August 2014, its age in years when it died was $41 + 114 = 155$.

5. **A** $\frac{1}{25} = \frac{4}{100} = 0.04$. So $\frac{1}{25} + 0.25 = 0.04 + 0.25 = 0.29$.

6. **C** Let there be g girls in Gill's school. Then there are $(g - 30)$ boys at the school. So $g + g - 30 = 600$. Therefore $2g = 630$, that is $g = 315$.

7. **A** As a distance of 8 km is roughly equal to 5 miles, $1.2\,\text{km} \approx \frac{1.2 \times 5}{8}\,\text{miles} = \frac{6}{8}\,\text{miles} = 0.75\,\text{miles}$.

8. **A** By factorising the numerator, it is seen that;
$$\frac{2+4+6+8+10+12+14+16+18+20}{1+2+3+4+5+6+7+8+9+10} = \frac{2(1+2+3+4+5+6+7+8+9+10)}{1+2+3+4+5+6+7+8+9+10} = 2.$$

9. **E** All four numbers may be obtained: $36 = 20 + 16$; $195 = 201 - 6$; $207 = 201 + 6$; $320 = 20 \times 16$.

10. **D** When a square is folded exactly in half, the shape obtained is a rectangle or a right-angled isosceles triangle. So to determine which of the given shapes can be obtained from a second fold we need to test which shapes form a rectangle or a right-angled isosceles triangle when joined with the image formed when the shape is reflected about an edge. Of the options given, only D does not do this. Of the others, shape A is formed by using fold line 1 first, followed by fold line 3. For shape B the fold lines are 3 followed by 4. For shapes C and E, which are similar, the fold lines are 2 followed by 5.

11. **C** A number is divisible by 4 if and only if its last two digits are divisible by 4. Since 34 is not divisible by 4, we deduce that 1234 is not a multiple of 4. Of the other options, 12 is even and so is a multiple of 2; the sum of the digits of 123 is 6, which is a multiple of 3, so 123 is a multiple of 3; 12 345 has a units digit of 5 and so is a multiple of 5. Finally, 123 456 is even and has a digit sum of 21, a multiple of 3. So 123 456 is a multiple of 2 and of 3 and is therefore a multiple of 6.

12. **B** Five hundred and twenty five thousand six hundred minutes is equal to
$$\frac{525\,600}{60}\,\text{hours} = 8760\,\text{hours} = \frac{8760}{24}\,\text{days} = 365\,\text{days}.$$
So the length of time in the song is the number of minutes in a year, unless it is a leap year.

13. **C** The position of the 5 is immaterial to the question asked, so let it be placed in the top circle. Now 4 differs by 1 from 5 so neither a nor d equals 4. Therefore either $b = 4$ or $c = 4$. It doesn't matter which it is, because the answer will be symmetric. So let $b = 4$. Since 3 differs by 1 from 4, neither a nor c can be 3, so $d = 3$. This leaves us with 1 and 2 to place. As 2 cannot be next to 3, $c \neq 2$ so $c = 1$ and $a = 2$. Therefore the sum of the numbers in the two circles adjacent to the circle containing 5 is $3 + 2 = 5$.

14. **D** As $AB = AC$, triangle ABC is isosceles. So $\angle ABC = \angle ACB = \frac{1}{2}(180° - 40°) = 70°$ as $\angle BAC = 40°$ and the angle sum of a triangle is $180°$. Triangle BCD is also isosceles as $BD = BC$, so $\angle BDC = \angle BCD = 70°$. Considering triangle ABD: $\angle BDC = \angle DAB + \angle ABD$ as an exterior angle of a triangle is equal to the sum of the two interior opposite angles. So $\angle ABD = \angle BDC - \angle DAB = 70° - 40° = 30°$.

15. E All four expressions are perfect squares: $1^3 + 2^3 = 1 + 8 = 9 = 3^2$;
$1^3 + 2^3 + 3^3 = 1 + 8 + 27 = 36 = 6^2$; $1^3 + 2^3 + 3^3 + 4^3 = 1 + 8 + 27 + 64 = 100$
$= 10^2$; $1^3 + 2^3 + 3^3 + 4^3 + 5^3 = 1 + 8 + 27 + 64 + 125 = 225 = 15^2$.
(It is not a coincidence that all four expressions are squares: the sum of the
cubes of the first n integers is equal to the square of the sum of the first n
integers for all positive integers n. For example: $1^3 = 1^2$; $1^3 + 2^3 = (1 + 2)^2$;
$1^3 + 2^3 + 3^3 = (1 + 2 + 3)^2$; $1^3 + 2^3 + 3^3 + 4^3 = (1 + 2 + 3 + 4)^2$ *etc.)*

16. B We imagine all the squares being black and consider
changing as few as possible to white in order to satisfy the
conditions required. First note that the colour of the centre
square has no effect on the symmetries involved. So we will
leave that black. If we change one corner to white, the opposite corner must also
be changed to white to give the rotational symmetry. The diagram still has
reflective symmetry. If you instead try changing a non-corner square to white,
the opposite one must be. And you again have reflective symmetry. That shows
we need to change more than two squares. The rotational symmetry means that
the next possiblity is to change 4 squares to white. And the diagram shown
shows that it is possible, with four white squares, to have rotational but not
reflective symmetry. That means that, in the problem as stated, the maximum
number of black squares is 5.

17. C Initially there are 48 children of whom $\frac{3}{8}$ are boys and $\frac{5}{8}$ are girls, so there are 18
boys and 30 girls. When more boys join, there are still 30 girls but now they
form $\frac{3}{8}$ of the total. So the total number of pupils is now $\frac{8}{3} \times 30 = 80$, of whom
$80 - 30 = 50$ are boys. Hence the number of boys joining is $50 - 18 = 32$.

18. D First note that when two numbers are added together the only possible carry
from any column is 1. Now, looking at the tens column of the sum, we see that
$E + E$ leaves a total of E in the column. Since E is non-zero, the only way that
this can happen is that there is a carry of 1 from the units column. So we have
$1 + E + E = 10 + E$, so $1 + E = 10$, that is $E = 9$. Looking at the units column
we see that $E + E = 18$, so $S = 8$ and there is a carry of 1 to the tens column.
The addition sum may now be solved: $899 + 899 = 1798$. So $X = 7$.

19. B Let p be the total number of pears. Then $12 + \frac{p}{9} = \frac{1}{2}\left(p - \frac{p}{9}\right) = \frac{4p}{9}$. So
$12 = \frac{3p}{9} = \frac{p}{3}$. Therefore $p = 3 \times 12 = 36$. So the number of pieces of fruit in
each box is $\frac{12 + 36}{3} = 16$.

20. E The length of s, half the perimeter of the cyclic quadrilateral, is
$\frac{1}{2}(4 + 5 + 7 + 10)$ cm $= 13$ cm. So the required area, in cm^2, is
$\sqrt{(13-4)(13-5)(13-7)(13-10)} = \sqrt{9 \times 8 \times 6 \times 3} = \sqrt{9 \times 144} = 3 \times 12 = 36$.

21. A The area of the shaded triangle is $\frac{1}{2} \times 3 \times 6 = 9$. The area of the square grid
is $6 \times 6 = 36$, and the area of the triangle which is not part of the area of the
pentagon is $\frac{1}{2} \times 3 \times 3 = \frac{9}{2}$. So the area of the pentagon is $36 - \frac{9}{2} = \frac{63}{2}$.
Hence the required fraction is $9 \div \frac{63}{2} = 9 \times \frac{2}{63} = \frac{2}{7}$.

22. **E**   In order to join the four triangles together it is required to join together at least three pairs of edges, which consequently are not part of the perimeter of the resulting parallelogram. The four triangles have a total of 12 edges, so the maximum number of edges which 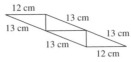 can be part of the perimeter of the parallelogram is $12 - 3 \times 2 = 6$. For the perimeter to be as large as possible, all four 13 cm edges should be included together with two of the 12 cm edges, if this is possible. The diagram shows how it may be accomplished. So the largest possible perimeter is $(4 \times 13 + 2 \times 12)\,\text{cm} = 76\,\text{cm}$.

23. **B**   Note first that the fourth square has side length 3, the fifth square has side length 4 and the sixth square has side length 7. As described in the question, the seventh square is placed alongside the sixth square, the fourth square and one of the first three unit squares. However, it may be seen that the side length of the seventh square is equal to the sum of the side lengths of the fifth and sixth squares, which is $4 + 7 = 11$. Similarly, the eighth square is placed along the fourth, fifth and seventh squares, but its side length is the sum of the side lengths of the sixth and seventh squares, which is $7 + 11 = 18$. The spiral sequence continues in the same way and therefore the side length of any subsequent square may be calculated by adding together the side lengths of the two previous squares in the sequence. So from the fourth square onwards the side lengths of the squares are 3, 4, 7, 11, 18, 29, 47, 76, 123, ... Hence the side length of the twelfth square is 123.

(All of the positive integers in the sequence from the side length of the fourth square onwards are members of the sequence of Lucas numbers – a Fibonacci sequence with first term 2 and second term 1.)

24. **D**   First note that as there are four tiles to be placed and all three colours must be used, every arrangement of tiles consists of two of one colour and one each of the other two colours. Let the colours be R, G and B and consider the arrangements in which there are two tiles of colour R. These two tiles may be placed in six different ways: RR**, R*R*, R**R, *RR*, *R*R and **RR. For each of these arrangements of R tiles, there are two possible ways of placing the remaining G tile and B tile – the G tile may go in the first remaining space or the second remaining space and then there remains only one space for the B tile. So the number of arrangements in which there are two R tiles is $2 \times 6 = 12$. By the same reasoning, we see that there are 12 different arrangements in which there are two G tiles and 12 different arrangements in which there are two B tiles. So the total number of different arrangements is $3 \times 12 = 36$.

25. **D**   First note that there are 25 squares on the board. As each domino occupies two squares, the number of squares left uncovered must be odd. The diagram on the right shows that it is possible for Beatrix to place the dominoes so that there are seven uncovered spaces when it is not possible for her to place any more dominoes.
Of the options given, it is not possible to obtain eight uncovered spaces as the number of them must be odd and it has been shown that seven uncovered spaces is possible so the correct answer is seven.

(For a proof that it is not possible to obtain more than seven uncovered spaces, please see the extended solutions on the UKMT website.)

The JMC answers

The table below shows the proportion of pupils' choices. The correct answer is shown in bold. [The percentages are rounded to the nearest whole number.]

Qn	A	B	C	D	E	Blank
1	0	**28**	2	56	12	1
2	**95**	2	0	0	1	1
3	0	1	2	2	**93**	1
4	1	3	**89**	4	1	1
5	**50**	4	3	31	9	3
6	4	1	**50**	41	1	2
7	**65**	12	4	8	6	4
8	**83**	3	4	4	2	3
9	4	8	23	22	**38**	4
10	9	12	8	**60**	8	2
11	1	7	**78**	1	11	2
12	20	**52**	12	7	5	3
13	8	9	**51**	12	14	6
14	10	25	12	**30**	14	9
15	12	17	25	18	**19**	8
16	14	**21**	10	10	5	40
17	4	4	**38**	18	5	31
18	4	9	7	**22**	5	52
19	10	**24**	8	4	5	48
20	2	4	11	4	**11**	66
21	**7**	12	8	6	4	63
22	8	9	9	8	**6**	61
23	3	**12**	5	5	3	70
24	10	8	9	**7**	4	63
25	9	12	6	**8**	3	62

JMC 2016: Some comments on the pupils' choices of answers as expressed in the feedback letter to schools

It was good to see the number of pupils who achieved very high scores. They will be invited to take part in either the Junior Mathematical Olympiad (JMO) or Junior Kangaroo follow up competitions, depending on their scores. We hope that their excellent achievement in the Junior Mathematical Challenge will gain them appropriate recognition and congratulations in your school.

It was good to see that the average score this year of around 50 was higher than last year. The performance of pupils on many of the early questions was encouraging. However, there were two exceptions. As these are questions dealing with basic numeracy, this is a concern.

It may be that pupils rush into Question 1 before their brains are completely focused on mathematics. Perhaps this explains the worrying outcome on this question, which fewer than 30% of pupils nationally answered correctly.

From the table enclosed with your results you will be able to judge the performance of your own pupils. If many of them chose the wrong option D, we hope you will find the time to emphasize to them where they went wrong.

It is a standard convention (often known as BIDMAS) that in evaluating an expression such as $6 - 5 \times 4$, the multiplication is carried out before the subtraction so that $6 - 5 \times 4 = 6 - 20 = -14$. However it looks as though half of all the pupils evaluated the expression in option D as $(6 - 5) \times 4 = 1 \times 4 = 4$, and so thought this had the value closest to 1.

If many of your pupils made this mistake, it would be a good exercise for them to try this sum on their calculators. They should all obtain the correct answer. This might help to convince them that 'multiplications before additions and subtractions' is the standard convention. The Extended Solutions to the JMC paper provide some more exercises for your pupils on this topic. If they evaluate the expression given in Exercise 1.1 (d) correctly, they should then be asked to find an expression of a similar kind for next year. The Extended Solutions may be downloaded from the UKMT homepage or (along with the short solutions) from our Junior Challenge page.

The other easy question with a disappointing outcome was Question 5. Although just over half the pupils nationally got this question right, we hoped for an even better performance. It might prove valuable to have a classroom discussion of how it can be seen that option D could not possibly be correct.

The profile of marks obtained is shown below.

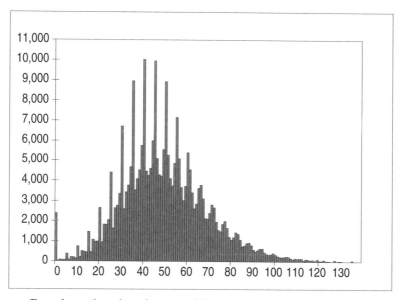

Bar chart showing the actual frequencies in the 2016 JMC

On the basis of the standard proportions used by the UKMT, the cut-off marks were set at

GOLD – 81 or over   SILVER – 65 to 80   BRONZE – 51 to 64

A sample of one of the certificates is shown on the next page.

The follow-up round to the Junior Challenge consists of the Junior Olympiad and Kangaroo (JMOK).

Candidates who scored 113 or more in the Junior Challenge automatically qualified for the Olympiad, and 986 were invited via this route. As with our other Olympiads, schools were allowed to enter non-automatic candidates on payment of a fee. The number who entered by this route was 195.

Candidates who scored 93 to 112 were invited to sit the multiple-choice Junior Kangaroo. There were 5,427 automatic entries; we do not accept discretionary (paid-for) entries for Kangaroo competitions.

UK Junior Mathematical Challenge
2016

of

received a

GOLD CERTIFICATE

Institute
and Faculty
of Actuaries

Professor Chris Budd, OBE
Chairman, United Kingdom Mathematics Trust

THE UNITED KINGDOM JUNIOR MATHEMATICAL CHALLENGE

The Junior Mathematical Challenge (JMC) is run by the UK Mathematics Trust. The JMC encourages mathematical reasoning, precision of thought, and fluency in using basic mathematical techniques to solve interesting problems. It is aimed at pupils in years 7 and 8 in England and Wales, S1 and S2 in Scotland and years 8 and 9 in Northern Ireland. The problems on the JMC are designed to make students think. Most are accessible, yet challenge those with more experience; they are also meant to be memorable and enjoyable.

Mathematics controls more aspects of the modern world than most people realise – from iPods, cash machines, telecommunications and airline booking systems to production processes in engineering, efficient distribution and stock-holding, investment strategies and 'whispering' jet engines. The scientific and industrial revolutions flowed from the realisation that mathematics was both the language of nature, and also a way of analysing – and hence controlling – our environment. In the last fifty years, old and new applications of mathematical ideas have transformed the way we live.

All of these developments depend on mathematical thinking – a mode of thought whose essential style is far more permanent than the wave of technological change which it has made possible. The problems on the JMC reflect this style, which pervades all mathematics, by encouraging students to think clearly about challenging problems.

The UK JMC has grown out of a national challenge first run in 1988. In recent years over 250,000 pupils have taken part from around 3,700 schools. Certificates are awarded to the highest scoring 40% of candidates (Gold : Silver : Bronze 1 : 2 : 3). From 2014, Certificates of Participation were awarded to all participants.

There is an Intermediate and Senior version for older pupils. All three events are organised by the United Kingdom Mathematics Trust and are administered from the School of Mathematics at the University of Leeds.

The UKMT is a registered charity. For more information about us please visit our website at www.ukmt.org.uk

Donations to support our work would be gratefully received and can be made at www.donate.ukmt.org.uk

The JMC follow-on events

The Junior Kangaroo is a one-hour multiple-choice paper with 25 questions for the UK and by invitation only. It was offered to around 5,000 UK candidates who scored just below the Junior Olympiad qualifying score. The qualification mark was 93 to 112.

Junior Kangaroo Mathematical Challenge

Tuesday 14th June 2016

Organised by the United Kingdom Mathematics Trust

The Junior Kangaroo allows students in the UK to test themselves on questions set for young mathematicians from across Europe and beyond.

RULES AND GUIDELINES (to be read before starting):

1. Do not open the paper until the Invigilator tells you to do so.

2. Time allowed: **1 hour**.
   No answers, or personal details, may be entered after the allowed hour is over.

3. The use of rough paper is allowed; **calculators** and measuring instruments are **forbidden**.

4. Candidates in England and Wales must be in School Year 8 or below.
   Candidates in Scotland must be in S2 or below.
   Candidates in Northern Ireland must be in School Year 9 or below.

5. **Use B or HB pencil only**. For each question mark *at most one* of the options A, B, C, D, E on the Answer Sheet. Do not mark more than one option.

6. Five marks will be awarded for each correct answer to Questions 1 - 15.
   Six marks will be awarded for each correct answer to Questions 16 - 25.

7. *Do not expect to finish the whole paper in 1 hour*. Concentrate first on Questions 1-15. When you have checked your answers to these, have a go at some of the later questions.

8. The questions on this paper challenge you **to think**, not to guess. Though you will not lose marks for getting answers wrong, you will undoubtedly get more marks, and more satisfaction, by doing a few questions carefully than by guessing lots of answers.

Enquiries about the Junior Kangaroo should be sent to: Maths Challenges Office, School of Mathematics, University of Leeds, Leeds, LS2 9JT.
(Tel. 0113 343 2339)
http://www.ukmt.org.uk

1. At which of these times is the angle between the minute hand and the hour hand of a clock equal to 150°?

   A 9 pm   B 8 pm   C 6 pm   D 5 pm   E 4 pm

2. Twelve people, and no more, can sit evenly spaced around a large square table. Rohan arranges eight of these square tables in a row to make one long rectangular table. What is the maximum number of people that can sit evenly spaced around this long table?

   A 48   B 54   C 60   D 80   E 96

3. A ball and a bat cost £90 in total. Three balls and two bats cost £210 in total. How much does a bat cost?

   A £20   B £30   C £40   D £50   E £60

4. It takes 9 litres of paint to cover the surface of the cube on the left.

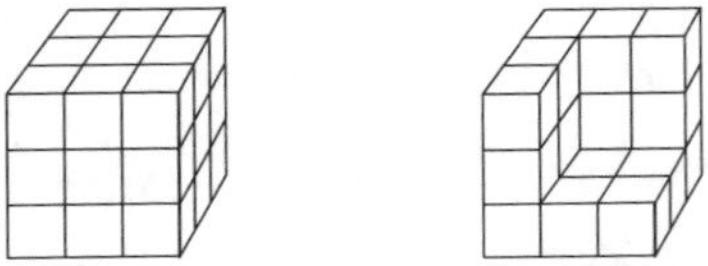

   How much paint would it take to cover the surface of the shape on the right?

   A 9 litres   B 8 litres   C 6 litres   D 4 litres   E 2 litres

5. What is 10% of 30% of 50% of 7000?

   A 15   B 105   C 150   D 501   E 510

6. Miss Spelling has enough sheets of paper to give each pupil in her class 3 sheets and have 31 sheets left over. Alternatively, she could give each pupil 4 sheets and have 8 sheets left over. How many sheets of paper does she have?

   A 31   B 34   C 43   D 91   E 100

7. Which of the following nets can be used to build the partial cube shown in the diagram?

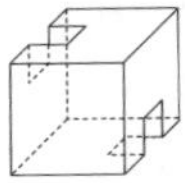

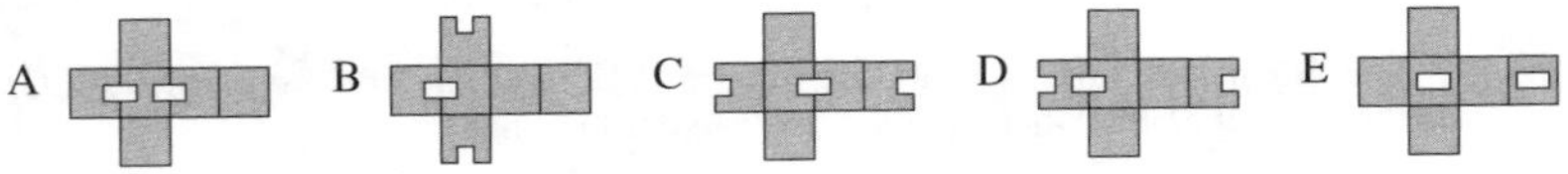

8. One angle of an isosceles triangle is 30°. Which of the following could be the difference between the other two angles?

   A 30°   B 60°   C 70°   D 80°   E 90°

9. A piece of paper in the shape of a regular hexagon, as shown, is folded so that the three marked vertices meet at the centre O of the hexagon. What is the shape of the figure that is formed?

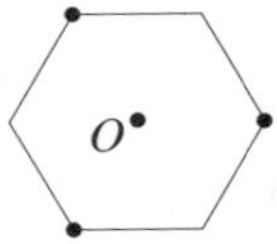

   A Six-pointed star   B Dodecagon   C Hexagon
   D Square   E Equilateral Triangle

10. Four circles of radius 5 cm touch the sides of a square and each other, as shown in the diagram. On each side of the square, an equilateral triangle is drawn to form a four-pointed star.

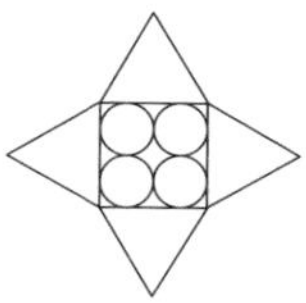

   What is the perimeter of the star?

   A 40 cm   B 80 cm   C 120 cm   D 160 cm   E 200 cm

11. Joey calculated the sum of the largest and smallest two-digit numbers that are multiples of three. Zoë calculated the sum of the largest and smallest two-digit numbers that are not multiples of three. What is the difference between their answers?

   A 2   B 3   C 4   D 5   E 6

12. The diagram shows a rectangle $ABCD$ in which AB = 1 metre and AD = 4 metres. The points E and G are the midpoints of AD and AB and the points F and H are the midpoints of AE and AG.

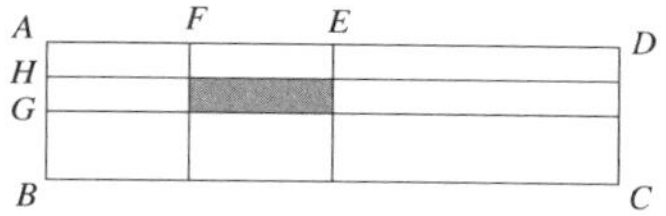

   What is the area of the shaded rectangle?

   A $\frac{1}{16}$ m^2 B $\frac{1}{8}$ m^2 C $\frac{1}{4}$ m^2 D $\frac{1}{2}$ m^2 E 1 m^2

13. The tens digit of a two-digit number is three more than the units digit. When this two-digit number is divided by the sum of its digits, the answer is 7 remainder 3. What is the sum of the digits of the two-digit number?

   A 5   B 7   C 9   D 11   E 13

14. How many different cubes are there with three faces coloured red and three faces coloured blue?

   A 1   B 2   C 3   D 4   E 5

15. The diameter of the circle shown is 10 cm. The circle passes through the vertices of a large rectangle which is divided into 16 identical smaller rectangles.

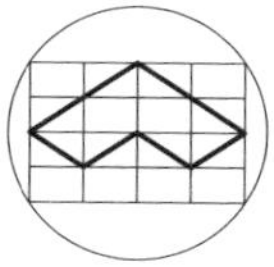

   What is the perimeter of the shape drawn with a dark line?

   A 10 cm   B 16 cm   C 20 cm   D 24 cm   E 30 cm

16. The diagram shows part of a river which has two islands in it. There are six bridges linking the islands and the two banks as shown. Leonhard goes for a walk every day in which he walks over each bridge exactly once. He always starts at point A, goes first over bridge

   1 and always finishes at point B. What is the maximum number of days that he can walk without repeating the order in which he crosses the bridges?

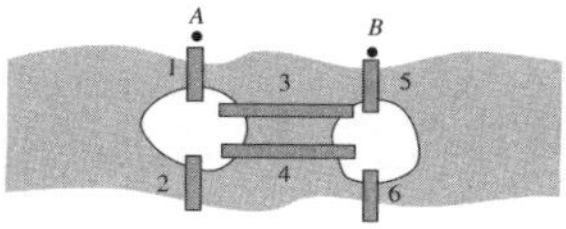

   A 2   B 4   C 5   D 6   E More than 6

17. The square $ABCD$ consists of four congruent rectangles arranged around a central square. The perimeter of each of the rectangles is 40 cm. What is the area of the square $ABCD$?

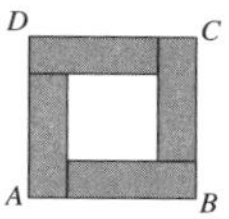

   A 400 cm^2 B 200 cm^2 C 160 cm^2 D 120 cm^2 E 80 cm^2

18. When Ellen went to the shop, she found she could spend all her money on 6 cans of cola and 7 croissants or on 8 cans of cola and 4 croissants. If she decided to buy only croissants, how many croissants could she buy?

    A 12   B 13   C 15   D 16   E 25

19. Adam, Bill and Chris went swimming 15 times last summer. Adam paid for everyone eight times and Bill paid for everyone seven times. At the end of the summer, Chris calculated that he owed £30. How should he split this between Adam and Bill so that each has paid the same amount?

    A £22 to Adam and £8 to Bill   B £20 to Adam and £10 to Bill
    C £18 to Adam and £12 to Bill   D £16 to Adam and £14 to Bill
    E £15 to Adam and £15 to Bill

20. The diagram shows five congruent right-angled isosceles triangles. What is the total area of the triangles?

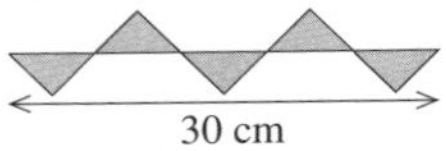

    A 25 cm^2 B 30 cm^2 C 35 cm^2 D 45 cm^2 E 60 cm^2

    30 cm

21. In Carl's pencil case there are nine pencils. At least one of the pencils is blue. In any group of four pencils, at least two have the same colour. In any group of five pencils, at most three have the same colour. How many pencils are blue?

    A 1   B 2   C 3   D 4   E More information needed

22. Lewis drives from London to Brighton at an average speed of 60 mph. On the way back, he gets stuck in traffic and his average speed is only 40 mph. What is his average speed for the whole journey?

    A 55 mph B 50 mph C 48 mph D 45 mph E Impossible to determine

23. In the addition sum below, a, b and c stand for different digits.

$$
\begin{array}{r}
a\,b\,c \\
+\ \ a\,c\,b \\
\hline
c\,4\,a.
\end{array}
$$

    What is the value of $a + b + c$?

    A 20   B 19   C 18   D 17   E 16

24. The lengths of three adjacent sides of a quadrilateral are equal. The angle between the first and second of these sides is 60° and the angle between the second and third of these sides is 100°. What is the largest angle of the quadrilateral?

    A 130°   B 140°   C 145°   D 150°   E 160°

25. The whole numbers from 1 to 2016 inclusive are written on a blackboard. Moritz underlines all the multiples of two in red, all the multiples of three in blue and all the multiples of four in green. How many numbers does Moritz underline exactly twice?

    A 1008   B 1004   C 504   D 336   E 168

Solutions were provided.

Solutions to 2016 Junior Kangaroo

1. **D** At all the times given, the minute hand is pointing to 12. When the minute hand is pointing to 12 and the angle between the hands is 150°, the hour hand has turned $\frac{150}{360} = \frac{5}{12}$ of a complete turn. Therefore the hour hand will point at 5 and the time will be 5 pm. (There are other times when the angle between the hands is 150° but, of these, only at 7 pm does the minute hand point to 12 and 7 pm is not one of the times given.)

2. **B** The number of people who can sit on each side of the square table is $12 \div 4 = 3$. When eight of these tables are arranged to make a long rectangular table, there will be room for $8 \times 3 = 24$ people on each long side and for three extra people at each end. Hence, the number of people that can sit round the long table is $2 \times 24 + 2 \times 3 = 48 + 6 = 54$.

3. **E** Since one ball and one bat cost £90, two balls and two bats cost $2 \times £90 = £180$. Now, since three balls and two bats cost £210, one ball costs £210 − £180 = £30. Therefore a bat costs £90 − £30 = £60.

4. **A** The surface areas of the two solids are the same. Hence the same amount of paint is required to cover them. Therefore it would take 9 litres of paint to cover the surface of the second solid.

5. **B** The calculation is equivalent to $\frac{1}{10} \times \frac{3}{10} \times \frac{5}{10} \times 7000 = 1 \times 3 \times 5 \times 7 = 105$.

6. **E** Let the number of pupils in the class be x. The information in the question tells us that $3x + 31 = 4x + 8$, which has solution $x = 23$. Hence the number of sheets of paper Miss Spelling has is $3 \times 23 + 31 = 100$.

7. **C** Nets A and D would produce cubes with holes on two edges of the same face. Net E would produce a cube with a hole in the centre of two opposite faces while net B would produce a cube with one hole on an edge and two small holes. The given partial cube has holes on two opposite edges and therefore its net will have a hole on the edge of four different faces.

Hence only net C can be used to build the required shape.

8. **E** Since one angle of the isosceles triangle is 30°, there are two possibilities. Either the other two angles are equal, in which case the difference between them is 0°, or one of the other angles is 30°. In this case, since angles in a triangle add to 180°, the second missing angle is 120° and hence the difference between the two missing angles is 120° − 30° = 90°.

9. **E** Label vertices A, B, C, D, E and F as shown. Since the hexagon is regular, it can be divided into six equilateral triangles as shown. Therefore quadrilateral $OABC$ is a rhombus and hence its diagonal AC is a line of symmetry. Therefore, if vertex B is folded onto O, the fold will be along AC. Similarly, if vertices D and F are folded onto O, the

folds will be along CE and EA respectively. Hence the figure that is formed will be a triangle and, since all three of the rhombuses $OABC$, $OCDE$ and $OEFA$ are made out of two congruent equilateral triangles, the lengths of their diagonals AC, CE and EA will be equal. Hence the shape ACE that is formed is an equilateral triangle.

10. D The radius of each of the circles is 5 cm and hence the diameter of each is 10 cm. The length of the side of the square is equal to the sum of the diameters of two circles and hence is equal to 20 cm. The length of each side of the equilateral triangle is equal to the length of the side of the square. Hence the perimeter of the star, which is made up of eight sides of congruent equilateral triangles, is 8×20 cm $= 160$ cm.

11. B Joey's two numbers are 99 and 12 and hence his sum is 111. Zoë's two numbers are 98 and 10 and hence her sum is 108. Therefore the difference between their answers is $111 - 108 = 3$.

12. C

Since E is the midpoint of AD and F is the midpoint of AE, the length of FE is $\frac{1}{2} \times \frac{1}{2} \times 4$ m $= 1$ m. Similarly, since G is the midpoint of AB and H is the midpoint of AG, the length of HG is $\frac{1}{2} \times \frac{1}{2} \times 1$ m $= \frac{1}{4}$ m. Therefore the area of the shaded rectangle is $\left(1 \times \frac{1}{4}\right)$ m^2 $= \frac{1}{4}$ m^2.

13. B Let the units digit of the number be x. Hence the tens digit of the number is $x + 3$ and the sum of the digits of the number is $2x + 3$. The information in the question tells us that $10(x + 3) + x = 7(2x + 3) + 3$. Hence $11x + 30 = 14x + 24$ which has solution $x = 2$. Therefore the sum of the digits of the two-digit number is $2 \times 2 + 3 = 7$.

14. B Consider the case where two opposite faces are coloured red. Whichever of the four remaining faces is also coloured red, the resulting arrangement is equivalent under rotation to a cube with top, bottom and front faces coloured red. Hence, there is only one distinct colouring of a cube consisting of three red and three blue faces with two opposite faces coloured red. Now consider the case where no two opposite faces are coloured red. This is only possible when the three red faces share a common vertex and, however these faces are arranged, the resulting arrangement is equivalent under rotation to a cube with top, front and right-hand faces coloured red. Hence there is also only one distinct colouring of a cube consisting of three red and three blue faces in which no two opposite faces are coloured red. Therefore there are exactly two different colourings of the cube as described in the question.

15. C The diagonals of a rectangle bisect each other at the midpoint of the rectangle. Hence, the midpoint of a rectangle is equidistant from all four vertices and is the centre of a circle through its vertices.

In this case, the diameter of the circle is 10 cm. This is equal to the sum of the lengths of the diagonals of four of the smaller rectangles. Hence the diagonal of each small rectangle has length 2.5 cm. The perimeter of the marked shape is made up of eight diagonals of the small rectangles and hence has length 8×2.5 cm $= 20$ cm.

16. D   Since Leonhard's walk always goes over bridge 1 first, it must conclude by going over bridge 5 to enable him to reach B. Note also that bridges 2 and 6 must be crossed consecutively, in some order, as they are the only way to get to and from the opposite bank to the one from which he started and is to finish and so can be considered together.

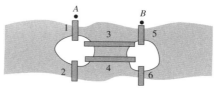

Hence the number of days he can walk without repeating the order in which he crosses the bridges is the same as the number of ways of choosing ordered crossings of bridges 3, 4 and the pair 2 and 6. These can be chosen in six different ways (three choices for the first bridge, two for the second and then only one choice for the third). Hence Leonhard can walk for six days without repeating the order in which he crosses the bridges.

(The six orders are 126345, 126435, 134265, 136245, 143265 and 146235.)

17. A   Let the length of each of the rectangles be x cm and the width be y cm. The perimeter of each of the rectangles is 40 cm and hence $2x + 2y = 40$. Therefore $x + y = 20$. From the diagram we can see that the length of each side of the square $ABCD$ is $(x + y)$ cm. Therefore the square $ABCD$ has side-length 20 cm. Hence the area of $ABCD$ is (20×20) cm^2 $= 400$ cm^2.

18. D   Let the cost of a can of cola be x pence and the cost of a croissant be y pence. The information in the question tells us that $6x + 7y = 8x + 4y$ and that both sides of the equation represent the total amount of money Ellen has. Hence $3y = 2x$. Therefore the total amount of money she has is $3 \times 3y + 7y$ pence $= 16y$ pence. Hence she could buy 16 croissants if she bought only croissants.

19. C   If each person paid their fair share, each would have paid five times. Therefore Adam has paid on an extra three occasions and Bill has paid on an extra two occasions. Hence the £30 Chris owes should be divided in the ratio 3:2. Therefore Adam should get $\frac{3}{5} \times £30 = £18$ and Bill should get $\frac{2}{5} \times £30 = £12$.

20. D   Consider one of the right-angled isosceles triangles as shown.

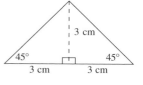

The longest side is $(30/5)$ cm $= 6$ cm. The triangle can be divided into two congruent right-angled isosceles triangles with base 3 cm and hence with height 3 cm. Therefore the area of each of the original triangles is $(\frac{1}{2} \times 6 \times 3)$ cm^2 $= 9$ cm^2. Hence the total shaded area is 5×9 cm$^2 = 45$ cm^2.

21. C   The information that in any group of four pencils, at least two have the same colour, tells us that there are at most three different coloured pencils in Carl's pencil case. The information that in any group of five pencils, at most three have the same colour, tells us that there are at most three pencils of any single colour in the pencil case. Hence there are three pencils of each of the three different colours and so Carl's pencil case contains three blue pencils.

22. C Let the distance from London to Brighton be d miles. Since time = distance/speed, the times Lewis spent on the two parts of his journey were $\frac{d}{60}$ hours and $\frac{d}{40}$ hours. Hence the total time in hours that he travelled was

$$\frac{d}{60} + \frac{d}{40} = \frac{2d + 3d}{120} = \frac{5d}{120} = \frac{d}{24}.$$

Therefore his average speed for the whole journey was $2d \div \left(\frac{d}{24}\right)$ mph $= 48$ mph.

23. E
$$
\begin{array}{r}
a\,b\,c \\
+ \ a\,c\,b \\
\hline
c\,4\,a.
\end{array}
$$

Since c is the digit in the hundreds column of the answer, we can deduce that $c > a$. Therefore, there must be a carry from the units column to the tens column and hence $a = 4 - 1 = 3$. Since there will also be a carry from the tens column to the hundreds column, we have $c = a + a + 1 = 7$. Therefore, $7 + b = 13$ and hence $b = 6$. Therefore the value of $a + b + c$ is $3 + 6 + 7 = 16$.

24. A Consider the quadrilateral $PQRS$ as shown with $PQ = QR = RS$, $\angle RQP = 60°$ and $\angle SRQ = 100°$.

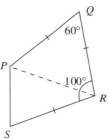

Draw line PR. Since $PQ = QR$ and $\angle PQR = 60°$, triangle PQR is equilateral and hence $PR = PQ = QR = RS$ and $\angle PRQ = 60°$. Since $\angle SRQ = 100°$, $\angle SRP = 100° - 60° = 40°$. Since $PR = RS$, triangle PRS is isosceles and hence $\angle RPS = \angle PSR = \frac{1}{2}(180° - 40°) = 70°$. Therefore the largest angle of the quadrilateral is $\angle QPS = 70° + 60° = 130°$.

25. C There is no number that is both a multiple of three and a multiple of four without also being a multiple of two. Hence, the numbers underlined exactly twice are those that are a multiple of two and of three but not of four and those that are a multiple of two and four but not of three. The first set of numbers consists of the set of odd multiples of six. Since $2016 \div 6 = 336$, there are 336 multiples of 6 in the list of numbers and hence $336 \div 2 = 168$ odd multiples of six that would be underlined in red and blue but not green. The second set of numbers consists of two out of every three multiples of four and, since $2016 \div 4 = 504$, there are $\frac{2}{3} \times 504 = 336$ numbers that would be underlined in red and green but not blue. Hence there are $168 + 336 = 504$ numbers that Moritz would underline exactly twice.

The Junior Mathematical Olympiad

UK Junior Mathematical Olympiad 2016

Organised by The United Kingdom Mathematics Trust

Tuesday 14th June 2016

RULES AND GUIDELINES :
READ THESE INSTRUCTIONS CAREFULLY BEFORE STARTING

1. Time allowed: 2 hours.

2. **The use of calculators, measuring instruments and squared paper is forbidden.**

3. All candidates must be in *School Year 8 or below* (England and Wales), *S2 or below* (Scotland), *School Year 9 or below* (Northern Ireland).

4. **Write in blue or black pen or pencil.**
    For questions in Section A *only the answer is required.* Enter each answer neatly in the relevant box on the Front Sheet. Do not hand in rough work.
    For questions in Section B you must give *full written solutions*, including clear mathematical explanations as to why your method is correct.
    Solutions must be written neatly on A4 paper. Sheets must be STAPLED together in the top left corner with the Front Sheet on top.
    Do not hand in rough work.

5. Questions A1-A10 are relatively short questions. Try to complete Section A within the first 30 minutes so as to allow well over an hour for Section B.

6. Questions B1-B6 are longer questions requiring *full written solutions*.
    This means that each answer must be accompanied by clear explanations and proofs.
    Work in rough first, then set out your final solution with clear explanations of each step.

7. These problems are meant to be challenging! Do not hurry. Try the earlier questions in each section first (they tend to be easier). Try to finish whole questions even if you are not able to do many. A good candidate will have done most of Section A and given solutions to at least two questions in Section B.

8. Answers must be FULLY SIMPLIFIED, and EXACT using symbols like π, fractions, or square roots if appropriate, but NOT decimal approximations.

DO NOT OPEN THE PAPER UNTIL INSTRUCTED BY THE INVIGILATOR TO DO SO!

The United Kingdom Mathematics Trust is a Registered Charity.

32

Section A

Try to complete Section A within 30 minutes or so. Only answers are required.

A1. Roger picks two consecutive integers, one of which ends in a 5. He multiplies his integers together and then squares the result.
What are the last two digits of his answer?

A2. Three isosceles triangles are put together to create a larger isosceles triangle, as shown.
What is the value of x?

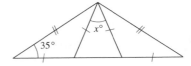

A3. The first term of a sequence is 0. Each term of the sequence after the first term is equal to $10p + 1$, where p is the previous term.
What is the sum of the first ten terms?

A4. The diagram shows a regular hexagon with area 48 m².
What is the area of the shaded triangle?

A5. Linda has a very thin sheet of paper measuring 20 cm by 30 cm. She repeatedly folds her paper in half by folding along the shorter line of symmetry. She finishes when she has a rectangle with area 75 cm².
What is the perimeter of her final rectangle?

A6. The points A, B, C, D and E lie in that order along a straight line so that $AB : BC = 1 : 2$, $BC : CD = 1 : 3$ and $CD : DE = 1 : 4$. What is $AB : BE$?

A7. A certain positive integer has exactly eight factors. Two of these factors are 15 and 21.
What is the sum of all eight factors?

A8. Julie and her daughters Megan and Zoey have the same birthday. Today, Julie is 32, Megan is 4 and Zoey is 1.
How old will Julie be when her age is the sum of the ages of Megan and Zoey?

A9. A circle of radius 18 cm is divided into three identical regions by the three semicircles, as shown.
What is the length of the perimeter of one of these regions?

A10. The diagram shows a rectangle with length 9 cm and width 7 cm. One of the diagonals of the rectangle has been divided into seven equal parts.
What is the area of the shaded region?

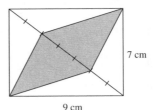

7 cm

9 cm

Section B

Your solutions to Section B will have a major effect on your JMO result. Concentrate on one or two questions first and then **write out full solutions** (not just brief 'answers').

B1. In a certain triangle, the size of each of the angles is a whole number of degrees. Also, one angle is 30° larger than the average of the other two angles.
What is the largest possible size of an angle in this triangle?

B2. The points A, B and C are the centres of three circles. Each circle touches the other two circles, and each centre lies outside the other two circles. The sides of the triangle ABC have lengths 13 cm, 16 cm and 20 cm.
What are the radii of the three circles?

B3. A large cube is made up of a number of identical small cubes. The number of small cubes that touch four other small cubes face-to-face is 168.
How many small cubes make up the large cube?

B4. In the trapezium $ABCD$, the lines AB and CD are parallel. Also $AB = 2DC$ and $DA = CB$.
The line DC is extended (beyond C) to the point E so that $EC = CB = BE$. The line DA is extended (beyond A) to the point F so that $AF = BA$.
Prove that $\angle FBC = 90°$.

B5. The board shown has 32 cells, one of which is labelled S and another F. The shortest path starting at S and finishing at F involves exactly nine other cells and ten moves, where each move goes from cell to cell 'horizontally' or 'vertically' across an edge.

How many paths of this length are there from S to F?

B6. For which values of the positive integer n is it possible to divide the first $3n$ positive integers into three groups each of which has the same sum?

UK Junior Mathematical Olympiad 2016 Solutions

A1   **00**   Since the integers are consecutive and one ends in a 5, the other integer ends in a 4 or a 6 and so is even. Hence the product of the two numbers is a multiple of 10. When this is squared, we obtain a multiple of 100 and so the final digits are 00.

A2   **40**

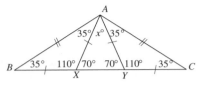

Using the angle sum of a triangle, the isosceles triangles ABX and ACY have angles of $35°$, $35°$ and $180° - 35° - 35° = 110°$. Angles on a straight line add to $180°$ and so $\angle AXY = \angle XYA = 180° - 110° = 70°$. Using the angle sum of a triangle again, we have $x = 180 - 70 - 70 = 40$.

Alternative Solution

Since $\triangle ABC$ is isosceles, $\angle ACB = 35°$.

Since $\triangle ABX$ is isosceles, $\angle BAX = 35°$.

Since $\triangle ACY$ is isosceles, $\angle CAY = 35°$.

Hence, from the angle sum in $\triangle ABC$ we have $x = 180 - 4 \times 35 = 40$.

A3   The sequence is 0, 1, 11, 111, 1111, 11111, 111111, 1111111, 11111111,
123456789   111111111, ... Hence the sum of the first 10 terms is 123456789.

A4.   **8 m²**   From the dissection shown, the area of the triangle is half of the area of a parallelogram which is itself a third of the area of the hexagon. So the triangle has area $\frac{1}{2} \times \frac{1}{3} \times 48$ m² $= 8$ m².

A5.   **35 cm**   Each fold reduces the area by half. Therefore we require three folds to reduce the area from 600 cm² to 75 cm².

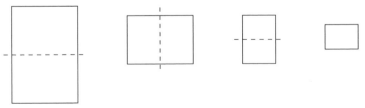

| 30 cm × 20 cm | 15 cm × 20 cm | 15 cm × 10 cm | 7.5 cm × 10 cm |

From the diagrams, we see that we have, in turn, areas of 600 cm², 300 cm², 150 cm² and 75 cm². The final shape has perimeter $2(7.5 + 10)$ cm $= 35$ cm.

A6. 1:32 We have $\qquad\qquad AB : BC = 1 : 2$

and $\qquad\qquad\qquad\quad BC : CD = 1 : 3 = 2 : 6$

and $\qquad\qquad\qquad\quad CD : DE = 1 : 4 = 6 : 24$

and so $\quad AB : BC : CD : DE = 1 : 2 : 6 : 24.$

Hence we have $\qquad AB : BE = 1 : (2 + 6 + 24) = 1 : 32$

$A \; B \qquad C \qquad\qquad D \qquad\qquad\qquad\qquad\qquad\qquad\qquad\qquad\qquad\qquad E$

A7. 192 We have $15 = 1 \times 3 \times 5$ and $21 = 1 \times 3 \times 7$. The integer we require is therefore a multiple of $1 \times 3 \times 5 \times 7 = 105$. However, 105 has the eight factors 1, 3, 5, 7, 15, 21, 35 and 105 and any (larger) multiple of 105 would have more than eight factors. Hence 105 is the integer we require and the sum of its factors is

$$1 + 3 + 5 + 7 + 15 + 21 + 35 + 105 = 192.$$

A8. 59 Suppose this happens in x years' time. Julie's age will be $32 + x$, Megan's age will be $4 + x$ and Zoey's age will be $1 + x$. Thus $1 + x + 4 + x = 32 + x$ and, subtracting $5 + x$ from each side of this equation, we have $x = 27$.

In 27 years' time, Julie will be 59, Megan 31 and Zoey 28. Notice that $31 + 28 = 59$ as required.

A9. 30π Each region has a perimeter consisting of the perimeters of a third of a circle of radius 18 cm and two semicircles of radius 9 cm. Using the fact that the perimeter of a circle is π times its diameter, the required perimeter (in cm) is $\frac{1}{3} \times \pi \times 36 + 2 \times \frac{1}{2} \times \pi \times 18 = 30\pi$.

A10. 27 The 14 small triangles shown have equal heights and bases of equal length. Thus they have equal areas and their total area is that of the rectangle. The area of the rectangle is $7\,\text{cm} \times 9\,\text{cm} = 63\,\text{cm}^2$.

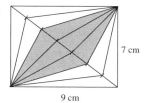

7 cm

9 cm

The area we require is made up of six small triangles.

Hence, the required area is $\frac{6}{14} \times 63\,\text{cm}^2 = 27\,\text{cm}^2$.

B1 In a certain triangle, the size of each of the angles is a whole number of degrees. Also, one angle is 30° larger than the average of the other two angles.

What is the largest possible size of an angle in this triangle?

Solution

Let two of the angles measure $a°$ and $b°$. Then the third angle is $\left(30 + \frac{1}{2}(a + b)\right)°$. The angle sum of a triangle is 180° which gives $180° = \left(a + b + 30 + \frac{1}{2}(a + b)\right)° = \left(30 + \frac{3}{2}(a + b)\right)°$ and so $\frac{3}{2}(a + b) = 150$, giving $a + b = 100$. The sizes of all the angles are integers so that the largest either a or b can be is 99. This gives a triangle with angles 1°, 80° and 99° and so the largest possible such angle is 99°.

B2 The points A, B and C are the centres of three circles. Each circle touches the other two circles, and each centre lies outside the other two circles. The sides of the triangle ABC have lengths 13 cm, 16 cm and 20 cm.

What are the radii of the three circles?

Solution

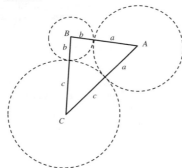

Since the circles touch, for each pair of circles, the distance between their centres is the sum of their radii. Let the radii of the three circles (in cm) be a, b and c. Then we can form equations for the lengths of the sides of the triangle:

$$a + b = 13$$
$$b + c = 16$$
$$a + c = 20.$$

Adding these equations together, we obtain

$$2a + 2b + 2c = 49.$$

So $a + b + c = 24\frac{1}{2}$. But $a + b = 13$ giving $c = 11\frac{1}{2}$. Then $b = 16 - 11\frac{1}{2} = 4\frac{1}{2}$ and $a = 20 - 11\frac{1}{2} = 8\frac{1}{2}$.

B3. A large cube is made up of a number of identical small cubes. The number of small cubes that touch four other small cubes face-to-face is 168.

How many small cubes make up the large cube?

Solution

On a face of the large cube, the cubes not on an edge touch five other faces and the internal cubes not on a face touch six other faces. Small cubes which touch four other faces lie along an edge and are not at a corner (those touch 3 other faces). A cube has 12 edges. Now $\frac{168}{12} = 14$ so that means each edge of the large cube has 14 small cubes which touch four other cubes and two small corner cubes. Therefore an edge of the large cube has length 16 and so the total number of small cubes is $16 \times 16 \times 16 = 4096$.

Alternative Solution

The large cube has 8 corner cubes each of which has 3 faces which touch matching cubes. The cubes which lie on the edges between a pair of corner cubes each have 4 faces which touch matching cubes and we know there are 168 of these. A cube has 12 edges so dividing 168 by 12 gives 14 which tells us that each edge of the large cube has 16 small cubes in it. Thus the number of small cubes is $16 \times 16 \times 16 = 4096$.

B4. In the trapezium *ABCD*, the lines *AB* and *CD* are parallel. Also *AB* = 2*DC* and *DA* = *CB*. The line *DC* is extended (beyond *C*) to the point *E* so that *EC* = *CB* = *BE*. The line *DA* is extended (beyond *A*) to the point *F* so that *AF* = *BA*.
Prove that ∠*FBC* = 90°.

Solution

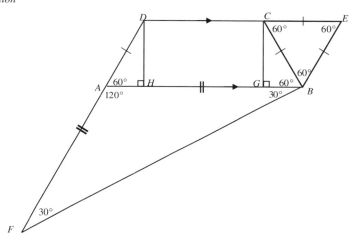

Since *EC* = *CB* = *BE*, the triangle *ECB* is equilateral and each of its angles is 60°.

ED and *AB* are parallel so ∠*ABC* = ∠*BCE* = 60° (alternate angles).

Draw perpendiculars from *C* and *D* to *AB* to meet *AB* at *G* and *H*. The right-angled triangles *DAH* and *CBG* have hypotenuses of equal length and *DH* = *CG* so triangles *DAH* and *CGB* are congruent {RHS}. Thus ∠*DAH* = ∠*CBG* = 60°.

DAF is a straight line so that ∠*BAF* = 180° − 60° = 120°.

Triangle *AFB* is isosceles with ∠*AFB* = ∠*FBA* = ½(180° − 120°) = 30° (angle sum of a triangle).

Therefore

$$∠FBC = ∠FBA + ∠ABC = 30° + 60° = 90°.$$

B5. The board shown has 32 cells, one of which is labelled S and another F. The shortest path starting at S and finishing at F involves exactly nine other cells and ten moves, where each move goes from cell to cell 'horizontally' or 'vertically' across an edge.

How many paths of this length are there from S to F?

Solution

From S, there are two starting paths: and we can represent the number of

paths to reach a square like this: .

There is only one way to travel along the edges and we can build up our diagram like this, noticing that each square not on an edge can only be reached from the left or from

below 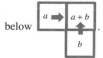 .

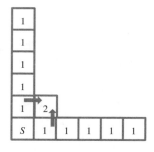

1	6	11	16	26	52
1	5	5	5	10	26
1	4			5	16
1	3			5	11
1	2	3	4	5	6
S	1	1	1	1	1

Since F is 5 steps above and 5 steps to the right of S, each of the 10 moves can only be upwards or to the right and so there are 52 paths from S to F.

B6. For which values of the positive integer n is it possible to divide the first $3n$ positive integers into three groups each of which has the same sum?

Solution

$n = 1$: it is impossible to place the integers 1, 2 and 3 into three groups with the same sum.

$n = 2$: $1 + 2 + 3 + 4 + 5 + 6 = 21$ and so we want to place these integers into three groups, each of which add to 7. The groups are $(1, 6)$, $(2, 5)$ and $(3, 4)$.

$n = 3$: $1 + 2 + 3 + 4 + 5 + 6 + 7 + 8 + 9 = 45$ and so we want to place these integers into three groups, each of which adds to 15. Such a grouping is $(1, 2, 3, 4, 5)$, $(6, 9)$ and $(7, 8)$.

It would not be sensible to continue to look at each value of n, so we look at what happens when we move from $3n$ to $3(n + 2)$.

Let us assume that we can place $3n$ integers into three groups with the same sum. For the first $3(n + 2)$ integers we must include an extra six integers $3n + 1$, $3n + 2$, $3n + 3$, $3n + 4$, $3n + 5$ and $3n + 6$ to deal with $3(n + 2) = 3n + 6$.

When we add the six new integers together, we obtain $18n + 21$ meaning we increase the sum by a third of this, $6n + 7$, to each group to make new groups with the same sum.

So we add pairs to our original three groups: $3n + 1$ with $3n + 6$ to one group; $3n + 2$ with $3n + 5$ to another group and $3n + 3$ with $3n + 4$ to the third group.

However, we know we can obtain three groups with the same sum for $n = 2$ and $n = 3$ and now we can also obtain three groups for each of $n = 4, 6, 8, \ldots$ and so every even integer, in the same way from $n = 3$ we have $n = 5, 7, 9, \ldots$ and so every odd integer greater than 1.

Thus the values of n for which the first $3n$ positive integers can be placed in three groups with the same sum are all values of $n > 1$.

The marking and results

The pupils' scripts began arriving very rapidly and the marking took place in Leeds on the weekend of 25th and 26th June. The discussions as to how marks should be given and for what were ably led by Mary Teresa Fyfe. A full list of markers appears in the Volunteers section.

As has been stated, the object of the JMO is for pupils to be *challenged*, possibly in ways they have not been before. Some participants may find all of Section B rather beyond them, but it is hoped that they achieve a degree of satisfaction from Section A. Satisfaction is an important aspect of this level of paper; nevertheless, those who do succeed in tackling Section B deserve credit for that and such credit is mainly dependent on getting solutions to questions in Section B which are 'perfect' or very nearly so.

Based on the total of both A and B sections, book prizes and certificates are awarded. The top scoring 25% of all candidates receive a Certificate of Distinction. Of those scoring below this, candidates who make a good attempt at the paper (usually a score of 8+, but may be moderated based on the score distribution) will receive a Certificate of Merit. Of the remaining candidates, those who qualified automatically for the JMO via the JMC receive a Certificate of Qualification. Other candidates (discretionary) are only eligible for Distinction and Merit certificates. The top 50 scorers will be awarded a book prize; in 2016 this was *Cakes, Custard, Category Theory* by Eugenia Cheng.

Medals are awarded on a different basis to certificates and prizes. The medal-awarding total will be the Section A mark + Section B marks that are 5 or more. The top 210 will receive a medal; gold: silver: bronze 30:60:120.

Average marks were slightly higher than in 2015. The numbers of medals awarded were: 33 Gold, 68 Silver and 119 Bronze.

The list below includes all the medal winners in the 2016 JMO. Within each category, the names are in alphabetical order.

Special mention should be made of Wilfred Ashworth, Robin Bradfield, Ben Fearnhead, Thomas Frith, Otoharu Kawaguchi, Linus Luu, James Tan and Thien Udomsrirungruang who now have two JMO gold medals each and Freddie Hand who has three.

The results and all the extras (books, book plates, certificates and medals) were posted to schools by the middle of July.

GOLD MEDALS

Arlan Abzhanov	Herschel Grammar School, Slough
Tahmeed Ali	Latymer School, London
Arthur Ashworth	Sutton Grammar School for Boys, Surrey
Wilfred Ashworth	Sutton Grammar School for Boys, Surrey
Peter Ball	King Edward VI Grammar S., Chelmsford
Duncan Bouchard	St Leonard's School, Fife
Robin Bradfield	Cargilfield Preparatory, Edinburgh
Avishek Das	City of London School
Ben Fearnhead	Lancaster Royal Grammar School
Thomas Frith	Horsforth School, Leeds
David Han	King George V School, Hong Kong
Freddie Hand	Judd School, Tonbridge, Kent
Tom Harvey	Bottisham Village College, Cambridgeshire
Emily Hudson	Wallington High School for Girls, Surrey
Otoharu Kawaguchi	Clifton Lodge School, London
Avish Kumar	Westminster Under School
Ines Lefranc	St Paul's Girls' School, Hammersmith
Rhys Lewis	Sir Thomas Picton School, Haverfordwest
Linus Luu	St Olave's Grammar School, Kent
Yuhka Machino	Millfield Preparatory School, Somerset
Ilya Misyura	Westminster Under School
Chenxin Qiu	Douglas Academy, East Dunbartonshire
Adrian Sahani	Westminster Under School
Oscar Selby	Westminster Under School
Jihwan Shin	UWCSEA Dover Campus, Singapore
James Tan	Queen Elizabeth's School, Barnet
Vaclav Trpisovsky	Open Gates Boarding S., Czech Republic
Thien Udomsrirungruaag	Shrewsbury International School, Thailand
Orca Vanichjakvong	Shrewsbury International School, Thailand
Jenni Voon	John Flamstead Community S., Derbyshire
Ted Xiong	Ashcroft Technology Academy, London
David Xu	Merchant Taylors' Boys School, Liverpool
John Yu	The Portsmouth Grammar School

SILVER MEDALS

Kenan Ai	The British School in Tokyo Showa
Seth Bailey	King Edward's School, Birmingham
Eliane Boyer	St Bede's Prep School, Eastbourne
Fin Brickman	Dragon School, Oxford
Jude Burling	The Perse School, Cambridge
Nathan Burn	Bishop Wordsworth's School, Salisbury
James Chen	Chetham's School of Music, Manchester
Daoyi Chen	Manor High School, Leicester
Brandon Chin	Garden International School, Malaysia
Wonjin (Sunny) Choi	North London Collegiate S. Jeju, South Korea
Prompt Chotanaphuti	Shrewsbury International School, Thailand
Vamshi Darisi	Reading School
Jack Dennis	St Martin's Academy, nr Nuneaton
Kira Dhariwal	Wycombe High School, Buckinghamshire
Francesc Diceci	St Paul's Girls' School, Hammersmith
Marwan Gedeon Achi	Dubai College
Oliver Gunton	Aylesbury Grammar School
Aditya Gupta	Repton School Dubai
Anant Gupta	Whitgift School, Surrey
Lorin Hallam	Matthew Arnold School, Oxford
Jack Haynes	Reading School
Edward Hilditch	Davenies School, Buckinghamshire
Rikako Hirai	St Paul's Girls' School, Hammersmith
Seongho Hong	Junior King's School, nr Canterbury
Michael Hua	Beijing Dulwich International School
Olivia Jackson	St Peter's Academy, Stoke-on-Trent
Claire S Kim	Dulwich College Seoul
Peter Kippax	King Edward VI Camp Hill S. for Boys, Birmingham
Kitty Knight	Oxford High School
Kai Lam	Whitgift School, Surrey
Serin Lee	North London Collegiate S. Jeju, South Korea
Michael Lin	The Perse School, Cambridge
Owen Mackenzie	Glyn School, Ewell, Surrey
Alexander Man	Latymer School, London
Samuel Millington	Newquay Tretherras
Jonah Milnes	D'Overbroeck's College, Oxford

Phoenix Mombru	St Paul's Girls' School, Hammersmith
Eunju Moon	International School of Luxembourg
Conall Moss	Parmiter's School, Watford
Alex Mousley	Newquay Tretherras
Jack Murphy	Hampton School, Middlesex
Yuki Nagai	Rossall School, Lancashire
Kanakdurga Nanda	King Edward VI Camp Hill S. for Girls, Birmingham
Daniel Naylor	Matthew Arnold School, Oxford
Vlad Penzyev	Hampton School, Middlesex
Kiran Raja	Manchester Grammar School
Felix Robertson	Queens Park Community School, London
Anshul Sajip	Queen Elizabeth's School, Barnet
Ethan Saw Yi Hern	West Island School (ESF), Hong Kong
Freja Schaap	St Paul's Girls' School, Hammersmith
Rituraj Sharma	Westminster Under School
Daniel Shergold	St Olave's Grammar School, Kent
Kiran Shiatis	Judd School, Tonbridge, Kent
Andrew Spielmann	Colet Court School, London
Ben Stokes	Rutlish School, London
Paris Suksmith	Harrow International School, Bangkok
Ashwin Tennant	Abingdon Prep School, Oxon
Arseny Uskov	Merchant Taylor's Prep, Hertfordshire
Ryan Voecks	University College School, London
Alexander Walker	The Perse School, Cambridge
Tommy Walker Mackay	Stretford Grammar School, Manchester
Tom Wall	Watford Grammar School for Boys
Levi Woolf	Ratton School, Eastbourne
Fuyi Xu	Queen Ethelburga's College, N. Yorks
William Yang	King Edward VI Camp Hill S. for Boys, Birmingham
Taewook Yeo	Coombe Boys' School, Surrey
Eric Yin	Dulwich College Shanghai
Emma Zhang	St Paul's Girls' School, Hammersmith

BRONZE MEDALS

Solal Afofa	British School Al-Khubairat, Abu Dhabi
Taha Ahmed	The Priory Academy LSST, Lincoln
Zakariya Alamin	Northampton School for Boys
Ayham Alkhader	Colet Court School, London

Otto Arends Page	Mill Hill County High School, London
Bhuvan Arora	King George V School, Hong Kong
Lena Atipunumphai	Shrewsbury International School, Thailand
Ewan Azlan Luk	Reading School
Julie Beck	Dulwich College Seoul
Aarit Bhattacharya	Papplewick School, Ascot
Benjamin Bishop	King Edward VI Grammar S., Chelmsford
Emily Bleakley	Royal High School, Bath
Jacob Brown	All Hallows Catholic College, Macclesfield
Alex Buckley	Manchester Grammar School
Sam Buick	Adams' Grammar School, Shropshire
John Robin Carlyon	City of London School
Ben Carton	Park House School, Berkshire
Christian Cases	Tiffin School, Kingston-upon-Thames
Dominic Catizone	British School of Chicago, Illinois, USA
Ami Che	King Edward VI High S. for Girls, Birmingham
Erin Choi	Dulwich College Seoul
Woojin (Sam) Choi	North London Collegiate S. Jeju, South Korea
Soum Choudhuri	UWCSEA Dover Campus, Singapore
David Coope	Westminster Under School
Rosalind Coward	Wycombe High School, Buckinghamshire
Matthew Cresswell	Hampton School, Middlesex
Johnny Cubbon	Colet Court School, London
Sarah Dauris	Wycombe Abbey School, High Wycombe
Beatrice De Goede	Manchester High School for Girls
Ashmi Deb	Hutchesons' Grammar School, Glasgow
Vittoria Dessi	St Paul's Girls' School, Hammersmith
Lewis Edmond	Sawston Village College, Cambridgeshire
Sara El-Khamlichi	Bancroft's School, Essex
James Emery	Hampton School, Middlesex
Alex Ford	Ryecroft Middle School, Staffs
Josef Fruhauf	Open Gates Boarding S., Czech Republic
Rowan Galler	Judd School, Tonbridge, Kent
Anchal Garg	The Royal Latin School, Buckingham
Josh Gould	Bottisham Village College, Cambridgeshire
Mihir Goyal	UWCSEA Dover Campus, Singapore
Maxi Grindley	Hampton School, Middlesex
Maksym Grykshtas	King Edward VI Grammar S., Chelmsford

Christopher Guo	Wellington College International Shanghai
Aaryan Gupta	Latymer School, London
Aditya Hahesh	The High School of Glasgow
Moonis Haider	Bishop Vesey's Grammar S., Sutton Coldfield
Isabelle Ho	Henrietta Barnett School, London
Benjamin Hobson Taher	King Edward VI Camp Hill S. for Boys, Birmingham
Yong June Hong	Frankfurt International School
Evan Hopewell	Nottingham High School
Tian Hsu	St Paul's Girls' School, Hammersmith
Elliot Isaac	Colet Court School, London
Sean Jaffe	Summer Fields School, Oxford
Ryunosuk Kawakami	Dulwich College Singapore
Yoonjin Kim	St Paul's Girls' School, Hammersmith
Bella Kim	North London Collegiate S. Jeju, South Korea
Shubh Lashkery	Taipei European School
Ryan Lee	Dulwich College Seoul
Francesca Lee	North London Collegiate School
Joe Levine	Wallington County Grammar School, Surrey
Jiawen Li	St Paul's Girls' School, Hammersmith
Harvey Lin	Papplewick School, Ascot
Nihar Lohan	Magdalen College School, Oxford
Max Ma	Wilson's School, Surrey
Eleanor MacGillivray	King's School Ely, Cambridgeshire
Gavin McWhinnie	Balwearie High School, Kirkcaldy
Tanishq Mehta	Queen Elizabeth's School, Barnet
Sieun Min	St Nicholas School, Sao Paulo, Brazil
James Morgan	Ulverston Victoria High School, Cumbria
Luke Mulholland	King's School, Chester
Akhila Natarajan	Bancroft's School, Essex
Pearl Ng	West Island School (ESF), Hong Kong
Filip Olszewski	Queen Elizabeth's School, Barnet
Johan Orly	Westminster Under School
Tom O'Sullivan	Colet Court School, London
James Painter	Bell Baxter High School, Fife
Devan Patel	King Edward's School, Birmingham
Leo Petchey	South Hunsley School and Sixth Form C., East Yorks
Daniel Phillips	Belper School, Derbyshire
Benjamin Proctor	Swanmore Technology College, Hampshire

Gao Qu	The Stephen Perse Foundation, Cambridge
Daniel Radzik-Rahman	Queen Elizabeth's School, Barnet
Luke Rennells	Simon Langton Boys' Grammar. S, Canterbury
Benjamin Robson	Bartholomew School, Oxon
Jago Rowe	Parmiter's School, Watford
Grace Ruddick	Ralph Allen School, Bath
Chae Yeon Ryu	UWCSEA Dover Campus, Singapore
Jio Ryu	Wycombe Abbey School, High Wycombe
Shimaq Sakeel Mohamed	Queen Elizabeth's School, Barnet
Abhinav Santhiramohan	Queen Elizabeth's School, Barnet
Robert Seabourne	Lavington School, Wiltshire
Luke Sharkey	St Andrew's and St Bride's H. S., East Kilbride
Kishan Sharma	King Edward's School, Birmingham
Matthew Simpson	Larbert High School, nr Falkirk
Theodore Sinclair	King's College School, London
Ryan Smith	King Edward VI Grammar S., Chelmsford
Dan Suciu	Queen Elizabeth's School, Barnet
Adam Sukky	Norlington School, London
Jieun (Olivia) Sung	North London Collegiate S. Jeju, South Korea
Jeffrey Tan	Aylesbury Grammar School
Gemma Taylor	Oxford High School
Archie Thomas	Alleyn's School, Dulwich
Liz Thorn	St Paul's Girls' School, Hammersmith
Anastazie Towers	Weydon School, Farnham, Surrey
Leosha Trushin	Dean Close Preparatory School, Cheltenham
Liam Turner	Colyton Grammar School, Devon
Niklas Vainio	Westminster Under School
Pun Waiwitlikhit	Shrewsbury International School, Thailand
Larry Wang	Lomond School, Argyll and Bute
James Wu	Magdalen College School, Oxford
Amy Xu	Chesterton Community College, Cambridge
David Xu	Haberdashers' Aske's School for Boys, Herts
Angela Yang	Central Lancaster High School
Yuheng (Jacky) Yao	British International S., Phuket, Thailand
Rupert Yeung	Westminster Under School
Jack Yu	Tiffin School, Kingston-upon-Thames
Jimmy Yuan	King Edward's School, Birmingham
Annie Zhu	Egglescliffe School, nr Stockton-on-Tees
George Zou	Beijing Dulwich International School

The Intermediate Mathematical Challenge and its follow-up events

The Intermediate Mathematical Challenge (IMC) was held on Thursday 4th February 2016, and over 215,000 pupils took part. There were several different Intermediate Mathematical Olympiad and Kangaroo (IMOK) follow-up competitions and pupils were invited to the one appropriate to their school year and mark in the IMC. Around 500 candidates in each of Years 9, 10 and 11 sat the Olympiad papers (Cayley, Hamilton and Maclaurin respectively) and approximately 3500 more in each year group took a Kangaroo paper. We start with the IMC paper.

UK INTERMEDIATE MATHEMATICAL CHALLENGE

THURSDAY 4TH FEBRUARY 2016

Organised by the **United Kingdom Mathematics Trust**
and supported by

Institute
and Faculty
of Actuaries

RULES AND GUIDELINES (to be read before starting)

1. Do not open the paper until the Invigilator tells you to do so.

2. Time allowed: **1 hour**.
   No answers, or personal details, may be entered after the allowed hour is over.

3. The use of rough paper is allowed; **calculators** and measuring instruments are **forbidden**.

4. Candidates in England and Wales must be in School Year 11 or below.
   Candidates in Scotland must be in S4 or below.
   Candidates in Northern Ireland must be in School Year 12 or below.

5. **Use B or HB pencil only**. Mark *at most one* of the options A, B, C, D, E on the Answer Sheet for each question. Do not mark more than one option.

6. *Do not expect to finish the whole paper in 1 hour.* Concentrate first on Questions 1-15. When you have checked your answers to these, have a go at some of the later questions.

7. Five marks are awarded for each correct answer to Questions 1-15.
   Six marks are awarded for each correct answer to Questions 16-25.
   Each incorrect answer to Questions 16-20 loses 1 mark.
   Each incorrect answer to Questions 21-25 loses 2 marks.

8. Your Answer Sheet will be read only by a *dumb machine*. **Do not write or doodle on the sheet except to mark your chosen options**. The machine 'sees' all black pencil markings even if they are in the wrong places. If you mark the sheet in the wrong place, or leave bits of rubber stuck to the page, the machine will 'see' a mark and interpret this mark in its own way.

9. The questions on this paper challenge you to **think**, not to guess. You get more marks, and more satisfaction, by doing one question carefully than by guessing lots of answers.
   The UK IMC is about solving interesting problems, not about lucky guessing.

The UKMT is a registered charity
http://www.ukmt.org.uk

1. What is the value of $6102 - 2016$?

   A 3994   B 4086   C 4096   D 4114   E 4994

2. Which of the following fractions is closest to 1?

   A $\dfrac{7}{8}$ B $\dfrac{8}{7}$ C $\dfrac{9}{10}$ D $\dfrac{10}{11}$ E $\dfrac{11}{10}$

3. How many of these five expressions give answers which are *not* prime numbers?

   $1^2 + 2^2$ $2^2 + 3^2$ $3^2 + 4^2$ $4^2 + 5^2$ $5^2 + 6^2$

   A 0   B 1   C 2   D 3   E 4

4. Amrita is baking a cake today. She bakes a cake every fifth day. How many days will it be before she next bakes a cake on a Thursday?

   A 5   B 7   C 14   D 25   E 35

5. When travelling from London to Edinburgh by train, you pass a sign saying 'Edinburgh 200 miles'. Then, $3\frac{1}{2}$ miles later, you pass another sign saying 'Half way between London and Edinburgh'.

   How many miles is it by train from London to Edinburgh?

   A 393   B $396\frac{1}{2}$ C 400   D $403\frac{1}{2}$ E 407

6. One third of the animals in Jacob's flock are goats, the rest are sheep. There are twelve more sheep than goats.

   How many animals are there altogether in Jacob's flock?

   A 12   B 24   C 36   D 48   E 60

7. In the diagram, what is the value of x?

   A 23   B 24   C 25   D 26   E 27

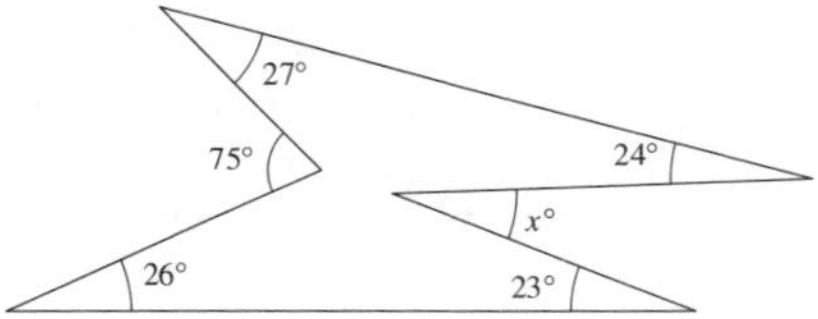

8. What is the value of $2.017 \times 2016 - 10.16 \times 201.7$?

   A 2.016   B 2.017   C 20.16   D 2016   E 2017

9. The world's fastest tortoise is acknowledged to be a leopard tortoise from County Durham called Bertie. In July 2014, Bertie sprinted along a 5.5 m long track in an astonishing 19.6 seconds.

   What was Bertie's approximate average speed in km per hour?

   A 0.1   B 0.5   C 1   D 5   E 10

10. The angles of a quadrilateral taken in order are $x°$, $5x°$, $2x°$ and $4x°$. Which of the following is the quadrilateral?

    A kite   B parallelogram   C rhombus   D arrowhead   E trapezium

11. The net shown consists of squares and equilateral triangles. The net is folded to form a rhombicuboctahedron, as shown.

   When the face marked P is placed face down on a table, which face will be facing up?

   A   B   C   D   E

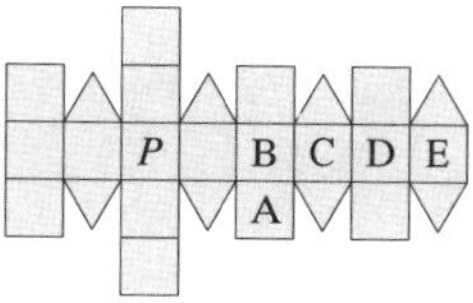

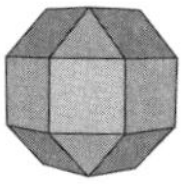

12. The sum of two numbers a and b is 7 and the difference between them is 2.

   What is the value of $a \times b$?

   A $8\frac{1}{4}$ B $9\frac{1}{4}$ C $10\frac{1}{4}$ D $11\frac{1}{4}$ E $12\frac{1}{4}$

13. The diagram shows a heptagon with a line of three circles on each side. Each circle is to contain exactly one number. The numbers 8 to 14 are distributed as shown and the numbers 1 to 7 are to be distributed to the remaining circles. The total of the numbers in each of the lines of three circles is to be the same.

   What is this total?

   A 18   B 19   C 20   D 21   E 22

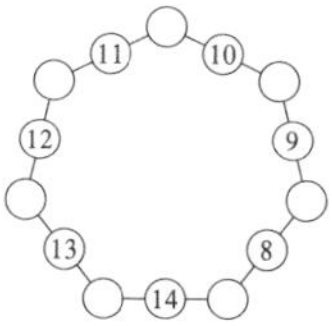

14. Tegwen has the same number of brothers as she has sisters. Each one of her brothers has 50% more sisters than brothers.

   How many children are in Tegwen's family?

   A 5   B 7   C 9   D 11   E 13

15. The circle has radius 1 cm. Two vertices of the square lie on the circle. One edge of the square goes through the centre of the circle, as shown.

   What is the area of the square?

   A $\frac{4}{5}$ cm^2 B $\frac{\pi}{5}$ cm^2 C 1 cm^2 D $\frac{\pi}{4}$ cm^2 E $\frac{5}{4}$ cm^2

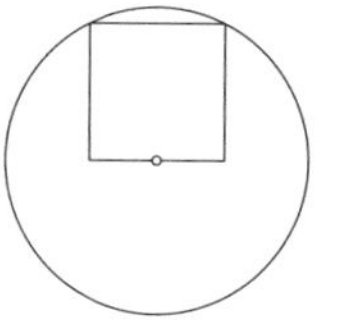

16. How many of the following positive integers are divisible by 24?

   $$2^2 \times 3^2 \times 5^2 \times 7^3 \qquad 2^2 \times 3^2 \times 5^3 \times 7^2 \qquad 2^2 \times 3^3 \times 5^2 \times 7^2 \qquad 2^3 \times 3^2 \times 5^2 \times 7^2$$

   A 0   B 1   C 2   D 3   E 4

17. The shaded region in the diagram, bounded by two concentric circles, is called an *annulus*. The circles have radii 2 cm and 14 cm.

   The dashed circle divides the area of this annulus into two equal areas.

   What is its radius?

   A 9 cm   B 10 cm   C 11 cm   D 12 cm   E 13 cm

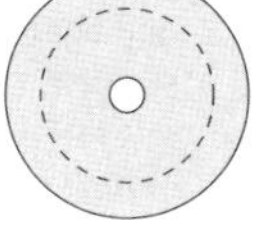

18. The sum of the areas of the squares on the sides of a right-angled isosceles triangle is 72 cm^2.

   What is the area of the triangle?

   A 6 cm^2 B 8 cm^2 C 9 cm^2 D 12 cm^2 E 18 cm^2

19. A list of positive integers has a median of 8, a mode of 9 and a mean of 10.

   What is the smallest possible number of integers in the list?

   A 5   B 6   C 7   D 8   E 9

20. Two semicircles are drawn in a rectangle as shown.
    What is the width of the overlap of the two semicircles?
    A 3 cm   B 4 cm   C 5 cm   D 6 cm   E 7 cm

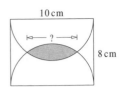

———————

21. The diagram shows a regular octagon. What is the ratio of the area
    of the shaded trapezium to the area of the whole octagon?

    A 1 : 4   B 5 : 16   C 1 : 3   D $\sqrt{2}$: 2   E 3 : 8

22. In a particular group of people, some always tell the truth, the rest always lie. There are 2016
    in the group. One day, the group is sitting in a circle. Each person in the group says, "Both the
    person on my left and the person on my right are liars."
    What is the difference between the largest and smallest number of people who could be telling
    the truth?

    A 0   B 72   C 126   D 288   E 336

23. A Saxon silver penny, from the reign of Ethelbert II in the eighth
    century, was sold in 2014 for £78 000. A design on the coin depicts
    a circle surrounded by four equal arcs, each a quarter of a circle, as
    shown. The width of the design is 2 cm.
    What is the radius of the small circle, in centimetres?

    A $\frac{1}{2}$ B $2 - \sqrt{2}$ C $\frac{1}{2}\sqrt{2}$ D $5 - 3\sqrt{2}$ E $2\sqrt{2} - 2$

24. Every day, Aimee goes up an escalator on her journey to work. If she stands still, it takes her
    60 seconds to travel from the bottom to the top. One day the escalator was broken so she had
    to walk up it. This took her 90 seconds.
    How many seconds would it take her to travel up the escalator if she walked up at the same
    speed as before while it was working?

    A 30   B 32   C 36   D 45   E 75

25. The tiling pattern shown uses two types of tile, regular hexagons
    and equilateral triangles, with the length of each side of the
    equilateral triangles equal to half the length of each side of the
    hexagons. A large number of tiles is used to cover a floor.
    Which of the following is closest to the fraction of the floor that is
    shaded black?

    A $\frac{1}{8}$ B $\frac{1}{10}$ C $\frac{1}{12}$ D $\frac{1}{13}$ E $\frac{1}{16}$

The IMC solutions

As with the Junior Challenge, a solutions leaflet was sent out.

Institute
and Faculty
of Actuaries

UK INTERMEDIATE MATHEMATICAL CHALLENGE

THURSDAY 4TH FEBRUARY 2016

Organised by the **United Kingdom Mathematics Trust**
from the School of Mathematics, University of Leeds

SOLUTIONS LEAFLET

This solutions leaflet for the IMC is sent in the hope that it might provide all concerned with some alternative solutions to the ones they have obtained. It is not intended to be definitive. The organisers would be very pleased to receive alternatives created by candidates.

For reasons of space, these solutions are necessarily brief. Extended solutions, and some exercises for further investigation, can be found at:

http://www.ukmt.org.uk/

The UKMT is a registered charity

1. **B** $6116 - 2016 = 4100$, so $6102 - 2016 = 4100 - 14 = 4086$.

2. **D** The difference between the given options and 1 is $\frac{1}{8}$, $\frac{1}{7}$, $\frac{1}{10}$, $\frac{1}{11}$ and $\frac{1}{10}$ respectively. As $\frac{1}{11}$ is the smallest of these fractions, $\frac{10}{11}$ is closest to 1.

3. **B** The values of the five expressions are 5, 13, 25, 41 and 61 respectively. Of these, only 25 is non-prime.

4. E   Amrita bakes every 5 days and Thursdays come every 7 days. So the next time Amrita bakes on a Thursday will be in 35 days time since 35 is the lowest common multiple of 5 and 7.

5. A   By train, the distance in miles of the second sign from Edinburgh is $200 - 3\frac{1}{2}$. This sign is halfway between London and Edinburgh, so the distance in miles between the two cities is $2(200 - 3\frac{1}{2}) = 400 - 7 = 393$.

6. C   Let g and s be the number of goats and sheep respectively. Then $s = 2g$ and $12 = s - g = 2g - g = g$. Hence the number of animals is $s + g = 3g = 36$.

7. C   The angles at a point sum to $360°$ so
$75 + z = 360$ and $y + x = 360$.
Therefore $75 + z + y + x = 720$.
The sum of the interior angles of a
hexagon is $4 \times 180° = 720°$.
Therefore

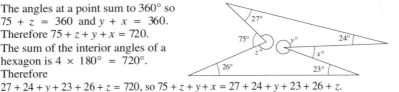

$27 + 24 + y + 23 + 26 + z = 720$, so $75 + z + y + x = 27 + 24 + y + 23 + 26 + z$.
Hence $75 + x = 27 + 24 + 23 + 26 = 100$. So $x = 100 - 75 = 25$.

8. E $2.017 \times 2016 - 10.16 \times 201.7 = 201.7 \times 20.16 - 10.16 \times 201.7$
$= 201.7(20.16 - 10.16) = 201.7 \times 10 = 2017$.

9. C   Bertie travelled 5.5 m in 19.6 s, which is just less than one-third of a minute. So his average speed was approximately 16.5 m per minute, which is equal to 990 m in one hour, as $16.5 \times 60 = 990$. Now 990 m = 0.99 km, so Bertie's approximate average speed was 1 km per hour.

10. E   The sum of the interior angles of a quadrilateral is
$360°$, so $x + 5x + 2x + 4x = 360$, that is
$12x = 360$. Therefore $x = 30$ and the angles of
the quadrilateral, taken in order, are $30°$, $150°$,
$60°$ and $120°$. The diagram shows the shape of the quadrilateral.

Since $30 + 150 = 180$, we see that AB and DC are parallel. Since it has no equal angles, it is not a rhombus or a parallelogram so it is a trapezium.

11. D   When the net is folded up to form the
rhombicuboctahedron, the left-hand
edge of the square marked X is joined
to the right-hand edge of the square
marked E so that the eight squares at
the centre of the net form a band
around the solid. In this band, the square opposite square P is the square which is four squares away from P, that is square D. So if the square marked P is placed face down on a table, then the square marked D will be facing up.

12. D   Assume that $a > b$. Then $a + b = 7$ and $a - b = 2$. Adding these two equations together gives $2a = 9$. So $a = \frac{9}{2}$ and hence $b = 7 - \frac{9}{2} = \frac{14-9}{2} = \frac{5}{2}$.
Therefore $a \times b = \frac{9}{2} \times \frac{5}{2} = \frac{45}{4} = 11\frac{1}{4}$.

13. B   In the seven lines each of the integers from 1 to 7 is used twice and each of the integers from 8 to 14 is used once. So the sum of the numbers in the seven lines is $(1 + 2 + \ldots + 14) + (1 + 2 + \ldots + 7) = 105 + 28 = 133$. Therefore the total of the numbers in each line is $133 \div 7 = 19$.

It is left as an exercise for the reader to show that it is possible to complete the diagram so that the total of the three numbers in each line is indeed 19.

14. D   Let there be g girls and b boys in Tegwen's family. Then, as she has the same number of brothers as she does sisters, $b = g - 1$. Also, each of her brothers has 50% more sisters than brothers. Therefore $g = \frac{3}{2}(b - 1)$. So $b + 1 = \frac{3}{2}(b - 1)$ and hence $2b + 2 = 3b - 3$. Rearranging this equation gives $b = 5$. So $g = 5 + 1 = 6$. Therefore there are $5 + 6 = 11$ children in Tegwen's family.

15. A   Let the length of the side of the square be $2x$ cm. Then, using Pythagoras' Theorem in the triangle shown, $(2x)^2 + x^2 = 1^2$. So $4x^2 + x^2 = 1$. Therefore $x^2 = \frac{1}{5}$ and the area of the square is $4x^2$ cm^2 $= \frac{4}{5}$ cm^2.

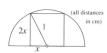

16. B   The prime factorisation of $24 = 2^3 \times 3$. Therefore all multiples of 24 must include both 2^3 and 3 in their prime factorisation. Of the options given, only the last includes 2^3. As it is also a multiple of 3, it is a multiple of 24.

17. B   Let the radius of the dashed circle be r cm. Then one of the equal areas is bounded by circles of radii of 14 cm and r cm, whilst the other is bounded by circles of radii of r cm and 2 cm. So $\pi \times 14^2 - \pi r^2 = \pi r^2 - \pi \times 2^2$. Dividing throughout by π gives $196 - r^2 = r^2 - 4$. So $2r^2 = 200$, that is $r^2 = 100$. Therefore $r = 10$ (since $r > 0$).

18. C   Let the length of each of the shorter sides of the triangle be x cm and the length of its hypotenuse be y cm. Then, by Pythagoras' Theorem: $x^2 + x^2 = y^2$. So $y^2 = 2x^2$. Also, $x^2 + x^2 + y^2 = 72$, so $4x^2 = 72$, that is $x^2 = 18$. Now the area of the triangle, in cm^2, is $\frac{1}{2} \times x \times x = \frac{1}{2}x^2 = 9$.

19. B   From the information given, there are at least two 9s in the list, since 9 is the mode, and at least one number greater than 10, since 10 is the mean. So there are at least three numbers greater than 8 in the list. Therefore the list must contain at least six numbers, as the median of the numbers is 8. Moreover, it is possible to find suitable lists of six numbers with sum 60 (as the mean is 10), for example 1, 2, 7, 9, 9, 32.

20. D   In the diagram, O is the centre of the lower semicircle, A and C are the points of intersection of the two semicircles and B is the point at the centre of the rectangle and also of the overlap. Now OA is a radius of the semicircle so OA has length 5 cm. Also OB is half the height of the rectangle so has length 4 cm. Angle ABO is a right angle. So triangle ABO is a $(3, 4, 5)$ triangle and hence $AC = 2 \times 3$ cm $= 6$ cm.

21. A   Let a be the side length of the octagon and b be as shown on the diagram. The square in the centre is a by a, each rectangle is a by b and the triangles are each half of a b by b square. Applying Pythagoras' Theorem to a triangle shows that $a^2 = 2b^2$. So the shaded area is $b^2 + ab = b^2 + \sqrt{2}b^2 = b^2(1 + \sqrt{2})$. Similarly the total area of the figure is $a^2 + 4ab + 2b^2 = 4b^2 + 4\sqrt{2}b^2 = b^2(4 + 4\sqrt{2})$. Therefore the ratio required is $(1 + \sqrt{2}) : (4 + 4\sqrt{2}) = 1 : 4$.

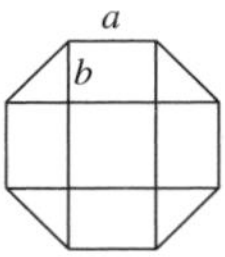

22. E   For brevity, let T denote a truth teller and L a liar. Clearly each T has to have an L on each side. Each L either (i) has a T on each side or (ii) has an L on one side and a T on the other side. The largest number of Ts will occur if (i) is always the case. This gives the arrangement TLTLTL… which, since 2 divides 2016, joins up correctly after going round the table. In this case the number of Ts is $\frac{1}{2} \times 2016$. The smallest will occur if case (ii) always is the case. This gives the arrangement LLTLLTLLT… which, since 3 divides 2016, also joins up correctly. In this case the number of Ts is $\frac{1}{3} \times 2016$. The difference is $\frac{1}{6} \times 2016 = 336$.

23. B   The diagram shows part of the figure, to which have been added A and C, centres of two of the quarter-circle arcs, B and D, points of intersection of two arcs, and E, the centre of the small circle. In cm, the radii of each arc and the small circle are R and r respectively. Firstly, note that $\angle BCD$ is a right angle as arc BD is a quarter of a circle. Therefore, by Pythagoras' Theorem $R^2 + R^2 = 2^2$ so $R = \sqrt{2}$. Consider triangle ACE: from the symmetry of the figure we deduce that $\angle AEC = \frac{1}{4} \times 360° = 90°$. So, by Pythagoras' Theorem $(R + r)^2 + (R + r)^2 = (2R)^2 = 4R^2$. Therefore $(R + r)^2 = 2R^2 = 2 \times 2 = 4$. Hence $R + r = 2$, so $r = 2 - R = 2 - \sqrt{2}$.

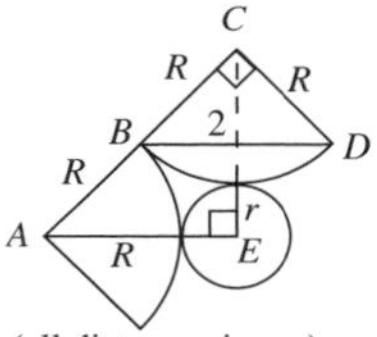

(all distances in cm)

24. C   Let the distance from the bottom of the escalator to the top be d. Then, when she stands still, Aimee travels $d/60$ every second. When she is walking, Aimee travels $d/90$ every second. So when Aimee walks up the working escalator, the distance which she travels every second is $\dfrac{d}{60} + \dfrac{d}{90} = \dfrac{3d + 2d}{180} = \dfrac{5d}{180} = \dfrac{d}{36}$. So the required number of seconds is 36.

25. D   The tiled area may be considered to be a tessellation of the figure shown, except for the dotted lines. For every hexagonal tile, there are two triangular tiles. The diagram shows that the area of each hexagonal tile is 24 times the area of each triangular tile. As there are two triangular tiles to each hexagonal tile, the ratio of the fraction of the floor shaded black to that which is shaded grey is $2 : 24 = 1 : 12$. Therefore, in the repeating pattern of tiles, the fraction which is shaded black is 1/13.

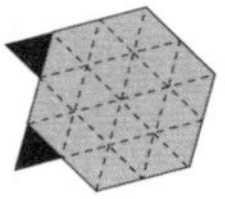

The exact ratios given are for the infinite plane. Since we are dealing with a finite floor, this is approximate since the edges are unpredictable, but close to correct since the numbers involved are large.

The answers

The table below shows the proportion of pupils' choices. The correct answer is shown in bold. [The percentages are rounded to the nearest whole number.]

Qn	A	B	C	D	E	Blank
1	2	**91**	5	1	0	1
2	5	5	13	**66**	9	2
3	3	**53**	15	11	15	1
4	7	11	7	10	**62**	2
5	**49**	6	2	5	35	2
6	2	12	**77**	5	1	2
7	20	13	**44**	11	6	6
8	5	7	10	30	**40**	6
9	23	29	**23**	13	5	6
10	13	11	17	26	**27**	5
11	5	5	16	**64**	6	3
12	17	11	12	**48**	6	5
13	13	**36**	15	15	11	10
14	29	35	12	**15**	4	5
15	**13**	9	37	23	8	9
16	12	**14**	9	3	3	58
17	6	**12**	3	13	2	64
18	4	6	**7**	7	12	65
19	8	**12**	11	4	3	62
20	3	5	7	**16**	2	67
21	**7**	8	8	2	7	68
22	11	3	3	3	**5**	75
23	6	**4**	4	2	2	81
24	19	2	**5**	7	2	65
25	3	3	8	**3**	6	77

IMC 2016: Some comments on the pupils' choice of answers as sent to schools in the letter with the results

Last year the mean score was low. The Problems Group therefore attempted to set a more accessible paper this year. It has been only partially successful. The mean score has risen from 35 in 2015 to 37 this year, which is still somewhat lower than we would wish. We have not been very successful in setting questions which are more interesting than routine problems, but which three-quarters of the pupils manage to get right.

With your results you will find tables showing the distribution of the response of your pupils to the individual questions, and the national distribution of answers which shows that only Questions 1 and 6 were answered correctly by more than three-quarters of all the pupils who took part.

In this letter we have space only to look at a few of the questions which we hoped would prove easy, but which many pupils failed to answer correctly.

Four of the expressions given in Question 3 work out to be prime numbers, and only one is not. Careless reading of the question will lead some pupils to choose option E, but what can we make of the 25% who seemed to think that 2 or 3 of the numbers are not primes? Did they fail to evaluate the expressions correctly, or are they not good at knowing which two-digit numbers are primes?

In Question 5 over a third of the pupils selected the wrong option 407. This suggests that they did not read the question carefully or failed to think clearly about the fact that the train was travelling *towards* Edinburgh.

Question 7 was intended to be an easy angle-chasing geometry question. The most popular wrong option 23° may have been chosen because two sides of the polygon look as though they might be parallel. We surmise that for other pupils the difficulty was that, although they may know that the interior angles of a regular hexagon are each 120°, they do not have secure knowledge about the total of the interior angles of an irregular hexagon. Therefore, there was no way they could answer the question other by making a guess based on the diagram.

The poor response to Question 9 is also disappointing. The choice of the wrong option 0.1 is not too surprising, as the best of us can lose a factor of 10 when doing an estimation of this kind under time pressure, but we are puzzled by the popularity of 0.5 as the correct answer.

Given the rather poor response to earlier numerical questions, it was encouraging to see that half the pupils answered Question 12 correctly.

The later questions are harder, and are used to help us select the pupils who are invited to take the Cayley, Hamilton and Maclaurin and Kangaroo papers. Many of these questions are very challenging and most students did not attempt them. Pupils who did well enough on these questions to qualify for one of the follow-on events should be congratulated on their excellent achievement. We hope that their success will gain recognition throughout your school.

The profile of marks obtained is shown below.

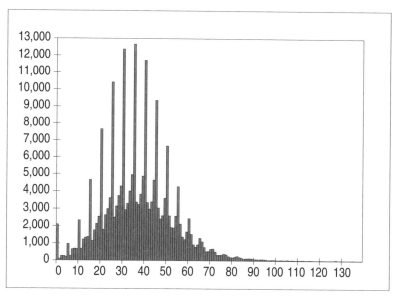

Bar chart showing the actual frequencies in the 2016 IMC

On the basis of the standard proportions used by the UKMT, the cut-off marks were set at

GOLD – 62 or over   SILVER – 50 to 61   BRONZE – 40 to 49

The certificates were virtually identical in design to those used for the JMC.

The cut-off scores for the follow-up competitions were

Year (E&W)	Minimum mark	Event	Minimum mark	Event
11	95	Maclaurin	66	Kangaroo Pink
10	89	Hamilton	66	Kangaroo Pink
9	81	Cayley	60	Kangaroo Grey

The Intermediate Mathematical Olympiad and Kangaroo

(a) *Kangaroo*

The 2016 Intermediate Kangaroo (a multiple choice paper with 25 questions) took place on Thursday 17th March. It was also held in many other countries across Europe and beyond with over five million candidates. As in previous years, the UKMT constructed two Kangaroo papers. Invitations were increased in 2016 by 10% to just under 10,500.

EUROPEAN 'KANGAROO' MATHEMATICAL CHALLENGE
'GREY' and 'PINK'
Thursday 17th March 2016

Organised by the United Kingdom Mathematics Trust and the Association Kangourou Sans Frontières

This competition is being taken by 6 million students in over 60 countries worldwide.

RULES AND GUIDELINES (to be read before starting):

1. Do not open the paper until the Invigilator tells you to do so.

2. Time allowed: **1 hour**.
   No answers, or personal details, may be entered after the allowed hour is over.

3. The use of rough paper is allowed; **calculators** and measuring instruments are **forbidden**.

4. Candidates in England and Wales must be in School Year 9 or below.
   Candidates in Scotland must be in S2 or below.
   Candidates in Northern Ireland must be in School Year 10 or below.

5. **Use B or HB non-propelling pencil only**. For each question mark *at most one* of the options A, B, C, D, E on the Answer Sheet. Do not mark more than one option.

6. Five marks will be awarded for each correct answer to Questions 1 - 15.
   Six marks will be awarded for each correct answer to Questions 16 - 25.

7. *Do not expect to finish the whole paper in 1 hour.* Concentrate first on Questions 1-15. When you have checked your answers to these, have a go at some of the later questions.

8. The questions on this paper challenge you **to think**, not to guess. Though you will not lose marks for getting answers wrong, you will undoubtedly get more marks, and more satisfaction, by doing a few questions carefully than by guessing lots of answers.

Enquiries about the European Kangaroo should be sent to:
UKMT, School of Mathematics, University of Leeds, Leeds, LS2 9JT.
(Tel. 0113 343 2339)
http://www.ukmt.org.uk

2016 European Grey Kangaroo Questions

1. The triangle in the diagram contains a right angle. What is the sum of the other two marked angles on the diagram?

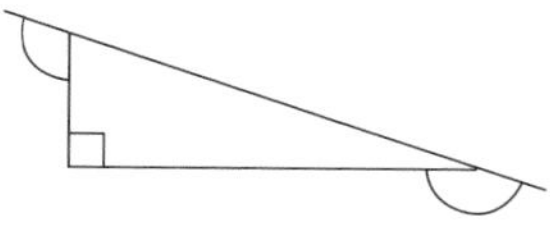

   A 150°   B 180°   C 270°   D 320°   E 360°

2. Jenny had to add 26 to a certain number. Instead she subtracted 26 and obtained −14. What number should she have obtained?

   A 28   B 32   C 36   D 38   E 42

3. Joanna turns over the card shown about its lower edge and then about its right-hand edge, as indicated in the diagram. What does she see?

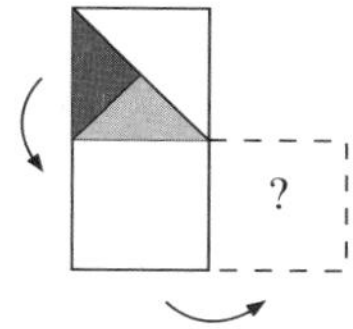

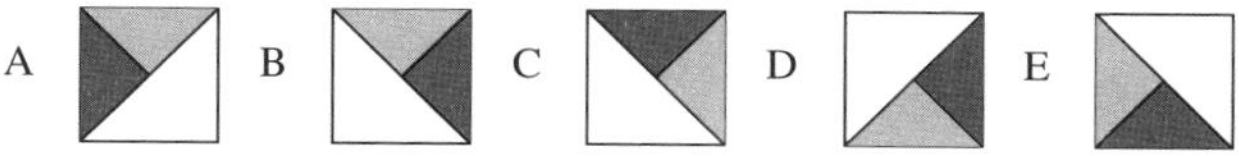

   A   B   C   D   E

4. In my school, 60% of the teachers come to school by bicycle. There are 45 teachers who come to school by bicycle. Only 12% come to school by car. How many teachers come to school by car?

   A 4   B 6   C 9   D 10   E 12

5. What is the total area in cm^2 of the shaded region?

   A 50   B 80   C 100   D 120   E 150

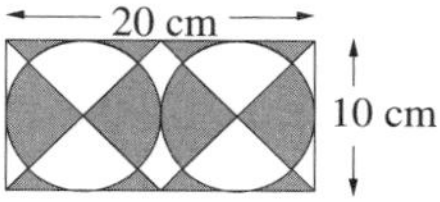

6. Two pieces of rope have lengths 1 m and 2 m. Alex cuts the pieces into several parts. All the parts have the same length. Which of the following could not be the total number of parts he obtains?

   A 6   B 8   C 9   D 12   E 15

7. Four towns P, Q, R and S are connected by roads, as shown. A race uses each road exactly once. The race starts at S and finishes at Q. How many possible routes are there for the race?

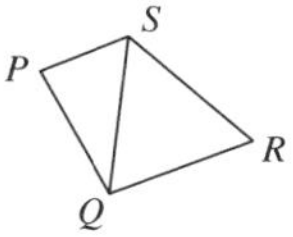

   A 10   B 8   C 6   D 4   E 2

8. Petra has 49 blue beads and one red bead. How many beads must Petra remove so that 90% of her beads are blue?

   A 4   B 10   C 29   D 39   E 40

9. Three equilateral triangles are cut from the corners of a large equilateral triangle to form an irregular hexagon, as shown in the diagram.

   The perimeter of the large equilateral triangle is 60 cm. The perimeter of the irregular hexagon is 40 cm. What is the sum of the perimeters of the triangles that were cut from the large triangle?

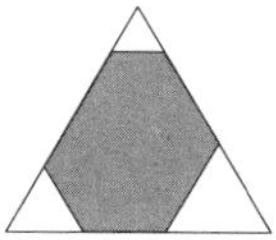

   A 60 cm   B 66 cm   C 72 cm   D 75 cm   E 81 cm

10. Tim, Tom and Tam are triplets (three brothers born on the same day). Their twin brothers Jon and Jim are exactly three years younger. Which of the following numbers could be the sum of the ages of the five brothers?

    A 36   B 53   C 76   D 89   E 92

11. A 3 cm wide strip is grey on one side and white on the other. Maria folds the strip, so that it fits inside a rectangle of length 27 cm, as shown. The grey trapeziums are identical. What is the length of the original strip?

    A 36 cm   B 48 cm   C 54 cm   D 57 cm   E 81 cm

12. Two kangaroos Bo and Ing start to jump at the same time, from the same point, in the same direction. After that, they each make one jump per second. Each of Bo's jumps is 6 m in length. Ing's first jump is 1 m in length, his second is 2 m, his third is 3 m, and so on. After how many jumps does Ing catch Bo?

    A 10   B 11   C 12   D 13   E 14

13. Ivor writes down the results of the quarter-finals, the semi-finals and the final of a knock-out tournament. The results are (not necessarily in this order): Bart beat Antony, Carl beat Damian, Glen beat Harry, Glen beat Carl, Carl beat Bart, Ed beat Fred and Glen beat Ed. Which pair played in the final?

    A Glen and Carl   B Glen and Harry   C Carl and Bart
             D Glen and Ed   E Carl and Damian

14. Seven standard dice are glued together to make the solid shown. The pairs of faces of the dice that are glued together have the same number of dots on them. How many dots are on the surface of the solid?

    A 24   B 90   C 95   D 105   E 126

15. There are twenty students in a class. Some of them sit in pairs so that exactly one third of the boys sit with a girl, and exactly one half of the girls sit with a boy. How many boys are there in the class?

    A 9   B 12   C 15   D 16   E 18

16. Inside a square of area 36 cm², there are shaded regions as shown. The total shaded area is 27 cm². What is the value of $p + q + r + s$?

    A 4 cm   B 6 cm   C 8 cm   D 9 cm   E 10 cm

17. Theo's watch is 10 minutes slow, but he believes it is 5 minutes fast. Leo's watch is 5 minutes fast, but he believes it is 10 minutes slow. At the same moment, each of them looks at his own watch. Theo thinks it is 12:00. What time does Leo think it is?

    A 11:30   B 11:45   C 12:00   D 12:30   E 12:45

18. Twelve girls met in a cafe. On average, they ate $1\frac{1}{2}$ cupcakes each, although no cupcakes were actually divided. None of them ate more than two cupcakes and two of them ate no cupcakes at all. How many girls ate two cupcakes?

    A 2   B 5   C 6   D 7   E 8

19. Little Red Riding Hood is delivering waffles to three grannies. She starts with a basket full of waffles. Just before she enters the house of each granny, the Big Bad Wolf eats half of the waffles in her basket. She delivers the same number of waffles to each granny. When she leaves the third granny's house, she has no waffles left. Which of the following numbers definitely divides the number of waffles she started with?

    A 4   B 5   C 6   D 7   E 9

20. The cube shown is divided into 64 small cubes. Exactly one of the cubes is grey, as shown in the diagram. Two cubes are said to be 'neighbours' if they have a common face. On the first day, the white neighbours of the grey cube are changed to grey. On the second day, the white neighbours of all the grey cubes are changed to grey.

    How many grey cubes are there at the end of the second day?

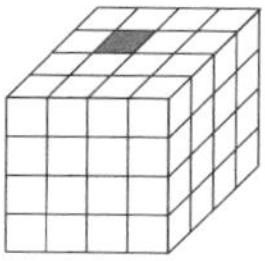

    A 11   B 13   C 15   D 16   E 17

21. Several different positive integers are written on a blackboard. The product of the smallest two of them is 16. The product of the largest two of them is 225. What is the sum of all the integers written on the blackboard?

    A 38   B 42   C 44   D 58   E 243

22. The diagram shows a pentagon. The lengths of the sides of the pentagon are given in the diagram.

    Sepideh draws five circles with centres A, B, C, D and E such that the two circles with centres at the ends of a side of the pentagon touch on that side. Which point is the centre of the largest circle that she draws?

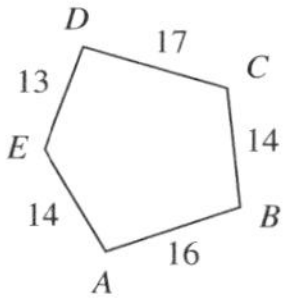

    A A B B C C D D E E

23. Katie writes a different positive integer on the top face of each of the fourteen cubes in the pyramid shown.

    The sum of the nine integers written on the cubes in the bottom layer is 50. The integer written on each of the cubes in the middle and top layers of the pyramid is equal to the sum of the integers on the four cubes underneath it. What is the greatest possible integer that she can write on the top cube?

    A 80   B 98   C 104   D 118   E 128

24. A train has five carriages, each containing at least one passenger. Two passengers are said to be 'neighbours' if either they are in the same carriage or they are in adjacent carriages. Each passenger has exactly five or exactly ten neighbours. How many passengers are there on the train?

    A 13   B 15   C 17   D 20   E There is more than one answer.

25. A $3 \times 3 \times 3$ cube is built from 15 black cubes and 12 white cubes. Five faces of the larger cube are shown.

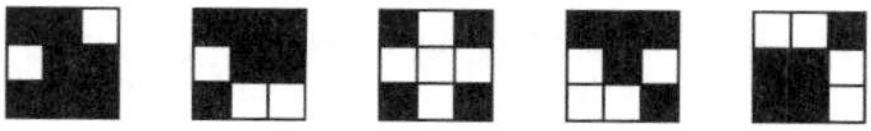

    Which of the following is the sixth face of the larger cube?

    A 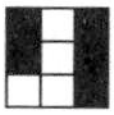   B 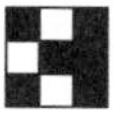   C    D 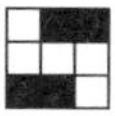   E

Solutions to the 2016 European Grey Kangaroo

1. **C** Since angles in a triangle add to 180° and one angle is given as 90°, the two blank angles in the triangle add to 90°. Since angles on a straight line add to 180°, the sum of the two marked angles and the two blank angles in the triangle is $2 \times 180° = 360°$. Therefore the sum of the two marked angles is $360° - 90° = 270°$.

2. **D** Jenny subtracted 26 instead of adding 26 and obtained -14. Therefore to obtain the answer she should have obtained, she must add two lots of 26 to -14. Therefore the number she should have obtained is $-14 + 2 \times 26 = -14 + 52 = 38$.

3. **B** When the card is turned about its lower edge, the light grey triangle will be at the top and the dark grey triangle will be on the left. When this is turned about its right-hand edge, the light grey triangle will be at the top and the dark grey triangle will be on the right. Therefore Joanna will see option B.

4. **C** The percentage of teachers coming to school by car is one fifth of the percentage of teachers coming to school by bicycle. Therefore, the number of teachers coming to school by car is $\frac{1}{5} \times 45 = 9$.

5. **C** The area of the whole rectangle is 200 cm². Suppose the rectangle is cut in two by a vertical cut joining the midpoints of its longer edges and the right-hand half is then given a quarter turn about its centre to produce the arrangement as shown. It can then be seen that every grey region has a corresponding white region of the same shape and size. Hence, the total area of the grey regions is half the area of the rectangle and so is 100 cm².

6. **B** Since all the parts cut are of the same length, Alex will obtain twice as many parts from his 2 metre piece of rope as he does from his 1 metre piece of rope. Hence, the total number of parts he obtains will always be a multiple of 3, and he can make it any multiple of 3. Of the options given, only 8 is not a multiple of 3 and so could not be obtained.

7. **C** Any route starts by going from S to P or S to Q or S to R. Any route starting S to P must then go to Q and then has the choice of going clockwise or anticlockwise round triangle QSR, giving two possible routes. By a similar argument, there are two routes that start S to R. For those routes that start by going from S to Q, there is then the choice of going clockwise or anticlockwise round quadrilateral $QPSR$, giving two more routes. Therefore there are six possible routes in total.

8. **E** For the one red bead to be 10% of the final number of beads, there must be nine blue beads representing 90% of the final number of beads. Therefore the number of beads Petra must remove is $49 - 9 = 40$.

9. **A** Let the lengths of the sides of the equilateral triangles that are cut off be x cm, y cm and z cm, as shown in the diagram.

The length of a side of the large equilateral triangle is $\frac{1}{3} \times 60$ cm $= 20$ cm. The perimeter of the irregular hexagon is 40 cm. Therefore we have

$40 = x + (20 - x - y) + y + (20 - y - z) + z + (20 - z - x)$. Hence $40 = 60 - (x + y + z)$ and therefore $x + y + z = 20$. Therefore the sum of the perimeters of the triangles cut off is $(3x + 3y + 3z)$ cm $= 60$ cm.

10. D   Let x be the age of each of Tim, Tom and Tam. Therefore the age of both Jon and Jim is $x - 3$. Therefore the sum of all their ages is $3x + 2(x - 3) = 5x - 6$ and $5x - 6$ can also be written as $5(x - 1) - 1$. Hence the sum of their ages is always one less than a multiple of 5. Of the options given, the only number for which this is true is 89 (when Tim, Tom and Tam are 19 and Jon and Jim are 16).

11. D   Let the length of the shorter of the two parallel sides of the grey trapeziums be x cm. Since the folded shape is 27 cm long and the strip is 3 cm wide, we have $3 + x + 3 + x + 3 + x + 3 + x + 3 = 27$ which has solution $x = 3$. Hence the length of the longer of the two parallel sides of the grey trapezium is $(3 + x + 3)$ cm $= 9$ cm. Also, since the height of each trapezium is equal to the width of the strip, the height is 3 cm and hence the height of each of the small rectangles is $(6 - 3)$ cm. Therefore the total length of the strip (along the edge marked in the diagram) is

$$(6 + 9 + 3 + 3 + 3 + 3 + 3 + 9 + 3 + 3 + 3 + 3 + 6) \text{ cm } = 57 \text{ cm}.$$

6 cm

27 cm

12. B   Since the two kangaroos jump at the same time and in the same direction, Ing will catch Bo when they have jumped the same distance. After n jumps, Bo has jumped $6n$ metres whereas Ing has jumped $(1 + 2 + 3 + \dots + n)$ metres. The sum of the whole numbers from 1 to n is given by the formula $\frac{1}{2}n(n + 1)$ (it is left as an exercise for the reader to prove this) and hence $\frac{1}{2}n(n + 1) = 6n$. Hence $n + 1 = 12$, which has solution $n = 11$. Therefore Ing will catch Bo after 11 jumps.

13. A   The pair who play in the final will have played three matches. Only Glen and Carl play three matches so they are the pair who play in the final.

14. D   A standard die has a total of 21 dots on its faces. The faces that are glued together have the same number of dots. Since the die in the centre of the solid has all its faces glued to other dice, the sum of the dots that are *not* on the surface of the solid is 2×21. Therefore, the number of dots on the surface of the solid is $7 \times 21 - 2 \times 21 = 5 \times 21 = 105$.

15. B   Let the number of boys in the class be x and let the number of girls be y. Since one third of the boys sit with a girl and one half of the girls sit with a boy, we have $\frac{1}{3}x = \frac{1}{2}y$ and hence $\frac{2}{3}x = y$. The total number of students in the class is 20. Therefore $x + \frac{2}{3}x = 20$. Hence $\frac{5}{3}x = 20$, which has solution $x = 12$. Therefore there are 12 boys in the class.

16. D   Since the area of the square is 36 cm², the length of a side of the square is 6 cm. Since the shaded area is 27 cm², the area not shaded is $(36 - 27)$ cm² $= 9$ cm². Let a cm, b cm and c cm be the lengths of the parts of the sides shown on the diagram. The area of a triangle is $\frac{1}{2} \times$ base $\times$ height.

Therefore $\frac{1}{2} \times a \times 6 + \frac{1}{2} \times b \times 6 + \frac{1}{2} \times c \times 6 = 9$ and hence $a + b + c = 3$. Therefore, since $(a + b + c) + (p + q + r + s)$ is the sum of the lengths of two sides of the square and so is equal to 12 cm, the value of $p + q + r + s$ is 9 cm.

17. D Since Theo thinks it is 12:00, his watch shows 12:05. Therefore, the correct time is 12:15 since Theo's watch is 10 minutes slow. Since Leo's watch is five minutes fast, at 12:15 his watch will show 12:20. However, Leo thinks his watch is 10 minutes slow so he thinks the time is 12:30.

18. E The total number of cupcakes eaten by the girls is $12 \times 1\frac{1}{2} = 18$. Two girls ate no cakes so the 18 cupcakes were eaten by 10 girls. Since no-one ate more than two cupcakes, the maximum number of cupcakes the 10 girls could have eaten is $10 \times 2 = 20$. For every girl who eats only one cupcake, the total of 20 is reduced by 1. Hence the number of girls who ate only one cupcake is $20 - 18 = 2$ and hence the number of girls who ate two cupcakes is 8.

19. D Let x be the number of waffles Little Red Riding Hood delivered to each of the grannies. She delivered x waffles to the third granny and so, since the Big Bad Wolf eats half of the waffles in her basket just before she enters each granny's house, she must have arrived with $2x$ waffles. Therefore she had $3x$ waffles before giving the second granny her waffles and hence had $2 \times 3x = 6x$ waffles when she arrived. Therefore she had $6x + x = 7x$ waffles before giving the first granny her waffles and hence had $2 \times 7x = 14x$ waffles in her basket when she arrived. Hence, since we do not know the value of x, the only numbers that definitely divide the number of waffles she started with are the numbers that divide 14, namely 1, 2, 7 and 14. Therefore, of the options given, only 7 definitely divides the number of waffles she started with.

20. E The diagram below shows the day on which certain cubes turned grey.

top layer   second layer   third layer

As can be seen, at the end of the second day there are $11 + 5 + 1 = 17$ grey cubes.

21. C The only ways to express 16 as the product of two different positive integers are 1×16 and 2×8. The only ways to express 225 as the product of two different positive integers are 1×225, 3×75, 5×45 and 9×25. Therefore, since both integers in the first pair must be smaller than both integers in the second pair, the only possible combination is for the two smallest integers to be 2 and 8 and for the two largest integers to be 9 and 25. There are no other integers written on the blackboard since they would need to be different from these four, be less than 9 and greater than 8. Hence the sum of the integers written on the blackboard is $2 + 8 + 9 + 25 = 44$.

22. A Let the radius of the circle with centre A be x cm. Therefore, since the circles drawn on each side of the pentagon touch, the radius of the circle with centre B is $(16 - x)$ cm. Similarly, the radius of the circle with centre C is $\left(14 - (16 - x)\right)$ cm $= (x - 2)$ cm, the radius of the circle with centre D is $\left(17 - (x - 2)\right)$ cm $= (19 - x)$ cm and the radius of the circle with centre E is $\left(13 - (19 - x)\right)$ cm $= (x - 6)$ cm. However, the radius of the circle with centre E is also equal to $(14 - x)$ cm since the circle with centre A has radius x cm. Therefore $14 - x = x - 6$, which has solution $x = 10$. Hence the radii of the circles centres A, B, C, D and E are 10 cm, 6 cm, 8 cm, 9 cm and 4 cm respectively. Therefore point A is the centre of the largest circle Sephideh draws.

23. **D** Let the integers written on the small cubes in the bottom layer be arranged as shown.

a	b	c
d	e	f
g	h	i

Hence, since the integers written on the cubes in the second and third layers are the sum of the integers on the four cubes underneath, the following is written on the cubes in the second layer.

$a + b + d + e$	$b + c + e + f$
$d + e + g + h$	$e + f + h + i$

Therefore the integer written on the top cube is

$$(a + b + d + e) + (b + c + e + f) + (d + e + g + h) + (e + f + h + i)$$
$$= (a + b + c + d + e + f + g + h + i) + (b + d + f + h) + 3e.$$

Since the sum of the integers on the bottom layer is 50, the integer written on the top cube is equal to $50 + (b + d + f + h) + 3e$. To maximise this, we first require e to be as large as possible which will be obtained when the other eight integers are as small as possible. Therefore $e = 50 - (1 + 2 + 3 + 4 + 5 + 6 + 7 + 8) = 14$. Secondly, $(b + d + f + h)$ should now be made as large as possible and hence b, d, f and h are 5, 6, 7 and 8 in any order. Therefore $(b + d + f + h) = 5 + 6 + 7 + 8 = 26$. Hence the greatest possible integer she can write on the top cube is $50 + 26 + 3 \times 14 = 118$.

24. **C** Let the numbers of passengers in the five carriages be p, q, r, s and t respectively with p, q, r, s and t all at least 1. Consider the neighbours of the passengers in the first and second carriages. Since each passenger has 5 or 10 neighbours, we have $p - 1 + q = 5$ or 10 and $p + q - 1 + r = 5$ or 10. Therefore $p + q = 6$ or 11 and $p + q + r = 6$ or 11. However, we know that $r \geqslant 1$ and hence $p + q \leqslant 10$ and therefore $p + q = 6$ and $r = 5$. Similarly, considering the neighbours of the passengers in the fourth and fifth carriages, we obtain $s + t = 6$ and (again) $r = 5$. Therefore, the total number of passengers in the train is $6 + 5 + 6 = 17$. (Note that while the total number of passengers in the train is uniquely determined, the arrangement of these passengers in all but the centre carriage is not unique.)

25. **A** Note first that a small cube in the centre of a face of the large cube will only appear on one face while a cube appearing on the edge of a face of the large cube will appear on two faces and a cube appearing at a corner of the face of the large cube will appear on three faces. Hence, the total number of white faces on the edge of the large cube is an even number and the total number of white faces on the corners of the large cube is a multiple of 3. The five faces shown contain 1 centre white face from 1 small white cube, 12 edge white faces and 5 corner white faces. Therefore, since the total number of white faces on the corners is a multiple of 3, the missing face contains 1 or 4 white faces at its corners. None of the options contains 4 white corners so the missing face contains one white corner as in options A and E, making 6 in total. These 6 faces come from $6 \div 3 = 2$ small white cubes. Both options A and E have two white faces on their edges, making 14 in total over the six faces from $14 \div 2 = 7$ white cubes. Hence the number of white cubes whose positions we know is $1 + 7 + 2 = 10$. The large cube is made with 12 small white cubes so there are still two more to be placed. One can be at the centre of the large cube and the only place the remaining cube can be is at the centre of the missing face. Therefore, the missing face contains one centre white face, two edge white faces and one corner white face. Hence, the missing face is A. (This proof shows that the only possible missing face for such a cube is face A. It is left to the reader to check that the five given faces and face A can indeed be fitted together consistently to form the faces of a cube.)

2016 European Pink Kangaroo Questions

1. Which of the following numbers is the closest to the value of $\dfrac{17 \times 0.3 \times 20.16}{999}$?

   A 0.01   B 0.1   C 1   D 10   E 100

2. Four of the following points are vertices of the same square. Which point is not a vertex of this square?

   A $(-1, 3)$ B $(0, -4)$ C $(-2, -1)$ D $(1, 1)$ E $(3, -2)$

3. When the positive integer x is divided by 6, the remainder is 3. What is the remainder when $3x$ is divided by 6?

   A 4   B 3   C 2   D 1   E 0

4. How many weeks are equivalent to 2016 hours?

   A 6   B 8   C 10   D 12   E 16

5. Little Lucas invented his own way to write down negative numbers before he learned the usual way with the minus sign in front. Counting backwards, he would write: 3, 2, 1, 0, 00, 000, 0000, ... What is the result of $000 + 0000$ in his notation?

   A 1   B 00000   C 000000   D 0000000   E 00000000

6. Marie changed her dice by replacing 1, 3, and 5 with -1, -3 and -5 respectively. She left the even numbers unchanged. If she throws two such dice, which of the following totals cannot be achieved?

   A 3   B 4   C 5   D 7   E 8

7. Angelo wrote down the word TEAM. He then swapped two adjacent letters around and wrote down the new order of the letters. He proceeded in this way until he obtained the word MATE. What is the least number of swaps that Angelo could have used?

   A 3   B 4   C 5   D 6   E 7

8. Sven wrote five different one-digit positive integers on a blackboard. He discovered that none of the sums of two different numbers on the board equalled 10. Which of the following numbers did Sven definitely write on the blackboard?

   A 1   B 2   C 3   D 4   E 5

9. Four numbers a, b, c, d are such that $a + 5 = b^2 - 1 = c^2 + 3 = d - 4$. Which of them is the largest?

   A a B b C c D d E more information required

10. A square is split into nine identical squares, each with sides of length one unit. Circles are inscribed in two of these squares, as shown. What is the shortest distance between the two circles?

    A $2\sqrt{2} - 1$ B $\sqrt{2} + 1$ C $2\sqrt{2}$ D 2   E 3

11. A tennis tournament was played on a knock-out basis. The following list is of all but one of the last seven matches (the quarter-finals, the semi-finals and the final), although not correctly ordered: Bella beat Ann; Celine beat Donna; Gina beat Holly; Gina beat Celine; Celine beat Bella; and Emma beat Farah. Which result is missing?

    A Gina beat Bella   B Celine beat Ann   C Emma beat Celine

    D Bella beat Holly   E Gina beat Emma

12. The large triangle shown has sides of length 5 units. What percentage of the area of the triangle is shaded?

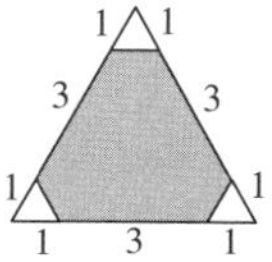

    A 80%   B 85%   C 88%   D 90%

    E impossible to determine

13. Sepideh is making a magic multiplication square using the numbers 1, 2, 4, 5, 10, 20, 25, 50 and 100. The products of the numbers in each row, in each column and in the two diagonals should all be the same. In the figure you can see how she has started. Which number should Sepideh place in the cell with the question mark?

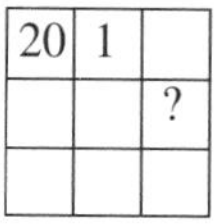

    A 2   B 4   C 5   D 10   E 25

14. Eight unmarked envelopes contain the numbers: 1, 2, 4, 8, 16, 32, 64, 128. Eve chooses a few envelopes randomly. Alie takes the rest. Both sum up their numbers. Eve's sum is 31 more than Alie's. How many envelopes did Eve take?

    A 2   B 3   C 4   D 5   E 6

15. Peter wants to colour the cells of a 3 × 3 square in such a way that each of the rows, each of the columns and both diagonals have cells of three different colours. What is the least number of colours Peter could use?

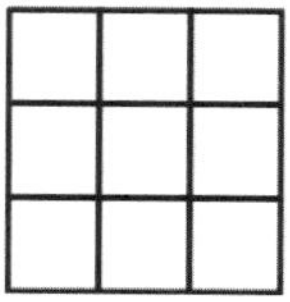

    A 3   B 4   C 5   D 6   E 7

16. The picture shows a cube with four marked angles, $\angle WXY$, $\angle XYZ$, $\angle YZW$ and $\angle ZWX$. What is the sum of these angles?

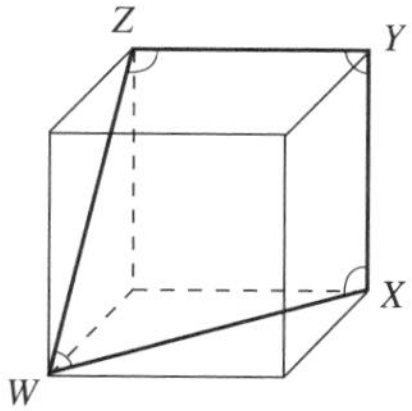

    A 315°   B 330°   C 345°   D 360°   E 375°

17. There are 2016 kangaroos in a zoo. Each of them is either grey or pink, and at least one of them is grey and at least one is pink. For every kangaroo, we calculate this fraction: the number of kangaroos of the other colour divided by the number of kangaroos of the same colour as this kangaroo (including himself). Find the sum of all the 2016 fractions calculated.

    A 2016   B 1344   C 1008   D 672   E more information required

18. What is the largest possible remainder that is obtained when a two-digit number is divided by the sum of its digits?

    A 13   B 14   C 15   D 16   E 17

19. A 5 × 5 square is divided into 25 cells. Initially all its cells are white, as shown. Neighbouring cells are those that share a common edge. On each move two neighbouring cells have their colours changed to the opposite colour (white cells become black and black ones become white).

    What is the minimum number of moves required in order to obtain the chess-like colouring shown on the right?

    A 11   B 12   C 13   D 14   E 15

20. It takes 4 hours for a motorboat to travel downstream from X to Y. To return upstream from Y to X it takes the motorboat 6 hours. How many hours would it take a wooden log to be carried from X to Y by the current, assuming it is unhindered by any obstacles? [Assume that the current flows at a constant rate, and that the motorboat moves at a constant speed relative to the water.]

    A 5   B 10   C 12   D 20   E 24

21. In the Kangaroo republic each month consists of 40 days, numbered 1 to 40. Any day whose number is divisible by 6 is a holiday, and any day whose number is a prime is a holiday. How many times in a month does a single working day occur between two holidays?

    A 1   B 2   C 3   D 4   E 5

22. Jakob wrote down four consecutive positive integers. He then calculated the four possible totals made by taking three of the integers at a time. None of these totals was a prime. What is the smallest integer Jakob could have written?

    A 12   B 10   C 7   D 6   E 3

23. Two sportsmen (Ben and Filip) and two sportswomen (Eva and Andrea) – a speed skater, a skier, a hockey player and a snowboarder – had dinner at a square table, with one person on each edge of the square. The skier sat at Andrea's left hand. The speed skater sat opposite Ben. Eva and Filip sat next to each other. A woman sat at the hockey player's left hand. Which sport did Eva do?

    A speed skating   B skiing   C hockey
              D snowboarding   E more information required

24. Dates can be written in the form DD.MM.YYYY. For example, today's date is 17.03.2016. A date is called 'surprising' if all 8 digits in its written form are different. In what month will the next surprising date occur?

    A March   B June   C July   D August   E December

25. At a conference, the 2016 participants were registered from P1 to P2016. Each participant from P1 to P2015 shook hands with exactly the same number of participants as the number on their registration form. How many hands did the 2016th participant shake?

    A 1   B 504   C 672   D 1008   E 2015

Solutions to the 2016 European Pink Kangaroo

1. **B** The calculation can be approximated as follows:
$$\frac{17 \times 0.3 \times 20.16}{999} \approx \frac{17 \times 3 \times 2}{1000} = \frac{51 \times 2}{1000} \approx \frac{100}{1000} = 0.1.$$

2. **A** By plotting the points, it is easy to check that $BCDE$ is a square. Since any three vertices of a square determine the fourth vertex, it is impossible to make a square using three of these points and the point A.

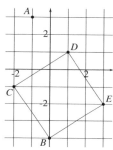

3. **B** The number x is 3 more than a multiple of 6, so $x = 6k + 3$ for some non-negative integer value of k. And then $3x = 3(6k + 3) = 18k + 9 = 6(3k + 1) + 3$. Hence $3x$ is 3 more than a multiple of 6, so leaves remainder 3 when divided by 6.

4. **D** By dividing by 4 and then by 6, we see that $2016 = 4 \times 504 = 4 \times 6 \times 84 = 24 \times 84$. So 2016 hours is 84 days and $84 = 7 \times 12$ so 2016 hours is 12 weeks.

5. **C** In Lucas's notation, the first zero represents the minus sign, and the number of other zeroes is the magnitude of the number, so 000 is -2 and 0000 is -3. Then $000 + 0000$ is $-2 + -3 = -5$, which is 000000 in Lucas's notation.

6. **D** Any odd score must be the sum of an even (positive) number and an odd (negative number). The largest odd total will be the largest even number added to the smallest odd number, which is $6 + -1 = 5$. Hence Marie cannot achieve 7. The others are achievable: $3 = 4 + -1; 4 = 2 + 2; 5 = 6 + -1; 8 = 4 + 4$.

7. **C** In order to get from TEAM to MATE, at some point M will have to pass each of T, E and A. Likewise Angelo will have to move A in front of T and E. So at least 5 swaps are required. The list: TEAM, TEMA, TMEA, MTEA, MTAE, MATE shows it can be done in five swaps.

8. **E** Sven can choose from $\{1, 2, 3, 4, 5, 6, 7, 8, 9\}$, but can choose at most one from each of the pairs that add to 10: $\{1, 9\}, \{2, 8\}, \{3, 7\}, \{4, 6\}$. Since this gives him a maximum of 4 integers, he must always pick the digit 5.

9. **D** Note that $d = c^2 + 7$, so $d > c$; $d = b^2 + 3$, so $d > b$; and $d = a + 9$, so $d > a$. Hence d is the largest.

10. **A** Each square has side-length 1 unit, so by Pythagoras' Theorem the diagonals have length $\sqrt{1^2 + 1^2} = \sqrt{2}$. The distance between the two circles consists of a whole diagonal and two part diagonals (from the corner of a square to the circle). This is the same as the length of two whole diagonals, minus a diameter, that is $2\sqrt{2} - 1$.

11. E The most matches that any player could play is three. Any player who wins twice will play in the final. Hence Celine and Gina must be the two finalists, and Gina beat Celine. This means Gina must have won three matches altogether, but only two are recorded. Hence the missing result must be that Gina beat someone.

All the other players must have lost once, but Emma has no loss recorded, so the missing result must be that Gina beat Emma.

Indeed, from the given information we can deduce that the pairings must have been as shown (using players' initials instead of their full names):

$$
\left.\begin{array}{l}
\left.\begin{array}{l}
\left.\begin{array}{l} A \\ B \end{array}\right\} - - B \\
\left.\begin{array}{l} C \\ D \end{array}\right\} - - C
\end{array}\right\} - - - C \\
\left.\begin{array}{l}
\left.\begin{array}{l} E \\ F \end{array}\right\} - - E \\
\left.\begin{array}{l} G \\ H \end{array}\right\} - - G
\end{array}\right\} - - - G
\end{array}\right\} G
$$

12. C By dissecting the triangle into smaller, identical triangles, we see that the shaded area is 22/25 of the larger triangle, which corresponds to $88/100 = 88\%$.

13. B Since each of the nine numbers appears exactly once in the three rows, the product of each of the three rows is equal to the product of all nine numbers, that is $1 \times 2 \times 4 \times 5 \times 10 \times 20 \times 25 \times 50 \times 100$. This equals $1 \times 2 \times 2^2 \times 5 \times 2 \times 5 \times 2^2 \times 5 \times 5^2 \times 2 \times 5^2 \times 2^2 \times 5^2 = 2^9 \times 5^9$.

Since the products of each of the three rows are equal, these products are equal to $\sqrt[3]{2^9 \times 5^9} = 2^3 \times 5^3$. So the 'magic product' is 1000.

By considering the top row, we can see that the top right cell must contain $1000 \div (20 \times 1) = 50$.

The only other way to get 1000 as the product of 1 and two of the remaining numbers is $1 \times 10 \times 100$. So 10 and 100 must fill the two spaces below 1. We cannot put the 100 in the centre since the products of the numbers on each diagonal would then be too large. So 10 goes in the centre and 100 below it. From the diagonal we see that the bottom right entry is 5 and so the middle number on the right is 4.

Note: It may interest readers to know that in a 3×3 multiplicative magic square the centre number is always the cube root of the magic total.

14. D The sum of the numbers in the envelopes is 255. Let E be the sum of Evie's numbers. Then Alie's numbers will have a total of $E - 31$. Hence we have $E + (E - 31) = 255$, giving $2E - 31 = 255$, so $2E = 286$ and $E = 143$. The only way to add up powers of two to get 143 is $128 + 8 + 4 + 2 + 1$, so Evie took 5 envelopes.

15. C   Peter needs three different colours for the top row, say colours A, B, C. The central cell must be different from each of these (as it lies on the same diagonal as A and also of C, and in the same column as B), say colour D.

Suppose it is possible to use only these four colours. Note that the bottom left cell must be different from A (same column), and different from C and D (same diagonal), hence it must be colour B. But then the bottom right cell must be different from A and D (same diagonal), from B (same row) and from C (same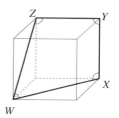

column). Hence a fifth colour is needed. The arrangement above shows that five colours are sufficient.

16. B   The lengths of WX, XZ and ZW are all equal (each being the diagonal of a square face), hence triangle WXZ is equilateral and angle ZWX is 60°.

The other angles are all 90°, so the total of all four angles is $90° + 90° + 90° + 60° = 330°$.

17. A   Let G be the number of grey kangaroos, and P the number of pink kangaroos, so $G + P = 2016$. For each grey kangaroo we calculate the fraction as $\frac{P}{G}$; and there are G of these, so the total of the fractions for grey kangaroos is $G \times \frac{P}{G} = P$.

Similarly the total of the fractions calculated for the pink kangaroos is G. Thus the total of all the fractions is $P + G = 2016$.

18. C   Since the remainder of a division is always less than the divisor used, we can begin our search for the largest possible remainder by looking at the largest possible divisor, that is the largest possible sum of the digits of a 2-digit number.

The largest possible sum of digits is $9 + 9 = 18$. And $99 \div 18$ has remainder 9.

The next largest is 17, which could come from 89 or 98. Doing the division, we see $89 \div 17$ has remainder 4 and $98 \div 17$ has remainder 13.

The next largest sum of digits is 16, which could come from 88, 97, 79. And division shows that $88 \div 16$ has remainder 8; $97 \div 16$ has remainder 1, and $79 \div 16$ has remainder 15 (the largest remainder so far).

Any sum of digits below 16 will have remainder below 15, so the remainder of 15 that we have achieved must be the largest possible.

19. B   Note that, for each black square that we wish to produce, there will need to be a move which makes it black. This move will not change the colour of any of the other squares which we wish to make black (since the desired black cells are not neighbouring). Since there are 12 such squares, we must necessarily make at least 12 moves.

However, we can show that 12 moves are sufficient. Consider a pair of black cells with a white cell between them. This colouring can be made in two moves as follows: Starting with WWW, change the colours of two adjacent cells to obtain BBW, then change the middle cell and the one on its right to obtain BWB. By pairing off the 12 black cells into 6 pairs as shown, it is possible to create 12 black cells in $6 \times 2 = 12$ moves.

20. E   Let D be the distance from X to Y, and let u be the speed of the boat and v be the speed of the current. When travelling downstream the overall speed of the boat in the current is $u + v$, and travelling upstream against the current it is $u - v$. Then using time $= \dfrac{\text{distance}}{\text{speed}}$, we get $\dfrac{D}{u + v} = 4$ for the journey downstream and $\dfrac{D}{u - v} = 6$ for the journey upstream. Inverting the equations gives $\dfrac{u + v}{D} = \dfrac{1}{4}$ or $4u + 4v = D \ldots$ (1) and $\dfrac{u - v}{D} = \dfrac{1}{6}$ or $6u - 6v = D \ldots$ (2). Multiplying (1) by 3 and (2) by 2, we get $12u + 12v = 3D \ldots$ (3) and $12u - 12v = 2D \ldots$ (4). Subtracting, (3) − (4) gives $24v = D$ which rearranges to $\dfrac{D}{v} = 24$ (hours), which is the time taken for the log to float downstream at the speed of the current alone.

21. A   Every multiple of 6 is a holiday. For $n > 0$, the days in between $6n$ and $6n + 6$ will contain three consecutive non-primes $6n + 2$ (divisible by 2), $6n + 3$ (divisible by 3) and $6n + 4$ (divisible by 2). Using H to represent a holiday, W a working day and ? for an unknown day, we see the numbers $6n$ to $6n + 6$ form the pattern H?WWW?H. We are searching for the pattern HWH but this will not fit into the pattern shown above. Hence, the only days that can possibly give HWH must occur in the first week of the month. The days 1, 2, 3, 4, 5, 6 have the pattern WHHWHH so contain one occurrence of HWH.

The first day of the month could possibly be a working day between two holidays, but a quick check shows that of course day 40 is also a working day.

22. C   Let n be the smallest of the integers. The four consecutive integers have sum $n + n + 1 + n + 2 + n + 3 = 4n + 6$. Then the four possible sums formed by taking three of these at a time are

$4n + 6 - n = 3n + 6$ (divisible by 3 so not prime)

$4n + 6 - (n + 1) = 3n + 5$ (if n is odd then this is even, so is not prime)

$4n + 6 - (n + 2) = 3n + 4$

$4n + 6 - (n + 3) = 3n + 3$ (divisible by 3 so not prime)

Hence we are looking for the smallest n for which neither $3n + 4$ nor $3n + 5$ is prime.

n	$3n + 4$	$3n + 5$
1	7 prime	8 not prime
2	10 not prime	11 prime
3	13 prime	14 not prime
4	16 not prime	17 prime
5	19 prime	20 not prime
6	22 not prime	23 prime
7	25 not prime	26 not prime

When $n = 7$, none of the four sums is prime.

23. A Put Andrea at the top of the table. Since Eva and Filip are next to each other, Ben must be next to Andrea. If Ben was to her right then he would be opposite the skier, whom we know is to her left. But Ben is opposite the speed skater. So Ben is to Andrea's left and he is the skier. We are now at the stage shown on the diagram.

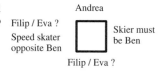

The hockey player is not opposite Ben, but has a woman to the left. Therefore the hockey player must be at the bottom of the table and Eva is on the left side of the table. So Eva is the speed skater.

24. B The smallest possible first digit in the year is 2. This eliminates December from the month, leaving only months that start with 0, or 10 (11 cannot be used because it has a repeated digit). So we will definitely use 0 for the month. Not using 0 or 2 for a day leaves us with 13 to 19, or 31, all of which use a 1. Since we are using 0 and 1 for the month and day, the earliest year we could have is 2345. The earliest month is then 06, and the earliest day that can be made is 17. This gives 17.06.2345. So the month is June.

25. D P2015 shakes hands with each of the other 2015 candidates (including P2016). In particular he shakes hands with P1, leaving P1 with no more handshakes to perform. P2014 then shakes hands with each of the candidates, not including P1. But then P2 has used up his two handshakes (once with P2015 and once with P2014). Proceeding in this way, we see that P2013 uses up the third shake for P3, P2012 uses up the fourth shake for P4, and so on, until we get towards the half-way point. The handshakes of P1009 again include P2016 and use up the 1007th shake for P1007. By this point, P2016 has shaken hands with each of P1009 to P2015, and now must provide the 1008th shake for P1008, a total of 1008 shakes for P2016.

(b) *The IMOK Olympiad*

 The United Kingdom Mathematics Trust

Intermediate Mathematical Olympiad and Kangaroo (IMOK)

Olympiad Cayley/Hamilton/Maclaurin Papers

Thursday 10th March 2016

READ THESE INSTRUCTIONS CAREFULLY BEFORE STARTING

1. Time allowed: 2 hours.

2. **The use of calculators, protractors and squared paper is forbidden.**
   Rulers and compasses may be used.

3. Solutions must be written neatly on A4 paper. Sheets must be STAPLED together in the top left corner with the Cover Sheet on top.

4. Start each question on a fresh A4 sheet.
   You may wish to work in rough first, then set out your final solution with clear explanations and proofs. *Do not hand in rough work.*

5. Answers must be FULLY SIMPLIFIED, and EXACT. They may contain symbols such as π, fractions, or square roots, if appropriate, but NOT decimal approximations.

6. Give full written solutions, including mathematical reasons as to why your method is correct.
   Just stating an answer, even a correct one, will earn you very few marks; also, incomplete or poorly presented solutions will not receive full marks.

7. **These problems are meant to be challenging!** The earlier questions tend to be easier; the last two questions are the most demanding.
   Do not hurry, but spend time working carefully on one question before attempting another. Try to finish whole questions even if you cannot do many; you will have done well if you hand in full solutions to two or more questions.

DO NOT OPEN THE PAPER UNTIL INSTRUCTED BY THE INVIGILATOR TO DO SO!

The United Kingdom Mathematics Trust is a Registered Charity.
Enquiries should be sent to: Maths Challenges Office,
School of Mathematics Satellite, University of Leeds, Leeds, LS2 9JT.
(Tel. 0113 343 2339)
http://www.ukmt.org.uk

2016 Olympiad Cayley Paper

All candidates must be in *School Year 9 or below* (England and Wales), *S2 or below* (Scotland), or *School Year 10 or below* (Northern Ireland).

C1. How many three-digit multiples of 9 consist only of odd digits?

C2. In a 6 × 6 grid of numbers:
   - (i) all the numbers in the top row and the leftmost column are the same;
   - (ii) each other number is the sum of the number above it and the number to the left of it;
   - (iii) the number in the bottom right corner is 2016.

   What are the possible numbers in the top left corner?

C3. All the telephone numbers in Georgetown have six digits and each of them begins with the digits 81. Kate finds the scrap of paper shown, with part of Jenny's telephone number on it.

   How many different possibilities are there for Jenny's telephone number?

C4. The diagram shows an equilateral triangle *ABC* and two squares *AWXB* and *AYZC*.

   Prove that triangle *AXZ* is equilateral.

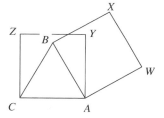

C5. Dean wishes to place the positive integers 1, 2, 3, ..., 9 in the cells of a 3 × 3 square grid so that:
   - (i) there is exactly one number in each cell;
   - (ii) the product of the numbers in each row is a multiple of four;
   - (iii) the product of the numbers in each column is a multiple of four.

   Is Dean's task possible? Prove that your answer is correct.

C6. The diagram shows two regular heptagons *ABCDEFG* and *APQRSTU*. The vertex *P* lies on the side *AB* (and hence *U* lies on the side *GA*). Also, *Q* lies on *OB*, where *O* is the centre of the larger heptagon.

   Prove that *AB* = 2*AP*.

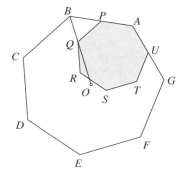

2016 Olympiad Hamilton Paper

> **All candidates must be in *School Year 10* (England and Wales), *S3* (Scotland), or *School Year 11* (Northern Ireland).**

H1. No digit of the positive integer N is prime. However, all the single-digit primes divide N exactly.

What is the smallest such integer N?

H2. The diagram shows two arcs. Arc AB is one eighth of a circle with centre C, and arc AC is one quarter of a circle with centre D. The points A and B are joined by straight lines to C, and A and C are joined by straight lines to D.

Prove that the area of the shaded triangle T is equal to the area of the shaded region R.

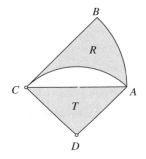

H3. Alex is given £1 by his grandfather and decides:
    (i)   to spend at least one third of the £1 on toffees at 5p each;
    (ii) to spend at least one quarter of the £1 on packs of bubblegum at 3p each; and
    (iii) to spend at least one tenth of the £1 on jellybeans at 2p each.

He only decides how to spend the rest of the money when he gets to the shop, but he spends all of the £1 on toffees, packs of bubblegum and jellybeans.

What are the possibilities for the number of jellybeans that he buys?

H4. The diagram shows a right-angled triangle ACD with a point B on the side AC.

The sides of triangle ABD have lengths 3, 7 and 8, as shown.

What is the area of triangle BCD?

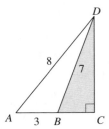

H5. James chooses five different positive integers, each at most eight, so that their mean is equal to their median.

In how many different ways can he do this?

H6. Tony multiplies together at least two consecutive positive integers. He obtains the six-digit number N. The left-hand digits of N are '47', and the right-hand digits of N are '74'.

What integers does Tony multiply together?

2016 Olympiad Maclaurin Paper

All candidates must be in *School Year 11* (England and Wales), *S4* (Scotland), or *School Year 12* (Northern Ireland).

M1. The positive integer N has five digits.
The six-digit integer P is formed by appending the digit 2 to the front of N.
The six-digit integer Q is formed by appending the digit 2 to the end of N.

Given that $Q = 3P$, what values of N are possible?

M2. A 'stepped' shape, such as the example shown, is made from 1×1 squares in the following way.

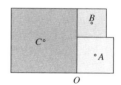

  (i) There are no gaps or overlaps.

  (ii) There are an odd number of squares in the bottom row (eleven in the example shown).

  (iii) In every row apart from the bottom one, there are two fewer squares than in the row immediately below.

  (iv) In every row apart from the bottom one, each square touches two squares in the row immediately below.

  (v) There is one square in the top row.

Prove that $36A = (P + 2)^2$, where A is the area of the shape and P is the length of its perimeter.

M3. The diagram shows three squares with centres A, B and C. The point O is a vertex of two squares.

Prove that OB and AC are equal and perpendicular.

M4. What are the solutions of the simultaneous equations:
$$3x^2 + xy - 2y^2 = -5;$$
$$x^2 + 2xy + y^2 = 1 ?$$

M5. The number of my hotel room is a three-digit integer. I thought that the same number could be obtained by multiplying together all of:

  (i) one more than the first digit;

  (ii) one more than the second digit;

  (iii) the third digit.

Prove that I was mistaken.

M6. The diagram shows two squares $APQR$ and $ASTU$, which have vertex A in common. The point M is the midpoint of PU.

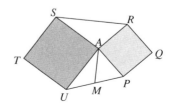

Prove that $AM = \frac{1}{2}RS$.

Solutions to the 2016 Olympiad Cayley Paper

C1. How many three-digit multiples of 9 consist only of odd digits?

Solution

We use the fact that 'an integer is a multiple of 9 when the sum of its digits is a multiple of 9, and not otherwise'.

Consider a three-digit integer with the required properties. Each digit is between 0 and 9, and none of them is zero, so the sum of the digits is between 1 and 27. Since we want the integer to be a multiple of 9, the sum of the digits is therefore 9, 18 or 27.

However, it is not possible to write 18 as a sum of three odd numbers, and the only way of making the sum of the digits equal to 27 is with 999, which is thus one possible integer. But the remaining question is 'how can we make the sum of the digits equal to 9?'

If one of the digits is 1, then we can make the remaining 8 in two ways:

1 + 7

giving the three integers 117, 171 and 711;

3 + 5

giving the six integers 135, 153, 315, 351, 513 and 531.

If we do not use a 1, then the only possible integer is 333.

Hence there are eleven three-digit multiples of 9 consisting only of odd digits.

C2. In a 6 × 6 grid of numbers:

    (i)   all the numbers in the top row and the leftmost column are the same;

    (ii)   each other number is the sum of the number above it and the number to the left of it;

    (iii)   the number in the bottom right corner is 2016.

What are the possible numbers in the top left corner?

Solution

Suppose we start by letting the number in the top left corner be t. Since, by rule (i), the numbers in the top row and left-hand column are all the same, we can fill them all in as t. Then we can use rule (ii) to fill in the rest of the grid, as shown.

t	t	t	t	t	t
t	$2t$	$3t$	$4t$	$5t$	$6t$
t	$3t$	$6t$	$10t$	$15t$	$21t$
t	$4t$	$10t$	$20t$	$35t$	$56t$
t	$5t$	$15t$	$35t$	$70t$	$126t$
t	$6t$	$21t$	$56t$	$126t$	$252t$

From rule (iii), we now obtain

$$252t = 2016.$$

Dividing each side by 252, we get

$$t = 8.$$

So the only possible number in the top left corner is 8.

C3. All the telephone numbers in Georgetown have six digits and each of them begins with the digits 81. Kate finds the scrap of paper shown, with part of Jenny's telephone number on it.

How many different possibilities are there for Jenny's telephone number?

Solution

The scrap of paper could read '1018' or '8101'.

Let us start by working out which parts of the phone number Kate could have been seeing. We show the scrap of paper as a rectangle.

8 |1018| d

There are ten possibilities for the unknown digit d.

81 |1018|

There is only one possibility.

|8101| cd

There are one hundred possibilities for the pair of unknown digits c and d.

81 |8101|

There is only one possibility.

However, all the possibilities in the first case—'81018d'—are also counted under the third case—'8101cd'.

Hence there are in fact 102 possibilities for Jenny's telephone number.

C4. The diagram shows an equilateral triangle ABC and two squares $AWXB$ and $AYZC$.

Prove that triangle AXZ is equilateral.

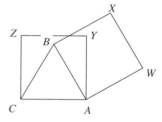

Solution

We start by studying the angles within the square $AYZC$, each of whose angles is 90°. Since the triangle ABC is equilateral, each of its angles is 60°. Hence

$$\angle BAY = \angle CAY - \angle CAB$$

$$= 90° - 60°$$

$$= 30°.$$

Also, $\angle ZAY = 45°$ since ZA is a diagonal of the square.

Now let us move over to the other square $AWXB$. We have $\angle BAX = 45°$ since AX is a diagonal.

Therefore

$$\angle ZAX = \angle ZAY - \angle BAY + \angle BAX$$

$$= 45° - 30° + 45°$$

$$= 60°.$$

Also, the two squares have the same size, because the triangle ABC is equilateral and so $AB = AC$. Thus AZ and AX are diagonals of squares of the same size, and hence $AZ = AX$.

It follows that the triangle AXZ is an equilateral triangle—it has two equal sides and the angle between them is 60°.

C5. Dean wishes to place the positive integers 1, 2, 3, ..., 9 in the cells of a 3 × 3 square grid so that:

    (i)   there is exactly one number in each cell;

    (ii)   the product of the numbers in each row is a multiple of four;

    (iii)   the product of the numbers in each column is a multiple of four.

Is Dean's task possible? Prove that your answer is correct.

Solution

We claim that Dean's task is impossible, and will prove our claim by contradiction.

Suppose Dean has placed the integers according to the given rules.

Now only one row contains 4, and only one row contains 8. But there are three rows, so there is at least one row R which contains neither 4 nor 8. From rule (ii), the product of the numbers in R is a multiple of 4 and hence R contains both 2 and 6.

In a similar way, there is at least one column C that contains neither 4 nor 8. From rule (iii), the product of the numbers in C is a multiple of 4 and hence C contains both 2 and 6.

As a result, both 2 and 6 are in the same row, and in the same column, which contradicts rule (i).

Therefore Dean's task is not possible.

C6. The diagram shows two regular heptagons *ABCDEFG* and *APQRSTU*. The vertex *P* lies on the side *AB* (and hence *U* lies on the side *GA*). Also, *Q* lies on *OB*, where *O* is the centre of the larger heptagon.

Prove that *AB* = 2*AP*.

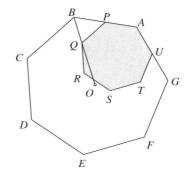

Solution

We will show that *PQ* = *PB*. Then it will follow that *AP* = *PB*, because *AP* and *PQ* are two sides of a regular heptagon, and hence that *AB* = 2*AP*.

Draw the lines *OA* and *OC* and extend *AB* to *X*, as shown.

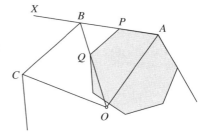

Now the angles *CBX* and *QPB* are equal because each is an exterior angle of a regular heptagon. Thus *BC* is parallel to *PQ* (corresponding angles converse), and therefore angle *OBC* is equal to angle *BQP* (alternate angles).

Consider triangles *OAB* and *OCB*. The side *OB* is common, the sides *OA* and *OC* are equal because *O* is the centre of the larger heptagon, and the sides *AB* and *BC* are equal because the heptagon is regular.

Thus triangles *OAB* and *OCB* are congruent (SSS), and therefore angle *OBC* is equal to angle *OBA*, which is the same as angle *PBQ*.

Hence the angles *PBQ* and *BQP* are equal. Therefore, using 'sides opposite equal angles are equal' in the triangle *BQP*, we get *PQ* = *PB* as required.

Solutions to the 2016 Olympiad Hamilton Paper

H1. No digit of the positive integer N is prime. However, all the single-digit primes divide N exactly.

What is the smallest such integer N?

Solution

The single-digit primes are 2, 3, 5 and 7. Each of them divides N, so that $2 \times 3 \times 5 \times 7$ divides N. Written another way, this means that N is a multiple of $2 \times 3 \times 5 \times 7 = 210$.

But one of the digits of 210 is the prime 2, so N is not 210, and one of the digits of $2 \times 210 = 420$ is also 2, so N is not 420 either. Furthermore, one of the digits of $3 \times 210 = 630$ is the prime 3, so N is not 630. However, none of the digits of $4 \times 210 = 840$ is a prime, so N can be 840.

We have ruled out all the smaller options, therefore the smallest possible integer N is 840.

H2. The diagram shows two arcs. Arc AB is one eighth of a circle with centre C, and arc AC is one quarter of a circle with centre D. The points A and B are joined by straight lines to C, and A and C are joined by straight lines to D.

Prove that the area of the shaded triangle T is equal to the area of the shaded region R.

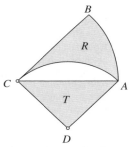

Solution

Let the radius DA be r, so that DC also equals r. Since arc AC is one quarter of a circle, $\angle CDA$ is $90°$. Hence, using Pythagoras' Theorem in the triangle ACD, we obtain $CA^2 = 2r^2$.

Now consider the segment S bounded by the arc AC and the chord AC, shown shaded in the following diagram.

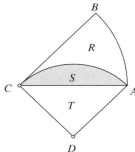

We shall combine this region with each of R and T—if the areas of the combined regions are equal, then the areas of R and T are equal.

The region obtained by combining R and S is one eighth of a circle with centre C and radius CA. Thus its area is

$$\tfrac{1}{8} \times \pi \times CA^2 = \tfrac{1}{8} \times \pi \times 2r^2$$
$$= \tfrac{1}{4}\pi r^2.$$

The region obtained by combining S and T is one quarter of a circle with centre D and radius DA. Thus its area is $\frac{1}{4}\pi r^2$.

Hence the areas of the regions obtained by combining S with each of T and R are equal. Therefore the area of T is equal to the area of R.

H3. Alex is given £1 by his grandfather and decides:
   (i)   to spend at least one third of the £1 on toffees at 5p each;
   (ii)   to spend at least one quarter of the £1 on packs of bubblegum at 3p each; and
   (iii) to spend at least one tenth of the £1 on jellybeans at 2p each.

He only decides how to spend the rest of the money when he gets to the shop, but he spends all of the £1 on toffees, packs of bubblegum and jellybeans.

What are the possibilities for the number of jellybeans that he buys?

Solution

It follows from decision (i) that Alex spends at least 35p on toffees; it follows from decision (ii) that he spends at least 27p on bubblegum; and it follows from decision (iii) that he spends at least 10p on jellybeans. Therefore, out of the total £1 that he will spend, he has to decide how to spend 28p.

He may spend the whole 28p on jellybeans, which is an extra 14 jellybeans.

He cannot spend 26p or 24p on jellybeans, because he cannot spend the remaining money (2p or 4p) on the other items.

But he may spend any even amount from 22p downwards on jellybeans, since the remaining money would then be an even amount from 6p to 28p, and he is able to spend this on toffees or bubblegum (or both), as the following table shows.

Remaining money	Toffees at 5p	Bubblegum at 3p
6p	0	2
8p	1	1
10p	2	0
12p	0	4
14p	1	3
16p	2	2
18p	0	6
20p	1	5
22p	2	4
24p	0	8
26p	1	7
28p	2	6

Note that in some cases there are other ways to spend the money.

Thus the number of additional jellybeans that he may buy is a number from 0 to 11, or is 14.

But these are in addition to the five he buys as a result of decision (iii). Therefore the number of jellybeans that he buys is a number from 5 to 16, or is 19.

84

H4. The diagram shows a right-angled triangle *ACD* with a point *B* on the side *AC*.

The sides of triangle *ABD* have lengths 3, 7 and 8, as shown.

What is the area of triangle *BCD*?

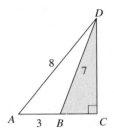

Solution

Let *BC* equal *b* and *CD* equal *h*, as shown in the following diagram.

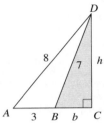

Using Pythagoras' Theorem in both the triangle *BCD* and the triangle *ACD*, we get the two equations

$$b^2 + h^2 = 7^2 \tag{1}$$

$$\text{and} \quad (b + 3)^2 + h^2 = 8^2. \tag{2}$$

Subtracting equation (1) from equation (2), we obtain

$$(b + 3)^2 - b^2 = 8^2 - 7^2.$$

Factorising the difference of two squares, we get

$$(b + 3 - b)(b + 3 + b) = (8 - 7)(8 + 7)$$

so that

$$3(2b + 3) = 15.$$

Therefore

$$b = 1.$$

Using equation (1), we now obtain $1 + h^2 = 7^2$, and so $h = \sqrt{48} = 4\sqrt{3}$.

Therefore the area of the triangle *BCD* is $\frac{1}{2} \times 1 \times 4\sqrt{3}$, that is, $2\sqrt{3}$.

H5. James chooses five different positive integers, each at most eight, so that their mean is equal to their median.

In how many different ways can he do this?

Solution

Since there are five different positive integers, the middle one is at least 3. But the five numbers are at most 8, so the middle one is at most 6.

However, the middle value is the median of the numbers, which we are told is equal to the mean. Let the integers, in increasing order, be a, b, c, d and e. Thus c is the median and therefore the mean.

Because c is the mean, $a + b + c + d + e = 5c$, and thus $(a + b) + (d + e) = 4c$. We know that $d + e$ is at most $7 + 8 = 15$, so that $a + b$ is at least $4c - 15$; also, $a + b$ is at most $(c - 2) + (c - 1) = 2c - 3$.

For each value of c, we first list the possible values of $a + b$. From $a + b$ we find $d + e$.

Finally, we list the possible values of a, b, d and e, using $0 < a < b < c < d < e$. The following table shows the results.

c	$a + b$	$d + e$	a	b	d	e
3	3	9	1	2	4	5
4	3	13	1	2	5	8
			1	2	6	7
	4	12	1	3	5	7
	5	11	2	3	5	6
5	5	15	1	4	7	8
			2	3	7	8
	6	14	2	4	6	8
	7	13	3	4	6	7
6	9	15	4	5	7	8

So altogether there are 10 ways for James to choose the integers.

H6. Tony multiplies together at least two consecutive positive integers. He obtains the six-digit number N. The left-hand digits of N are '47', and the right-hand digits of N are '74'.

What integers does Tony multiply together?

Solution

An integer is divisible by 4 when the number formed from the rightmost two digits is a multiple of 4, and not otherwise. But 74 is not a multiple of 4, so N is not divisible by 4.

However, when two even numbers are multiplied together, the result is a multiple of 4. We conclude that Tony's list of consecutive integers does not include two even numbers.

There are two possibilities: either he has multiplied three consecutive integers 'odd', 'even', 'odd'; or he has multiplied two consecutive integers. But when two consecutive integers are multiplied together the last digit is never 4—the only options for the last digits are $0 \times 1, 1 \times 2, 2 \times 3, 3 \times 4, 4 \times 5, 5 \times 6, 6 \times 7, 7 \times 8, 8 \times 9, 9 \times 0$, so the result ends in 0, 2, 6, 2, 0, 0, 2, 6, 2 or 0.

We are therefore trying to find an odd integer n such that $n \times (n+1) \times (n+2) = $ '47... 74'. We also know that $n + 1$ is not a multiple of 4.

Now $81 \times 82 \times 83$ fails because it ends in 6. It is also too big, since it is bigger than $80 \times 80 \times 80 = 512\,000$.

Also $73 \times 74 \times 75$ fails because it ends in 0. It is also too small, since it is smaller than $75 \times 75 \times 75 = 421\,875$.

The only remaining possibility is $77 \times 78 \times 79 = 474\,474$, which works.

Solutions to the 2016 Olympiad Maclaurin Paper

M1. The positive integer N has five digits.

The six-digit integer P is formed by appending the digit 2 to the front of N.
The six-digit integer Q is formed by appending the digit 2 to the end of N.

Given that $Q = 3P$, what values of N are possible?

Solution

We have $P = N + 200\,000$ and $Q = 10N + 2$. Hence

$$10N + 2 = 3 \times (N + 200\,000)$$

$$= 3N + 600\,000.$$

Therefore, subtracting $3N + 2$ from each side, we get

$$7N = 599\,998$$

and so, dividing each side by 7, we obtain

$$N = 85\,714.$$

Hence the only possible value of N is 85 714.

M2. A 'stepped' shape, such as the example shown, is made from 1×1 squares in the following way.

   (i)   There are no gaps or overlaps.

   (ii)   There are an odd number of squares in the bottom row (eleven in the example shown).

   (iii)   In every row apart from the bottom one, there are two fewer squares than in the row immediately below.

   (iv)   In every row apart from the bottom one, each square touches two squares in the row immediately below.

   (v)   There is one square in the top row.

Prove that $36A = (P + 2)^2$, where A is the area of the shape and P is the length of its perimeter.

Solution

Let n be the number of steps in the shape.

Now the top row consists of one square, and each subsequent row has two more squares than the one before. Hence the number of squares in the bottom row is $1 + 2(n - 1) = 2n - 1$.

The perimeter length P can be calculated by viewing the shape from four different directions and counting the number of horizontal or vertical segments. There are n vertical segments on each side (one for each row), making $2n$ in all. There are $2n - 1$ horizontal segments viewed from above, and the same number viewed from below, making $4n - 2$ in all. Therefore $P = 6n - 2$.

The area A is the total number of squares in the shape. But we may rearrange the shape into a square of side n, by dividing it into two pieces, rotating one of them by half a turn, and then recombining the squares, as shown in the diagrams.

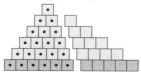

Thus $A = n^2$ and hence

$$36A = 36n^2$$
$$= (P + 2)^2.$$

M3. The diagram shows three squares with centres A, B and C. The point O is a vertex of two squares.

Prove that OB and AC are equal and perpendicular.

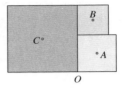

Solution

Let the three squares with centres A, B and C have sides of length $2a, 2b$ and $2c$ respectively. Then

$$c = a + b. \qquad (*)$$

Introduce coordinate axes as shown.

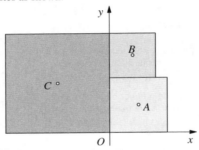

Then $A = (a, a)$, $B = (b, 2a + b)$ and $C = (-c, c)$.

Now consider the right-angled triangles OBF and ACP shown in the next diagram, where PA is parallel to the x-axis.

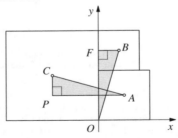

We have $BF = b$ and $OF = 2a + b$. Also $CP = c - a$ and $PA = c + a$. Using equation $(*)$, we get $CP = b$ and $PA = 2a + b$. Thus $CP = BF$ and $PA = OF$. Using either congruent triangles (SAS) or Pythagoras' Theorem, we therefore obtain $CA = OB$.

Now the gradient of OB is $\dfrac{FO}{BF}$ and the gradient of AC is $-\dfrac{CP}{PA}$. It follows that the product of these gradients is -1, and hence OB and AC are perpendicular.

M4. What are the solutions of the simultaneous equations:

$$3x^2 + xy - 2y^2 = -5;$$
$$x^2 + 2xy + y^2 = 1 ?$$

Solution

For convenience, we number the equations, as follows:

$$3x^2 + xy - 2y^2 = -5; \tag{1}$$
$$x^2 + 2xy + y^2 = 1. \tag{2}$$

By adding equation (1) to 5 × equation (2), we obtain

$$8x^2 + 11xy + 3y^2 = 0,$$

that is,

$$(8x + 3y)(x + y) = 0.$$

Thus either $8x + 3y = 0$ or $x + y = 0$.

In the first case, from equation (2) we obtain $25x^2 = 9$, so that $x = \pm\frac{3}{5}$. Because $8x + 3y = 0$, if $x = \frac{3}{5}$, then $y = -\frac{8}{5}$, and if $x = -\frac{3}{5}$, then $y = \frac{8}{5}$.

Checking, we see that each of these is also a solution to equation (1).

In the second case, from equation (2) we get $0 = 1$, so this is impossible.

Hence the solutions of the given simultaneous equations are $x = \frac{3}{5}, y = -\frac{8}{5}$; and $x = -\frac{3}{5}, y = \frac{8}{5}$.

Alternative

We may factorise the left-hand side of each of the given equations as follows:

$$(3x - 2y)(x + y) = -5; \tag{3}$$
$$(x + y)^2 = 1. \tag{4}$$

From equation (4) it follows that $x + y = \pm 1$.

When $x + y = 1$, from equation (3) we get $3x - 2y = -5$. Solving these two linear simultaneous equations, we obtain $x = -\frac{3}{5}$ and $y = \frac{8}{5}$.

Similarly, when $x + y = -1$, we obtain $x = \frac{3}{5}$ and $y = -\frac{8}{5}$.

Checking, we see that each of these is also a solution to the original equations.

Hence the solutions of the given simultaneous equations are $x = \frac{3}{5}, y = -\frac{8}{5}$; and $x = -\frac{3}{5}, y = \frac{8}{5}$.

M5. The number of my hotel room is a three-digit integer. I thought that the same number could be obtained by multiplying together all of:

    (i)   one more than the first digit;

    (ii)   one more than the second digit;

    (iii) the third digit.

Prove that I was mistaken.

Solution

Suppose that my hotel room number is 'abc', that is, $100a + 10b + c$.

If my belief is true, then

$$100a + 10b + c = (a + 1)(b + 1)c,$$

which we may rewrite as

$$(100 - (b + 1)c)a + (10 - c)b = 0. \tag{$*$}$$

Now $(b + 1)c$ is at most 90 because b and c are digits. Also, a is at least 1 because the room number is a three-digit integer. Hence $(100 - (b + 1)c)a$ is at least 10; in particular, it is positive.

Furthermore, $10 - c$ is at least 1 and b is at least zero, so $(10 - c)b$ is at least zero.

It follows that the left-hand side of equation $(*)$ is positive, which is not possible.

Hence my belief is mistaken.

M6. The diagram shows two squares $APQR$ and $ASTU$, which have vertex A in common. The point M is the midpoint of PU.

Prove that $AM = \frac{1}{2}RS$.

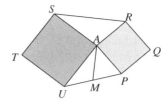

Solution

There are many methods, some of which use similar triangles or the cosine rule. The method we give below essentially only uses congruent triangles.

Let the point B be such that $AUBP$ is a parallelogram, as shown in the following diagram.

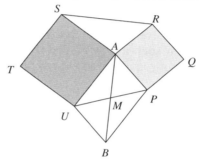

The diagonals of a parallelogram bisect one another. Therefore, because M is the midpoint of PU, it is also the midpoint of AB, in other words, $AM = \frac{1}{2}AB$.

Now we show that the triangles ABP and RSA are congruent.

Firstly, PA and AR are equal, because each is a side of the square $APQR$.

Also, $BP = UA$ because they are opposite sides of the parallelogram $AUBP$, and $UA = SA$ because each is a side of the square $ASTU$. Hence $BP = SA$.

Furthermore, because BP and UA are parallel, the angles BPA and PAU add up to $180°$ (allied angles, sometimes called interior angles). But $\angle RAP = 90°$ and $\angle UAS = 90°$ since each of them is an angle in a square. Then, by considering angles at the point A, we have

$$\angle SAR + 90° + \angle PAU + 90° = 360°,$$

so that the angles SAR and PAU add up to $180°$. Hence $\angle BPA = \angle SAR$.

In the triangles ABP and RSA, we therefore have

$$PA = AR,$$
$$\angle BPA = \angle SAR$$

and $\qquad BP = SA.$

Thus the triangles ABP and RSA are congruent (SAS). It follows that $AB = RS$.

But $AM = \frac{1}{2}AB$, so that $AM = \frac{1}{2}RS$, as required.

Comments on the IMOK Olympiad Papers and Scripts

General comments

Both candidates and their teachers will find it helpful to know something of the general principles involved in marking Olympiad-type papers. These preliminary paragraphs therefore serve as an exposition of the 'philosophy' which has guided both the setting and marking of all such papers at all age levels, both nationally and internationally.

What we are looking for, essentially, is solutions to problems. This approach is therefore rather different from what happens in public examinations such as GCSE, AS and A level, where credit is given for the ability to carry out individual techniques regardless of how these techniques fit into a protracted argument. Such marking is cumulative; a candidate may gain 60% of the available marks without necessarily having a clue about how to solve the final problem. Indeed, the questions are generally structured in such a way as to facilitate this approach, divided into many parts and not requiring an overall strategy for tackling a multi-stage argument.

In distinction to this, Olympiad-style problems are marked by looking at each question synoptically and deciding whether the candidate has some sort of overall strategy or not. An answer which is essentially a solution, but might contain either errors of calculation, flaws in logic, omission of cases or technical faults, will be marked on a '10 minus' basis. One question we often ask is: if we were to have the benefit of a two-minute interview with this candidate, could they correct the error or fill the gap? On the other hand, an answer which shows no sign of being a genuine solution is marked on a '0 plus' basis; up to 3 marks might be awarded for particular cases or insights. It is therefore important that candidates taking these papers realise the importance of the rubric about trying to finish whole questions rather than attempting lots of disconnected parts.

Cayley (comments from James Cranch)

IMOK Cayley is the UKMT's hardest individual competition designed for students in Year 9 in England and Wales, Year S2 in Scotland and Year 10 in Northern Ireland.

There are no easy marks: every one of the six problems is intended to be nonstandard, and getting any marks whatsoever requires some insight into it. The markscheme places very little weight on numerical answers: good ideas will get partial marks, and to get full marks, a fully reasoned and convincing account is required.

Our marking team, of sixteen people this year, spend two days together in the same room dealing with the many hundreds of scripts. I saw only a modest fraction of the scripts, but the team brought many unusual or interesting attempts at problems to me. Their insights have informed these comments, which I now present question-by-question.

1. Many students used divisibility facts (a number is a multiple of nine if and only if the sum of its digits is) to do this problem; some others generated multiples of nine and then restricted to those with the right sorts of digits. The former sort tended to be clear; the latter sort required more care.

   Several students had explanations of how to manufacture the numbers, based on the arithmetic of adding nines. These were sometimes hard to distinguish from numerology.

2. This was found to be the easiest problem on the paper. It was clear that the best way to start was by giving a variable name (such as n) to the common value of the cells in the leftmost column and the top row. But students who played around with some sample numbers were more likely to spot what was going on than they were by just guessing.

3. The majority of students who attempted this problem observed the reversibility of the scrap.

   Fewer gave a detailed account of each possible position of the scrap, for each of the two orientations: is it the first four digits, the middle four, or the last four? A tidy approach, starting with these questions and considering each case separately, provided a good chance of high marks.

   Many students missed the 'double count', however: one of the positions is possible, but all the possible phone numbers are counted with the scrap in another position. Recognising and dealing with this is an important combinatorial technique.

4. One fairly common approach was to deduce and then use the fact that the central quadrilateral in the figure is a kite. This was perhaps very natural and sensible, since it does look like a kite! Some justifications were correct, and others incomplete.

   We took the view that theorems which characterise kites are not common knowledge in classrooms (unlike isosceles triangles, for example: it is very commonly known that those can be characterised by having two equal sides or by having two equal angles), and so full detail should be required.

   This view was supported by the large number of inadequate justifications we saw: for example, some students claimed that this quadrilateral is a kite because it has a pair of opposite right angles (which is not true, of course: for example, a rectangle need not be a kite), and many such students had not even proved the other things (two equal sides, normally) required to characterise a kite.

Hence we were forced to penalise usage of kites unless justified perfectly, and to penalise them particularly heavily if the student had not provided enough material for an adequate justification.

Occasionally we saw proofs featuring unproved properties of the triangle whose vertices are Z, X and the intersection of YZ and BX. These properties are not obvious, and are about as hard to show as the original problem, so we considered this a grave shortcoming.

5. Many students did not work hard enough to distinguish contingent and necessary features of the configuration. As a result, many students had arguments which worked in insufficient generality.

Two different forms of this were seen commonly:

(i) saying that 4 and 8 are in some sense 'best off' if not put in the same column or row. Of course, one is trying to prove a general statement, that no configuration at all is good enough. If some configurations are worse than others, this needs to be justified, and to give a rigorous justification of this comes close to actually doing the problem properly.

(ii) saying that (for example) 8 'may as well' go in the top left corner, and 4 'may as well' go in the centre. Again, to give evidence that this is true is more or less to do the question.

6. A good approach to this problem is to spot, justify, and then use the isosceles triangles in the figure: triangles AOB and BPQ in particular.

In fact, a similar statement is true for any regular polygon with enough sides to make it possible to draw the diagram; understandably, no students spotted this.

Hamilton (comments from Stephen Power)

It was pleasing that the Hamilton paper allowed many candidates to engage successfully with a good number of questions. Very few scripts scored low marks and many scored well on two, three or even four questions. It was also encouraging to see the initiative shown in the face of challenging questions by many candidates and the many different approaches used.

Questions 3 and 5 were often attempted using some form of systematic listing and checking process and it was clear that the more logical and thorough the system used, the more successful it proved to be. A little more thought before entering into the case-checking phase may well have reduced the number of cases that needed to be taken into account and occasionally a method was seen that avoided this approach altogether. It would be good to think that some candidates will have learned the lesson that whenever possible they should look to understand and simplify rather than using brute force to subdue a problem.

The other general difficulty was that sometimes when a candidate found a solution that worked in the original problem they stopped at that point, presumably thinking they had finished. They failed to check for other solutions or, if they thought they had found all possible solutions, they did not prove that there were no more solutions. This difficulty was seen especially in answers to question 6.

Candidates need to realise that Olympiad problems are not just about finding a solution, they are about finding all possible solutions and justifying that all the solutions have been found.

1. This question proved to be relatively straightforward and many candidates found the correct answer. Care must be taken, however, to explain why each step is justified in order to achieve the highest marks.

   The most common method was to say that N is a multiple of the single-digit primes, and these have no common factors other than 1, so that N is a multiple of $2 \times 3 \times 5 \times 7 = 210$. The positive multiples of 210 are 210, 420, 630, 840, ... Of these, the first that does not use 2, 3, 5 or 7 as a digit is 840.

   Alternative methods used a combination of facts that follow from N being a multiple of 2, 3, 5 and 7. For example, since N is a multiple of 2 and 5, N ends in 0; multiples of 7 that end in 0 and only use the digits 1, 4, 6, 8, 9 or 0 are then checked to see whether they are multiples of 3.

2. This question was generally done well by those who attempted it. The shortest method used involved the unshaded segment S, say, and showing that

$$\text{area}(T + S) = \text{area}(R + S)$$

   so that

$$\text{area } T = \text{area } R.$$

   To do this, candidates used Pythagoras' Theorem to find the connection between the lengths of the radii and then found the areas of two sectors of circles.

   However, most candidates did not use S in this way. Instead, they found the area of triangle ACD in terms of their variable and then included that in their calculations for the area of R.

3. This question was found to be much harder than the opening two questions. It required the careful handling of a large number of possible combinations of sweets bought, as well as providing a clear explanation of why the method used was appropriate.

   Students first needed to work out how many sweets have to be bought to satisfy conditions (i) to (iii) and then they must check through the different ways of spending the remaining 28 pence. This case by case checking needs to be done painstakingly, and with visible justification.

Successful candidates often put this work into a table. There were also some successful arguments that included the idea of trading sweets from one possible combination to create another possible combination. For example, two packs of bubblegum can be exchanged for three jellybeans without affecting the overall cost.

4. This question was completed well by a good number of candidates.

   Usually candidates used Pythagoras' Theorem twice and then solved the two equations obtained simultaneously to find BC and CD; from these it is possible to find the area of triangle BCD.

   Some candidates successfully used trigonometry instead.

5. This was another question where candidates had to be systematic and thorough in their search for sets of numbers that satisfied the conditions given. Candidates could have looked at all 56 possibilities and deduced that only 10 of these work but with this amount of checking needed, it would be a very special student indeed who could carry out this approach accurately.

   A better method involves trying the possible values for the median, which can only take the values 3, 4, 5 and 6, and choosing the remaining numbers so they give the correct mean. An alternative is to think of needing to discard three of the 8 numbers to leave a set of numbers with a total which is a multiple of 5. The only possible totals are 30, 25, 20 and 15 and these give median/means of 6, 5, 4 and 3. The candidate would then need to choose the other remaining four numbers appropriately.

   Being clear about the approach being used and meticulous over accuracy were the keys to success.

6. This question was answered well by very few candidates. There were three key points:

   (i) N cannot be a product of two consecutive integers;

   (ii) N cannot be the product of four or more consecutive integers;

   (iii) the only possible product of three consecutive integers is $77 \times 78 \times 79$.

   The only possible last digits for a product of two consecutive integers are 0, 2 and 6, so that N cannot be a product of two consecutive integers.

   Also, 74 is not a multiple of 4, so that N cannot be a multiple of 4. Hence N cannot be a multiple of four or more consecutive integers, because they will necessarily include two even numbers and that would make N a multiple of 4.

   So N is a multiple of three consecutive integers. This can be refined, to say that N is of the form odd × even × odd since a number of the form even × odd × even is a multiple of 4, but this is not essential.

The problem has now been reduced to finding three consecutive integers whose product is '47??74'. This needs to be handled precisely, with explanation that the next possibilities above and below do not give the correct form so none further away will either.

Maclaurin (comments from Gerry Leversha)

1. This question was answered confidently by about 70% of the candidates. By far the most efficient method is to form the equation $10N + 2 = 3(200\,000 + N)$ which takes place-value into account.

   Many candidates, however, elected to treat the problem as a 'cryptarithm', shown alongside, in which letters stand for decimal digits. The values of the different letters can easily be found in the order

$$\begin{array}{r} 2\,A\,B\,C\,D\,E \\ \times\,3 \\ \hline A\,B\,C\,D\,E\,2 \end{array}$$

   E, D, C, B, A but solvers should discuss the role of 'carried on' digits in this process and also check that the first digit of the resulting product is indeed A.

   If you decide to begin with A and proceed from left to right, then there are complications because you do not know the contribution made by carries, and a case analysis is necessary.

2. The key to this problem is to decide on a variable N which describes a stepped shape and then derive a formula for each of A and P in terms of N; if these are correct, it is then simple to verify the desired relationship. If N was taken to be the number of rows in the shape, then A turned out to be the sum of the first N odd numbers, and it was acceptable to claim that this was equal to N^2. The situation when N was chosen as the number of squares in the bottom row was similar, although not quite as easy to analyse. Hence the criterion for a '10 minus' mark was a justified closed-form expression for P.

   Candidates who appeared to be pattern-spotting, by constructing a table of values of A and P and guessing formulae which fitted, were penalised heavily, even if the formulae turned out to be correct.

   The usual strategy for evaluating P was to view the shape from all four directions, noticing the perimeter is found by adding $b, b, 2b - 1, 2b - 1$ together, where b is the number of squares in the bottom row. However, other methods are available and any rigorous method was acceptable.

   No marks were given for special cases.

3. There are many ways of approaching this problem. A common method was to find congruent right-angled triangles with hypotenuses OB and AC. If these triangles also happen to be orientated at right-angles to each other, then the perpendicularity and equality follow at the same time. A key observation is that the side lengths of the two smaller squares add to give that of the large square. This leads to an easy proof using Pythagoras that $OB = AC$ but to show that the segments are perpendicular some argument involving rotation should be used.

Alternatively, this problem is readily susceptible to a coordinate argument, so long as the axes and origin are chosen sensibly. The perpendicularity requires consideration of gradients. Vectors and complex numbers can also be employed, but anyone who elects to use these methods ought to be familiar with dot product and the fact that multiplication by i results in an anticlockwise rotation through $90°$.

4. This is an intriguing algebra question, since it concerns two simultaneous quadratic equations. In general, this would lead to a quartic equation with up to four solutions, but it turns out that this has only two. If you are interested in geometry of curves, you might investigate what is happening in this case.

The criterion for achieving a '10 minus' solution was to form a quadratic expression in a single variable which would allow you to find solutions for (x, y).

Both expressions factorise, and the second equation yields the fact that $x + y = \pm 1$. The best way to deal with this is to consider the two cases separately. It turns out that using $y = 1 - x$ the resulting quadratic reduces to $5x = -3$ and using $y = -1 - x$ yields $5x = 3$; substituting back produces the relevant values of y. One common mistake was to forget the possibility $x + y = -1$, thereby losing a solution pair, and another was to obtain four solution pairs by staying at the quadratic level.

It is important to realise that algebraic manipulation of a pair of equations will yield values for variables which might not in fact be solutions. For example, if you square the equation $x = 1$ you obtain two values $x = \pm 1$; the negative value is, however, not a solution of the equation. This argument is blatantly erroneous, but the same result can be produced in a more subtle way, and so the general rule in solving systems of equations in Olympiads is that all solutions should be checked to see that they satisfy the original equations. In this case, we did not deem this necessary when the method used was clearly reversible (as in the model solution). However, other methods which led to a putative four solutions did require a checking phase in order to eliminate two inappropriate results.

5. This problem was perceived by most candidates as unusual, since they were required to prove that something could not happen. In this case, they had to show that the Diophantine equation $100a + 10b + c = (a + 1)(b + 1)c$ has no solutions if $1 \leqslant a \leqslant 9$ and $0 \leqslant b, c \leqslant 9$. A little experiment will suggest that this is because the left-hand side is too big, and so the argument will involve rearranging the equation in some way and then using consideration of sizes to show it is impossible to satisfy it. There are many good ways to do this; a particularly neat one rearranges the equation to $c(ab + a + b) = 10(10a + b)$ and then uses the facts that $c < 10$ and $b < 10$ (together with $a > 0$) to show that the right-hand side is strictly greater than the left.

Arguments of this type are always a bit delicate and it required some discipline to write down a watertight solution. Divisibility considerations are usually not relevant. A common mistake was to claim that if $c(ab + a + b) = 10(10a + b)$, then c has to be a factor of 10. Of course, it is conceivable that $c = 3$ and $ab + a + b$ has a factor of 10.

The markers were worried that this question might produce a large amount of systematic analysis of particular cases, which might have been very tedious to assess, but, perhaps as this is a late question in the paper, this did not happen.

6. This is a relatively straightforward exercise in geometry. Trained candidates might well have seen similar diagrams before and would realise that there were congruent triangles to be found within it. However, the model solution relied on constructing a parallelogram $AUVP$ and showing that the triangles SAR and AUV are congruent, from which the required deduction is immediate.

Alternative methods involved trigonometry (particularly the cosine rule and the recognition that $\cos(180° - \theta) = -\cos\theta$) and even Apollonius's median theorem. At least one candidate used complex numbers.

Marking

The marking was carried out on the weekend of 18th-20th March 2016 in Leeds. There were three marking groups led by James Cranch, Stephen Power and Gerry Leversha. The other markers are listed later in this book.

IMOK certificates

All participating students who qualified automatically were awarded a certificate. These came in three varieties: Qualification, Merit and Distinction.

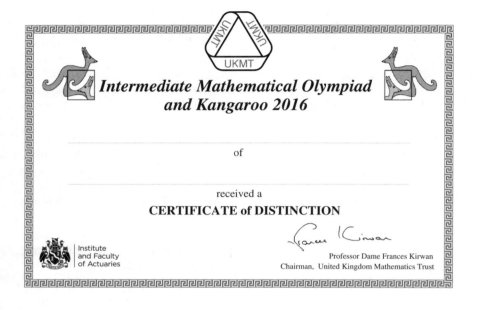

Intermediate Mathematical Olympiad and Kangaroo 2016

of

received a

CERTIFICATE of DISTINCTION

Professor Dame Frances Kirwan
Chairman, United Kingdom Mathematics Trust

Institute and Faculty of Actuaries

THE UKMT INTERMEDIATE MATHEMATICAL OLYMPIAD AND KANGAROO

The IMOK is the follow-on round for the Intermediate Mathematical Challenge and is organised by the UK Mathematics Trust. For each year group, the top scoring 500 or so IMC pupils are invited to participate in the Olympiad, and the next 3000 are invited to participate in the European Kangaroo. Schools may also enter additional pupils to the Olympiad upon payment of a fee; the Kangaroo is by invitation only.

The Olympiad is a two-hour examination which includes six demanding questions requiring full written solutions. The problems are designed to include interesting and attractive mathematics and may involve knowledge or understanding beyond the range of normal school work.

The one-hour multiple choice European Kangaroo requires the use of logic as well as mathematical understanding to solve amusing and thought-provoking questions. The 'Kangourou sans Frontières' is taken by students in over forty countries in Europe and beyond.

The UKMT is a registered educational charity. See our website www.ukmt.org.uk for more information.
Donations would be gratefully received and can be made at
www.donate.ukmt.org.uk if you would like to support our work in this way.

IMOK Olympiad awards

As in recent years, medals were awarded in the Intermediate Mathematical Olympiad. Names of medal winners are listed below. Book prizes were awarded to the top 50 or so in each age group. The Cayley prize was *How Not To Be Wrong: The Hidden Maths of Everyday Life* by Jordan Ellenberg; the Hamilton prize was *Things to Make and Do in the Fourth Dimension* by Matt Parker; and for Maclaurin, *The Irrationals A Story of the Numbers You Can't Count on* by Julian Havil.

IMOK

How many
positive
integers are
less than

2016

but have more
divisors?

IMOK medal winners

Cayley

Alimzhan Adil	Regent International School Dubai
Suyash Agarwal	St John's College, Cardiff
Edward Allen	Hampton School, Middlesex
Gianfranco Ameri	Westminster School
Nathaniel Ang Boon Han	Anglo-Chinese S. (Independent), Singapore
Reuel Armstrong	Winchester College
Gaurav Arya	King George V School, Hong Kong
Wilfred Ashworth	Sutton Grammar School for Boys, Surrey
Panda Atipunumphai	Shrewsbury International School, Thailand
Naomi Bazlov	King Edward VI H. S. for Girls, Birmingham
Duncan Bouchard	St Leonard's School, Fife
William Boyce	Hampton School, Middlesex
Robin Bradfield	Cargilfield Preparatory, Edinburgh
Agathian Bragadeesh	Hymers College, Hull
Peter Brealey	Winchester College
Fin Brickman	Dragon School, Oxford
Matthew Buckley	Eton College, Windsor
Dewi Chappel	Hockerill Anglo-European C., Bishop's Stortford
James Chen	Chetham's School of Music, Manchester
Xue Bang Chen	King Edward VI Camp Hill S. for Boys, Birmingham
William Ching	Westminster School
Soren Choi	Westminster School
Toby Cole	Kingston Grammar School, Surrey

Gustav Conradie	Eton College, Windsor
Brian Davies	St Edward's College, Liverpool
Rishit Dhoot	West Hill School, Lancashire
Ben Domb	Queen Elizabeth's School, Barnet
Andrew Dubois	Wellsway School, Bristol
James Edmiston	Magdalen College School, Oxford
Ben Fearnhead	Lancaster Royal Grammar School
Lizzie Freestone	The Perse School, Cambridge
Max French	Millfield School, Somerset
Abdullah Ghalib	Wilson's School, Surrey
Freddie Hand	Judd School, Tonbridge, Kent
Sarah Henderson	Highgate School, London
Andre Heycock	Wychwood School, Oxford
Jennifer Hu	Loughborough High School
Edward Hu	Queen Elizabeth's School, Barnet
Jason Ke	TASIS-England, Surrey
Hayyan Khan	Watford Grammar School for Boys
Rubaiyat Khondaker	Wilson's School, Surrey
Jina Kim	Concord College, Shrewsbury
Subin Kim	North London Collegiate S. Jeju, South Korea
Iris Kim	Seoul Foreign School
Sebastian Kreutz Wellsted	Dame Alice Owen's School, Herts
Avish Kumar	Westminster Under School
Chinh Le	British Vietnamese International School
Jungho Lee	Oundle School, Northants
Andrew Lee	Westminster Under School
Austen Leitch	Blenheim High School, Epsom
Rhys Lewis	Sir Thomas Picton School, Haverfordwest
Tony Lin	Wilson's School, Surrey
Nathan Lockwood	The Sele School, Hertford
Linus Luu	St Olave's Grammar School, Kent
Yuhka Machino	Millfield School, Somerset
Reuben Mason	Wallingford School, Oxon
Max McKeay	Fullbrook School, Surrey
Madoka Miyazaki	Henrietta Barnett School, London
Teddy Monro-Davies	St Paul's School, Barnes, London
George Monro-Davies	St Paul's School, Barnes, London

Alex Mousley	Newquay Tretherras
Emre Mutlu	British School of Chicago, Illinois, USA
Moe Okawara	The British School in Tokyo Showa
Euan Ong	Magdalen College School, Oxford
Robert Owen	Eton College, Windsor
Sonya Paramonova	Oundle School, Northants
Dillon Patel	King Edward VI S., Stratford-upon-Avon
William Peak	Simon Langton Boys' Gram. S., Canterbury
Daniel Phillips	Belper School, Derbyshire
Chenxin Qiu	Douglas Academy, East Dunbartonshire
Benedict Randall Shaw	Westminster School
Jessica Richards	South Wilts Grammar S. for Girls, Salisbury
Felix Robertson	Queens Park Community School, London
Tibor Rothschild	University College School, London
Adrian Sahani	Westminster Under School
Oscar Selby	Westminster Under School
Callan Sharples	Southlands High School, Chorley, Lancs
Yuanyuan Shen	North London Collegiate S. Jeju, South Korea
Vikram Singh	The Perse School, Cambridge
Fitz Steger-Lewis	Aylesbury Grammar School
Swasthihaa Surendran	Bancroft's School, Essex
Aron Thomas	Dame Alice Owen's School, Herts
Thien Udomsrirungrua	Shrewsbury International School, Thailand
Stephon Umashangar	Hampton School, Middlesex
Harry Vaughan	Tiffin School, Kingston-upon-Thames
Alex Walker	The Perse School, Cambridge
Tommy Walker Mackay	Stretford Grammar School, Manchester
Chuanqi Wang	Regent International School Dubai
Selina Wang	Burgess Hill School, West Sussex
Isaac Weaver	Ipswich School
Max Wong	Winchester College
David Xu	Merchant Taylors' Boys School, Liverpool
Alexander Yan	Bancroft's School, Essex
Norm Yeung	Westminster School
Yuki Yoshie	Merchant Taylors' School, Middlesex
Lauren Zhang	King Edward VI H. S. for Girls, Birmingham
Leon Zhang	King Edward VI Camp Hill S. for Boys, Birmingham

| Shiyan Zhu | Ashford School, Kent |
| Selena Zhu | St Margaret's School, Bushey, Herts |

Hamilton

Kiran Aberdeen	Queen Elizabeth's School, Barnet
Maxim Alexandroff Wilson	Westminster School
Taysir Barakat	Brighton College Abu Dhabi
Gaspard Baroudel	Westminster School
Daniel Bassett	Caistor Grammar School, Lincs
Emily Beckford	Lancaster Girls' Grammar School
Oliver Beken	Horndean Technology College, Hampshire
Sam Brown	Haberdashers' Aske's S. for Boys, Herts
David Bunn	Abingdon School
Ram Capoor	UWCSEA Dover Campus, Singapore
Elena Cates	The Perse School, Cambridge
Justin Chan	Torquay Boys' Grammar School
Matthew Chan	Lancaster Royal Grammar School
Wendy Cheng	Alleyn's School, Dulwich
Gordon Chi	German Swiss International S., Hong Kong
Jinheon Choi	British International S. of Shanghai (Puxi)
Nathan Chu	Winchester College
Matthew Chuang	YMCA of Hong Kong Christian College
Tom Connell	Ermysted's Grammar School, N. Yorks
Nathan Creighton	Mossbourne Community Acad., Hackney
Timothy De Goede	St James's C of E Secondary S., Bolton
Thomas Dhome-Casanova	St Paul's School, Barnes, London
Nicholas Dibb-Fuller	Hampton School, Middlesex
Ryan D'Souza	Hampton School, Middlesex
Ryan Elliot	High Storrs School, Sheffield
Thomas Finn	Bishop Bell C of E School, Eastbourne
Jorge Gallego	The English Montessori School Madrid
Daniel Gore	Westminster School
Arul Gupta	Eltham College, London
Darius Hagmann-Smith	The Cherwell School, Oxford
Faiz Haris Osman	British School of Brussels
Austin Harris	Highgate School, London
Robert Hillier	King Edward VI Camp Hill S. for Boys, Birmingham
Thomas Hillman	St Albans School

Zixiao Hu	Impington Village College, Cambridgeshire
Yifan Hu	Harrow International School, Bangkok
Shuqi Huang	St Swithun's School, Winchester
Phuong Huynh	Jerudong International School, Brunei
Takao Ito	Manchester Grammar School
Kunmin Jang	Ruthin School, Denbighshire
Brian Jeong Gyeom Kim	British International S. of Shanghai (Puxi)
Matthew Jolly	St Laurence School, Wiltshire
Isaac Kaufmann	City of London School
Minji Kim	North London Collegiate S. Jeju, South Korea
Senna Kim	North London Collegiate S. Jeju, South Korea
Sae Koyama	Rodborough Technology College, Surrey
Yao-Chih Kuo	The Perse School, Cambridge
Jon Lam	Marlborough College, Wiltshire
Georgina Lang	Moreton Hall School, Oswestry, Shropshire
Jamie Lear	Hurstpierpoint College, West Sussex
Alex Lee	Taipei European School
Dominic Lee	Parmiter's School, Watford
Haydon Leung	Colchester Royal Grammar School
James Lloyd-Williams	Westminster School
Amrit Lohia	Westminster School
Henry London	Magdalen College School, Oxford
Fraser Mason	St Mary's Music School, Edinburgh
Moses Mayer	The British International S. Jakarta, Indonesia
Anoushka Mazumdar	Manchester High School for Girls
Rupert McKay	Kings College School, Wimbledon
George Mears	George Abbot School, Guildford
Toby Mills	Trinity School, Croydon
Navonil Neogi	Tiffin School, Kingston-upon-Thames
Hugo Nestor-Sherman	Eton College, Windsor
Jasper Newbold	Hampton School, Middlesex
Minh Tuan Nguyen	Anglo-Chinese S. (Independent), Singapore
Lorcan O'Connor	University College School, London
Henry Pearson	Eton College, Windsor
Fred Phillips	Aylesbury Grammar School
Kian Power	Eton College, Windsor
Elijah Price	Reading School
Anish Ramakrishnan	St Paul's School, Barnes, London

Amy Rogers	Royal Grammar School Worcester
Juraj Rosinsky	Institut International de Lancy, Switzerland
Nick Scott	Dame Alice Owen's School, Herts
Andrea Sendula	Kenilworth School, Warwickshire
Zikai Shen	St Julian's School, Portugal
Yiqi Shi	Streatham and Clapham High S., London
Sanjay Singh	Eton College, Windsor
Harjivan Singh	Haberdashers' Aske's S. for Boys, Herts
Nishant Singhal	UWCSEA East Campus, Singapore
Alexander Song	Westminster School
Oliver Stubbs	Bristol Grammar School
Alevtina Studenikina	Cheltenham Ladies' College
Pasa Suksmith	Harrow School
Adam Thompson	St Paul's School, Barnes, London
Christopher Thorn	Eton College, Windsor
Niam Vaishnav	Queen Elizabeth's School, Barnet
Timothy Wallace	Hampton School, Middlesex
Alexander Wallace	Glenalmond College, Perth and Kinross
Anyi Wang	King Edward's School, Birmingham
George Wang	Epsom College, Surrey
Sean White	City of London School
Peter Woo	Hampton School, Middlesex
Isaac Wood	Redland Green School, Bristol
Yuqing Wu	Bangkok Patana School
Chris Yacoumatos	Eton College, Windsor
Shaobo Yang	Anglo-Chinese S, (Independent), Singapore
Tony Yang	North London Collegiate S. Jeju, South Korea
Julian Yu	British School Manila, Philippines

Maclaurin

Sameer Aggarwal	Merchant Taylors' School, Middlesex
Rahul Arya	King George V School, Hong Kong
Connie Bambridge-Sutton	Reigate Grammar School, Surrey
Luke Barratt	Backwell School, North Somerset
Sam Bealing	Bridgewater High School, Warrington
Emily Beatty	King Edward VII School, Sheffield
Connor Bennett	William Brookes School, Shropshire
Jonathan Bostock	Eltham College, London

Michael Brownlie	Pate's Grammar School, Cheltenham
Duyen Cao	Brooke House Coll., Market Harborough
Pengfei Chang	Jinan Foreign Language School, China
Alexander Chen	Westminster School
Yifei Chen	Graveney School, London
Yanyau Cheng	Discovery College, Hong Kong
Zieho Choi	British International S. of Shanghai (Puxi)
Bi Chongxuan	Jinan Foreign Language School, China
Aneesh Chopada	Queen Elizabeth's School, Barnet
George Clements	Norwich School
Leran Dai	Oswestry School, Shropshire
Louise Dai	Cheltenham Ladies' College
Raymond Douglas	Magdalen College School, Oxford
Jun Eshima	Eton College, Windsor
Reynold Fan	Concord College, Shrewsbury
Chris Finn	The Royal Grammar S., High Wycombe
George Garber	Oundle School, Northants
Elliot Gathercole	Cedars Upper School, Leighton Buzzard
Nicolas Geiseler Toran	Latymer Upper School, Hammersmith
Segev Gonen Cohen	Jews' Free School, London
Xueying Guo	Jinan Foreign Language School, China
Ziyi Guo	Chelsea Independent College
Zhengda Han	Jinan Foreign Language School, China
Edward Harris	St Paul's School, Barnes, London
Vera He	St Helen's School, Middlesex
James Hogge	Abingdon School
Samuel Howard	Stockport Grammar School
Charlie Hu	City of London School
Dong Hui Huang	Ipswich School
Isuru Jayasekera	Wilson's School, Surrey
Om Kanchanasakdichai	Winchester College
Wooseok Kang	British International S. of Shanghai (Puxi)
Ryan Kang	Westminster School
Zion Kim	Hampton School, Middlesex
Shikhar Kumar	Birkenhead School
Yiqing Lan	Queen Ethelburga's College, N. Yorks
Ryan Lee	Magdalen College School, Oxford
Charlotte Li	Malvern St James, Worcestershire
Hao Cheng Li	Anglo-Chinese S. (Independent), Singapore

Ruochen Li	Anglo-Chinese S. (Independent), Singapore
Zijia Li	Westbourne School, Vale of Glamorgan
Ziqi Li	Jinan Foreign Language School, China
Charlie Liao	Westbourne School, Vale of Glamorgan
Zien Lin	Anglo-Chinese S. (Independent), Singapore
Andy Liu	Wrekin College, Telford
Meng Ting Lu	Ulink College of Suzhou Industrial Park
Dmitry Lubyako	Eton College, Windsor
Callum McDougall	Westminster School
Sophie McInerney	Tonbridge Grammar School, Kent
Youngjae Moon	North London Collegiate S. Jeju, South Korea
Ritobrata Mukhopadhyay	Glasgow Academy
Junho Myung	The British School, New Delhi
Andy Nam	North London Collegiate S. Jeju, South Korea
Jungbeom Nam	UWCSEA Dover Campus, Singapore
Adi Nata	Anglo-Chinese S. (Independent), Singapore
Tuan Dung Nguyen	Anglo-Chinese S. (Independent), Singapore
Yuji Okitani	Tapton School, Sheffield
Hubert Ostoja-Petkowsk	London Oratory School
Sooyong Park	North London Collegiate S. Jeju, South Korea
Xin Qi	Jinan Foreign Language School, China
Melissa Quail	Longsands Academy, St Neots, Cambs
Cameron Richards	Sheringham High S. & VI Form Centre, Norfolk
Amelia Rout	Chislehurst & Sidcup Grammar S., Kent
Zichun Sang	Christ's Hospital, Horsham
Lee Shi Hao	Anglo-Chinese S. (Independent), Singapore
Rohan Shiatis	Judd School, Tonbridge, Kent
Christopher Sinnott	St Paul's School, Barnes, London
Phoenix Sremcevic	The Cherwell School, Oxford
James Sun	Reading School
Michael Thompson	Cavendish School, Eastbourne
Robert Thomson	The Perse School, Cambridge
Daniel Townsend	Colchester Royal Grammar School
Yuriy Tumarkin	Durham Johnston School
Arthur Ushenin	Eton College, Windsor
Laurence van Someren	Eton College, Windsor
Andrew Wang	Manchester Grammar School
Shuwen Wang	Jinan Foreign Language School, China
Verna Wang	Burgess Hill School, West Sussex

Yihe Wang	Anglo-Chinese S. (Independent), Singapore
Yuandong Wang	King's College Madrid
Naomi Wei	City of London Girls' School
Yannis Wells	Churston Ferrers Grammar School, Devon
Harvey Yau	Ysgol Dyffryn Taf, Carmarthenshire
Daniel Yue	King Edward's School, Birmingham
Mingshan Zhang	Albyn School, Aberdeen
Junge Zhang	Jinan Foreign Language School, China
Amelia Zhao	Westbourne School, Vale of Glamorgan
Mingqi Zhao	Shrewsbury School
Youyang Zhao	Bromsgrove School, Worcestershire

UKMT Summer Schools 2015-2016

Introduction

The first summer school was held in Queen's College, Oxford in July 1994. Dr. Tony Gardiner organised and ran the first five summer schools, from 1994 to 1998, when UKMT took over the organisation. From 1997 to 2012 they were held in Queen's College, Birmingham; for a few years the Trust then organised five annual summer schools, two being held in West Yorkshire and three in Oxford. In the year 2015-16, only four schools were held – two in West Yorkshire and two in Oxford.

Summer School for Girls

The Summer School for Girls was held in Oxford again this year between Sunday 16th August and Friday 21st August 2015. The accommodation was at Balliol College with teaching being held in the Andrew Wiles Building, at the Mathematical Institute. Somerville College provided the venue for lunch each day. There were 40 students from years 10 and 11 invited to attend, along with 5 senior students who had previously attended a summer school or other UKMT residential event. Their role was to assist the younger students throughout the week, as well as having the opportunity to attend more advanced sessions of their own. The director of the Summer School for Girls was Dr Lizzie Kimber.

National Mathematics Summer Schools (NMSS)

There were three other summer schools held this year, one in Oxford during the summer of 2015 and two in Leeds in July 2016.

Oxford Summer School

The school in Oxford was led by Dr Vicky Neale between Sunday 23rd August and Friday 28th August 2015. Accommodation for this school was at St Anne's College, with the teaching again being at the Mathematical Institute, in the Andrew Wiles Building. Lunches were taken at Somerville College.

Once again 40 junior students from years 10 and 11 were invited to attend, with 5 senior students assisting throughout the week, and also attending their own more advanced sessions.

Leeds Summer Schools

The first Leeds summer school this year was held at Woodhouse Grove School between Sunday July 10th and Friday July 15th 2016 and this was led by Dr Steven O'Hagan. The second week was also at Woodhouse

Grove, running from Sunday 17th July until Friday 22nd July 2016 and led by James Gazet (Eton College).

Both these schools were attended by 42 junior students, who were guided and assisted by 6 different senior students each week. Like the seniors in Oxford, these seniors had previously attended a summer school as a junior.

Students attending Summer Schools in 2015-2016

Summer School for Girls, 16th August – 21st August 2015

Melissa Agoro (Kingsdale School), Pippa Britton (Colfe's School), Kristina Buck (St Ninian's High School), Maria Calinescu (Oxford High School), Chloe Carr (Parkside School), Milly Cohen (Norton Hill School), Elizabeth Dearden-Williams (Upton-by-Chester High School), Annabelle Evans (James Allen's Girls' School), Heather Gault (Aberdeen Grammar School), Amelia Georgiou (Dame Alice Owen's School), Marie-Claire Grant-Adamson (Rye St Antony School), Charlotte Green (Settle College), Lucy Greenwood (New Hall School), Nia Hall (Priory School), Rebecca Hall (Ilkley Grammar School), Anna Hardisty (Beaumont School), Ruth Harris (Looe Community Academy), Elizabeth Hatton (Alcester Grammar School), Molly Ives (Stratford Grammar School for Girls), Rachel Jones (The Tiffin Girls' School), Jessie Kendrick (Thomas Telford School), Beth Likely (Arnold KEQMS), Niamh Lister (Penryn College), Amelia Livingston (Haberdashers' Monmouth Girls' School), Zoe Mitchell (Stroud High School), Milly Owen-Payne (Priestlands School), Sifa Poulton (The Grey Coat Hospital School), Rebecca Reiff Musgrove (Sevenoaks School), Emily Roberts (Hockerill Anglo-European College), Ruby Robinson (Colchester County High School for Girls), Rachel Sage (George Abbot School), Sheela Steele (King Ecgbert School), Rhea Suribhatia (Loughborough High School), Aisha Symmons (Caterham School), Laura Taylor (Gordon Schools), Jenifer Tipple (Durham High School for Girls), Rebecca Whittingham (Sturminster Newton High School), Hanna Whydle (Churchill Academy), Fiona Wilson (Wallington High School for Girls), Lianne Wu (Northampton High School) .

Seniors: Olivia Aaronson (St Paul's Girls School), Rosie Cates (The Perse Upper School), Clarissa Costen (Altrincham Girls' Grammar School), Kirsten Land (King's College London Mathematical School), Joanna Yass (North London Collegiate School).

Oxford NMSS 23rd August – 28th August 2015

Seren Barker (Sir John Lawes School), James Bayliss (Sutton Grammar School for Boys), Alex Benjamin (Bishop Luffa School), Callum Berry (St Michael's CE High School), Emily Brailsford (St Alban's High School for Girls), Katy Cartlidge (Colston's Girls' School), Toby Chamberlain (Malmesbury School), Thomas Cox (Trinity School), Adam Dillamore (Steyning Grammar School), Jack Dobson (Manor Community Academy), Nathan Domnitz (King David High School), Hannah Erlebach (Leicester High School for Girls), Adam Fleming (Langley Grammar School), Jonathan Ford (Sir Henry Floyd Grammar School), Jodie Fromage (John Warner School), Saul Gilbert (Twyford CofE High School), Ben Hayward (Reddish Vale High School), Callum House (Hinchley Wood School), Patricia Kelly (Townley Grammar School for Girls), Daria Konovalova (Eastbourne College), Shikhar Kumar (Birkenhead School), Juliette Littlewood (South Wilts Grammar School), Reuben Marbridge (All Saints School), Owen Messere (St Olave's Grammar School), Hugh Moorheard (Dunfermline High School), Sam Oldham (Alleyne's Academy), Poppy Parker (Kesteven & Grantham Girls' School), Rebecca Pimblett (Redland HS for Girls), Elena Saiu-Bell (St Benedict's Upper School), Anna Soligo (Lady Margaret School), Ross Sullivan (Cundall Manor Preparatory School), Samuel Sutherland (Wells Cathedral School), Maya Thomas (Wavell School), Charlotte Turner (St Leonards Mayfield), Alexandru Tudo Ulianov (Heaton Manor School), Saurav Vashisht (Sir Joseph Williamson's Maths School), Joseph Walker (De La Salle School), Max Warren (Elthorne Park High School), Robert Wooller (Downlands School), Pinhang Zhao (Kings School Rochester).

Seniors: Emma Brown (St Helen's School), Daniel Clark (Woodhouse Grove School), Solene Peroy (Lycee Francais Charles de Gaulle), George Robinson (Brooke Weston Academy), James Roper (Upton Court Grammar School).

Woodhouse Grove NMSS 10th July – 15th July 2016

Kate Adams (Tudor Grange Academy), Sameer Aggarwal (Merchant Taylors School), Patrick Akbar (Beechen Cliff School), Kaito Arai (American School in London), Ashesh Bati (The Costello School), Anna Beever (St Aidan's Church of England High School), Emma Bird (Northampton High School), Michael Brownlie (Pate's Grammar School), Matthew Colpus (Wallington County Grammar School), Tom Connell (Ermysted's Grammar School), Katie Cox (Gosforth Academy), Stanley Dodds (Weydon School), Caitlin Frank (Dr Challoner's High School), Elliot Gathercole (Cedars Upper School), Julian Gonzales (Ysgol Dinas

Bran), Lucy Greenwood (New Hall School), Aisling Hanrahan (Oxford High School), John Harber (Oxted School), Thomas Hillman (St Albans School), Callum Hobbis (Winston Churchill School), Samuel Howard (Stockport Grammar School), Dylan Lea (Winterbourne International Academy), Bruno Lindan (Simon Langton Boys' Grammar School), Hannah Lord (Bluecoat Academies Trust), Eden Ludgate (Castle Rushen High School), Robin Lyster (Matthew Arnold School), Izaac Mammadov (Latymer School), Sophie McInerney (Tonbridge Grammar School), Florence Miller (County Upper School), Kira Miller (St Marylebone CE School), Dylan Morris (Altrincham Grammar School for Boys), Elizabeth Oduekun (Kendrick School), Morgan Overton (Oakham School), Max Rose (Hitchin Boys' School), Charlotte Smith (Kingston Grammar School), Oliver Spacey (Outwood Academy Valley), Kitty Sparrowhawk (Beaconsfield High School), Morgan Steed (Queen Elizabeth High School), Harry Stuart (John Taylor High School), Henry Thake (Salesian College), Joe Tyler (Dame Alice Owen's School), Charlotte Waygood (Watford Grammar School for Girls).

Seniors: Samuel Ahmed (Kings College School, Wimbledon), Clarissa Costen (Altrincham Girls' Grammar School), Shaun Marshall (Shelley College), Alex Wardle-Solano (Wellingbrough School), Romy Williamson (St Anne's Catholic School), James Zhang (St Paul's School).

Woodhouse Grove NMSS 17th July – 22nd July 2016
Kiran Aberdeen (Queen Elizabeth's School), Luke Barratt (Backwell School), Daniel Bassett (Caistor Grammar School), Sam Bealing (Bridgewater High School), Emily Beckford (Lancaster Girls' Grammar School), Oliver Beken (Horndean Technology College), Connor Bennett (William Brookes School), Alice Birch (The Tiffin Girls' School), Loretta Bushell (St John Payne RC School), Elena Cates (The Perse School), Wendy Cheng (Alleyn's School), Nathan Creighton (Mossbourne Community Academy), Timothy De Goede (St James's C of E Secondary School), Nicholas Dibb-Fuller (Hampton School), Raymond Douglas (Magdalen College School), Thomas Finn (Bishop Bell C of E School), George Garber (Oundle School), Vera He (St Helen's School), Rachel Hewitt (St James Senior Girls' School), Robert Hillier (King Edward VI Camp Hill School for Boys), Zixiao Hu (Impington Village College), Takao Ito (Manchester Grammar School), Matthew Jolly (St Laurence School), Isaac Kaufmann (City of London School), Sae Koyama (Rodborough Technology College), Soumya Krishna Kumar (Bancroft's School), Georgina Lang (Moreton Hall School), Haydon Leung (Colchester Royal Grammar School), Anoushka Mazumdar (Manchester

High School for Girls), Navonil Neogi (Tiffin School), Lorcan O'Connor (University College School), Hubert Ostoja-Petkowsk (London Oratory School), Fred Phillips (Aylesbury Grammar School), Amy Rogers (Royal Grammar School Worcester), Amelia Rout (Chislehurst & Sidcup Grammar School), Andrea Sendula (Kenilworth School), Phoenix Sremcevic (The Cherwell School), Oliver Stubbs (Bristol Grammar School), Michael Thompson (Cavendish School), Yannis Wells (Churston Ferrers Grammar School), Isaac Wood (Redland Green School), Yifan Zhao (Tapton School).

Seniors: Emma Brown (St Helen's School), Matthew Chaffe (Littleover Community School), Harry Ellison-Wright (Bryanston School), Melissa Quail (Longsands School), Alice Vaughn-Williams (Nailsea School), Lennie Wells (St Paul's School).

Our thanks go to everyone who made these Summer Schools such a success, in particular: Balliol College, St Anne's College, Somerville College and the Mathematical Institute.

We also thank all our volunteers who work tirelessly to make these weeks a success, particularly the leaders of each week: James Gazet, Lizzie Kimber, Vicky Neale, Steven O'Hagan. A list of all the volunteers who helped at the summer schools can be found at the back of the Yearbook.

Senior Mathematical Challenge and British Mathematical Olympiads

The Senior Challenge took place on Thursday 5th November 2015, and over 82,000 pupils took part. Once again it was sponsored by the Institute and Faculty of Actuaries. Around 1000 candidates were invited to take part in the next stage, British Mathematical Olympiad Round 1, held on Friday 27th November 2015, with others able to enter on payment of a fee. The Senior Kangaroo was held on the same day, invitations to this were increased to around 4,000.

UK SENIOR MATHEMATICAL CHALLENGE

Thursday 5 November 2015

Organised by the **United Kingdom Mathematics Trust**

and supported by

Institute
and Faculty
of Actuaries

RULES AND GUIDELINES (to be read before starting)

1. Do not open the question paper until the invigilator tells you to do so.
2. **Use B or HB pencil only.** Mark *at most one* of the options A, B, C, D, E on the Answer Sheet for each question. Do not mark more than one option.
3. Time allowed: **90 minutes**.
   No answers or personal details may be entered on the Answer Sheet after the 90 minutes are over.
4. The use of rough paper is allowed.
   Calculators, measuring instruments and squared paper are forbidden.
5. Candidates must be full-time students at secondary school or FE college, and must be in Year 13 or below (England & Wales); S6 or below (Scotland); Year 14 or below (Northern Ireland).
6. There are twenty-five questions. Each question is followed by five options marked A, B, C, D, E. Only one of these is correct. Enter the letter A-E corresponding to the correct answer in the corresponding box on the Answer Sheet.
7. **Scoring rules**: all candidates start out with 25 marks;
   > 0 marks are awarded for each question left unanswered;
   > 4 marks are awarded for each correct answer;
   > **1 mark is deducted** for each incorrect answer.
8. **Guessing**: Remember that there is a penalty for wrong answers. Note also that later questions are deliberately intended to be harder than earlier questions. You are thus advised to concentrate first on solving as many as possible of the first 15-20 questions. Only then should you try later questions.

The United Kingdom Mathematics Trust is a Registered Charity.

http://www.ukmt.org.uk
© UKMT 2015

1. What is $2015^2 - 2016 \times 2014$?

   A −2015   B −1   C 0   D 1   E 2015

2. What is the sum of all the solutions of the equation $6x = \dfrac{150}{x}$?

   A 0   B 5   C 6   D 25   E 156

3. When Louise had her first car, 50 litres of petrol cost £40. When she filled up the other day, she noticed that 40 litres of petrol cost £50.

   By approximately what percentage has the cost of petrol increased over this time?

   A 50%   B 56%   C 67%   D 75%   E 80%

4. In the diagram, the smaller circle touches the larger circle and also passes through its centre. What fraction of the area of the larger circle is outside the smaller circle?

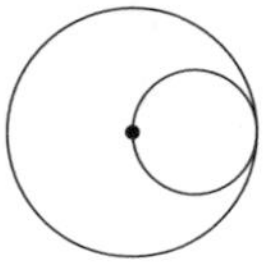

   A $\dfrac{2}{3}$ B $\dfrac{3}{4}$ C $\dfrac{4}{5}$ D $\dfrac{5}{6}$ E $\dfrac{6}{7}$

5. The integer n is the mean of the three numbers 17, 23 and $2n$. What is the sum of the digits of n?

   A 4   B 5   C 6   D 7   E 8

6. The numbers 5, 6, 7, 8, 9, 10 are to be placed, one in each of the circles in the diagram, so that the sum of the numbers in each pair of touching circles is a prime number. The number 5 is placed in the top circle.

   Which number is placed in the shaded circle?

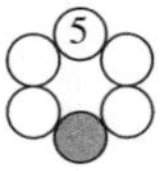

   A 6   B 7   C 8   D 9   E 10

7. Which of the following has the largest value?

   A $\dfrac{\left(\frac{1}{2}\right)}{\left(\frac{3}{4}\right)}$ B $\dfrac{1}{\left(\frac{\left(\frac{2}{3}\right)}{4}\right)}$ C $\dfrac{\left(\frac{\left(\frac{1}{2}\right)}{3}\right)}{4}$ D $\dfrac{1}{\left(\frac{2}{\left(\frac{3}{4}\right)}\right)}$ E $\dfrac{\left(\frac{1}{\left(\frac{2}{3}\right)}\right)}{4}$

8. The diagram shows eight small squares. Six of these squares are to be shaded so that the shaded squares form the net of a cube.

   In how many different ways can this be done?

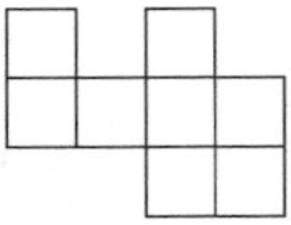

   A 10   B 8   C 7   D 6   E 4

9. Four different straight lines are drawn on a flat piece of paper. The number of points where two or more lines intersect is counted.

   Which of the following could **not** be the number of such points?

   A 1   B 2   C 3   D 4   E 5

10. The positive integer n is between 1 and 20. Milly adds up all the integers from 1 to n inclusive. Billy adds up all the integers from $n + 1$ to 20 inclusive. Their totals are the same. What is the value of n?

    A 11   B 12   C 13   D 14   E 15

11. Rahid has a large number of cubic building blocks. Each block has sides of length 4 cm, 6 cm or 10 cm. Rahid makes little towers built from three blocks stacked on top of each other. How many different heights of tower can he make?

A 6   B 8   C 9   D 12   E 27

12. A circle touches the sides of triangle PQR at the points S, T and U as shown. Also $\angle PQR = \alpha°$, $\angle PRQ = \beta°$ and $\angle TSU = \gamma°$. Which of the following gives γ in terms of α and β?

A $\frac{1}{2}(\alpha + \beta)$ B $180 - \frac{1}{2}(\alpha + \beta)$
C $180 - (\alpha + \beta)$ D $\alpha + \beta$
E $\frac{1}{3}(\alpha + \beta)$

13. The Knave of Hearts tells only the truth on Mondays, Tuesdays, Wednesdays and Thursdays. He tells only lies on all the other days. The Knave of Diamonds tells only the truth on Fridays, Saturdays, Sundays and Mondays. He tells only lies on all the other days. On one day last week, they both said, "Yesterday I told lies."

On which day of the week was that?

A Sunday   B Monday   C Tuesday   D Thursday   E Friday

14. The triangle shown has an area of 88 square units. What is the value of y?

A 17.6   B $2\sqrt{46}$ C $6\sqrt{10}$ D $13\sqrt{2}$ E $8\sqrt{5}$

15. Two vases are cylindrical in shape. The larger vase has diameter 20 cm. The smaller vase has diameter 10 cm and height 16 cm. The larger vase is partially filled with water. Then the empty smaller vase, with the open end at the top, is slowly pushed down into the water, which flows over its rim. When the smaller vase is pushed right down, it is half full of water.

What was the original depth of the water in the larger vase?

A 10 cm   B 12 cm   C 14 cm   D 16 cm   E 18 cm

16. Fnargs are either red or blue and have 2, 3 or 4 heads. A group of six Fnargs consisting of one of each possible form is made to line up such that no immediate neighbours are the same colour nor have the same number of heads. How many ways are there of lining them up from left to right?

A 12   B 24   C 60   D 120   E 720

17. The diagram shows eight circles of two different sizes. The circles are arranged in concentric pairs so that the centres form a square. Each larger circle touches one other larger circle and two smaller circles. The larger circles have radius 1. What is the radius of each smaller circle?

A $\frac{1}{3}$ B $\frac{2}{5}$ C $\sqrt{2}-1$ D $\frac{1}{2}$ E $\frac{1}{2}\sqrt{2}$

18. What is the largest integer k whose square k^2 is a factor of $10!$?
    $[10! = 10 \times 9 \times 8 \times 7 \times 6 \times 5 \times 4 \times 3 \times 2 \times 1.]$

    A 6   B 256   C 360   D 720   E 5040

19. Three squares are arranged as shown so that their
    bases lie on a straight line. Also, the corners P, Q and
    R lie on a straight line. The middle square has sides
    that are 8 cm longer than the sides of the smallest
    square. The largest square has sides of length 50 cm.

    There are two possible values for the length (in cm) of the sides of the smallest
    square. Which of the following are they?

    A 2, 32   B 4, 42   C 4, 34   D 32, 40   E 34, 42

20. A square ink pad has sides of length 1 cm. It is covered in black ink and carefully
    placed in the middle of a piece of white paper. The square pad is then rotated $180°$
    about one of its corners so that all of the pad remains in contact with the paper
    throughout the turn. The pad is then removed from the paper. What area of paper,
    in cm^2, is coloured black?

    A $\pi + 2$ B $2\pi - 1$ C 4   D $2\pi - 2$ E $\pi + 1$

21. The diagram shows a triangle XYZ. The sides
    XY, YZ and XZ have lengths 2, 3 and 4
    respectively. The lines AMB, PMQ and SMT
    are drawn parallel to the sides of triangle XYZ
    so that AP, QS and BT are of equal length.
    What is the length of AP?

    A $\dfrac{10}{11}$ B $\dfrac{11}{12}$ C $\dfrac{12}{13}$ D $\dfrac{13}{14}$ E $\dfrac{14}{15}$

22. Let $f(x) = x + \sqrt{x^2 + 1} + \dfrac{1}{x - \sqrt{x^2 + 1}}$. What is the value of $f(2015)$?

    A -1 B 0   C 1   D $\sqrt{2016}$ E 2015

23. Given four different non-zero digits, it is possible to form 24 different four-digit
    numbers containing each of these four digits. What is the largest prime factor of the
    sum of the 24 numbers?

    A 23   B 93   C 97   D 101   E 113

24. Peter has 25 cards, each printed with a different integer from 1 to 25. He wishes to
    place N cards in a single row so that the numbers on every adjacent pair of cards
    have a prime factor in common.
    What is the largest value of N for which this is possible?

    A 16   B 18   C 20   D 22   E 24

25. A function, defined on the set of positive integers, is such that $f(xy) = f(x) + f(y)$
    for all x and y. It is known that $f(10) = 14$ and $f(40) = 20$. What is the value of
    $f(500)$?

    A 29   B 30   C 39   D 48   E 50

Further remarks

The solutions are provided.

1.	D
2.	A
3.	B
4.	B
5.	A
6.	E
7.	B
8.	D
9.	B
10.	D
11.	C
12.	A
13.	E
14.	E
15.	C
16.	A
17.	C
18.	D
19.	A
20.	E
21.	C
22.	B
23.	D
24.	C
25.	C

UK SENIOR MATHEMATICAL CHALLENGE

Organised by the **United Kingdom Mathematics Trust**

supported by

Institute
and Faculty
of Actuaries

SOLUTIONS

Keep these solutions secure until after the test on

THURSDAY 5 NOVEMBER 2015

This solutions pamphlet outlines a solution for each problem on this year's paper. We have tried to give the most straightforward approach, but the solutions presented here are not the only possible solutions. Occasionally we have added a 'Note' at the end of a solution.

Please share these solutions with your students.

Much of the potential benefit of grappling with challenging mathematical problems depends on teachers making time for some kind of review, or follow-up, during which students may begin to see what they should have done, and how many problems they could have solved.

We hope that you and they agree that the first 15 problems could, in principle, have been solved by most candidates; if not, please let us know.

The UKMT is a registered charity.

© UKMT 2015

1. **D** The expression $2015^2 - 2016 \times 2014$ can be written as $2015^2 - (2015+1)(2015-1)$ which simplifies, using the difference of two squares, to $2015^2 - (2015^2 - 1) = 1$.

2. **A** Rearranging $6x = \dfrac{150}{x}$ gives $x^2 = \dfrac{150}{6}$, so $x^2 = 25$. This has two solutions, $x = 5$ and $x = -5$. Therefore the sum of the solutions is $5 + (-5) = 0$.

3. **B** When 50 litres of petrol cost £40, 1 litre cost $\dfrac{£40}{50}$ which is 80 pence. More recently, 1 litre cost $\dfrac{£50}{40} = 125$ pence. The percentage increase is then $\dfrac{\text{actual increase}}{\text{original price}} \times 100$ which is $\dfrac{45}{80} \times 100 = \dfrac{450}{8} = 56.25$. So the approximate increase is 56%.

4. **B** Let the radius of the smaller circle be r and so the radius of the larger circle is $2r$. The area of the smaller circle is then πr^2 and the area of the larger circle is $\pi \times (2r)^2$ which is $4\pi r^2$. The fraction of the larger circle which is outside the smaller circle is then $\dfrac{4\pi r^2 - \pi r^2}{4\pi r^2} = \dfrac{3\pi r^2}{4\pi r^2} = \dfrac{3}{4}$.

5. **A** The mean of 17, 23 and $2n$ is given to be n, so $\dfrac{17 + 23 + 2n}{3} = n$ which gives $40 + 2n = 3n$. As n is then 40, the sum of the digits of n is 4.

6. **E** The prime numbers which are the sums of pairs of numbers in touching circles are all odd as they are greater than 2. This means that any two adjacent circles in the diagram must be filled with one odd number and one even number. The number 10 may not be placed on either side of 5, since $10 + 5 = 15 = 3 \times 5$. So either side of the 5 must be 6 and 8. Below 6 and 8 must be 7 and 9 respectively leaving 10 to be placed in the shaded circle at the bottom.

7. **B** Evaluating each option gives

$$\text{A } \dfrac{\left(\frac{1}{2}\right)}{\left(\frac{3}{4}\right)} = \dfrac{1}{2} \times \dfrac{4}{3} = \dfrac{2}{3} \qquad \text{B } \dfrac{1}{\left(\frac{1}{6}\right)} = \dfrac{1}{\left(\frac{2}{12}\right)} = \dfrac{12}{2} = 6 \qquad \text{C } \dfrac{\frac{\left(\frac{1}{2}\right)}{3}}{4} = \dfrac{\left(\frac{1}{6}\right)}{4} = \dfrac{1}{24}$$

$$\text{D } \dfrac{1}{\frac{2}{\left(\frac{3}{4}\right)}} = \dfrac{1}{\left(\frac{8}{3}\right)} = \dfrac{3}{8} \qquad \text{E } \dfrac{\left(\frac{1}{3}\right)}{4} = \dfrac{\left(\frac{3}{2}\right)}{4} = \dfrac{3}{8}.$$

So B has the largest answer.

8. **D** Let the squares in the diagram be labelled as shown. Each of the nets formed from six squares must contain all of R, S and T. The net must also include one of P and Q (but not both as they will fold into the same position), and any two of U, V and W. This therefore gives $2 \times 3 = 6$ different ways.

9. **B** Possible configurations of four different straight lines drawn in a plane are shown here to give 1, 3, 4 and 5 points of intersection respectively. In order to have exactly 2 points of intersection, two of the straight lines would need to lie in the same position and so would not be 'different'.

10. **D** The total of the numbers from 1 to 20 is $\frac{1}{2} \times 20 \times (20 + 1) = 210$. If Milly and Billy have totals which are equal, their totals must each be 105. Milly's total, of the numbers from 1 to n, is $\frac{1}{2}n(n+1)$ so $\frac{1}{2}n(n+1) = 105$ which gives $n^2 + n = 210$. Therefore $n^2 + n - 210 = 0$ which factorises to give $(n+15)(n-14) = 0$. As n is a positive integer, $n = 14$.

11. C There are several different ways to count systematically the number of towers that Rahid can build. Here is one way.

All blocks the same size			Exactly two blocks the same size						All blocks of different sizes
10	6	4	4	6	4	10	6	10	4
10	6	4	10	10	6	6	4	4	6
10	6	4	10	10	6	6	4	4	10
Total height 30	18	12	24	26	16	22	14	18	20

So there are nine different heights of tower (as the height of 18cm can be made from $6 + 6 + 6$ or $10 + 4 + 4$).

12. A Each of the three sides of triangle PQR is a tangent to the circle. Two tangents to a circle which meet at a point are of equal length. So QU and QS are of equal length. Similarly $RT = RS$. This means that $\angle QUS = \angle QSU = \frac{1}{2}(180 - \alpha)$ and also $\angle RTS = \angle RST = \frac{1}{2}(180 - \beta)$. At S we can consider the sum of the three angles, so $\frac{1}{2}(180 - \alpha) + \gamma + \frac{1}{2}(180 - \beta) = 180$. Simplifying gives $90 - \frac{1}{2}\alpha + \gamma + 90 - \frac{1}{2}\beta = 180$ and so $\gamma = \frac{1}{2}(\alpha + \beta)$.

13. E

Knave of	Mon	Tue	Wed	Thu	Fri	Sat	Sun	Mon
Hearts	T	T	T	T	L	L	L	T
Diamonds	T	L	L	L	T	T	T	T

When a knave says "Yesterday I told lies" it could be that today he is telling the truth and he did indeed tell lies yesterday. In the table, this is a T preceded by an L.

It could also be that today he is lying, in which case he was in fact telling the truth yesterday. In the table, this is an L preceded by a T. The only day when one or the other of these options applies to each knave is Friday.

14. E

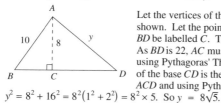

Let the vertices of the triangle be labelled A, B and D as shown. Let the point where the perpendicular from A meets BD be labelled C. The area of triangle ABD is given as 88. As BD is 22, AC must be 8. Considering triangle ABC and using Pythagoras' Theorem gives $BC = 6$. The remainder of the base CD is then $22 - 6 = 16$. Considering triangle ACD and using Pythagoras' Theorem again gives $y^2 = 8^2 + 16^2 = 8^2(1^2 + 2^2) = 8^2 \times 5$. So $y = 8\sqrt{5}$.

15. C Let the original water level in the larger vase be h cm. The volume of water at the start is then $\pi \times 10^2 \times h$ cm^3. The volume of water completely within the vase is constant, but when the smaller vase is pushed down, some of the water moves into it. In the end the depth of the water in the larger vase is the same as the height of the smaller vase itself, which is 16 cm. We are given that the final depth of water in the smaller vase is 8 cm. So the total volume of water is then $\pi \times 10^2 \times 16$ cm^3 less the gap in the top half of the smaller vase. So $\pi \times 10^2 \times h = \pi \times 10^2 \times 16 - \pi \times 5^2 \times 8$, giving $100\pi h = 1600\pi - 200\pi$ and therefore $h = 14$.

16. A Let the six Fnargs in their final positions be denoted by $F_1 F_2 F_3 F_4 F_5 F_6$. There are six choices for F_1. Once this Fnarg is chosen, the colours of the Fnargs must alternate all along the line and so we need only consider the number of heads. There are $3 - 1 = 2$ choices for F_2 as the number of heads for $F_2 \neq$ the number of heads for F_1. There is only one choice for F_3 as F_3 cannot have the same number of heads as F_2 or F_1 (F_3 and F_1 are the same colour and so have different numbers of heads). There is only one choice for F_4 as it is completely determined by F_3 and F_2, just as F_3 was completely determined by F_2 and F_1. There is only one choice for each of F_5 and F_6 as they are the last of each colour of Fnargs. The total number of ways of lining up the Fnargs is $6 \times 2 \times 1 \times 1 \times 1 \times 1$ which is 12.

17. C Let the radius of each of the smaller circles be r and let the centres of the circles be A, B, C and D in order. We are given that $ABCD$ is a square. When two circles touch externally, the distance between their centres equals the sum of their radii. Hence AB and BC have length $r + 1$ and AC has length $1 + 1 = 2$. By Pythagoras' Theorem $(r + 1)^2 + (r + 1)^2 = 2^2$, so $2(r + 1)^2 = 2^2 = 4$ and therefore $(r + 1)^2 = 2$. Square rooting both sides gives $r + 1 = \sqrt{2}$, as we must take the positive root, and so $r = \sqrt{2} - 1$.

18. D Expressed as a product of its prime factors, $10!$ is
$2 \times 5 \times 3 \times 3 \times 2 \times 2 \times 7 \times 2 \times 3 \times 5 \times 2 \times 2 \times 3 \times 2$ which is $2^8 \times 3^4 \times 5^2 \times 7$. This can be written as $(2^4 \times 3^2 \times 5)^2 \times 7$ so the largest integer k such that k^2 is a factor of $10!$ is $2^4 \times 3^2 \times 5$ which is 720.

19. A Let the length of the side of the smallest square be x cm. So the three squares have sides of lengths x cm, $(x + 8)$ cm and 50 cm respectively. The gradient of PQ is then $\frac{8}{x}$ and the gradient of PR is $\dfrac{50 - x}{x + x + 8}$. As P, Q and R lie on a straight line, $\dfrac{8}{x} = \dfrac{50 - x}{2x + 8}$ so $8(2x + 8) = x(50 - x)$. Expanding gives $16x + 64 = 50x - x^2$ and therefore $x^2 - 34x + 64 = 0$, giving $x = 2$ or 32.

20. E Let the corner of the square about which it is rotated be O and the opposite vertex of the square be A. As the circle is rotated through $180°$ about O, the vertex A travels along a semicircle whose centre is O. The area coloured black by the ink is then formed from two half squares and a semicircle. The square has side-length 1, so $OA = \sqrt{2}$. The total area of the two half squares and the semicircle is $2 \times (\frac{1}{2} \times 1 \times 1) + \frac{1}{2} \times \pi \times (\sqrt{2})^2$ which is $1 + \pi$.

21. C All of the triangles in the diagram are similar as they contain the same angles. The sides of each triangle are therefore in the ratio $2 : 3 : 4$. First consider triangle APM. Let $AP = x$, so that $AM = 2x$. Now considering triangle TBM, as $BT = x$, $BM = \frac{4x}{3}$. The quadrilateral $AMSX$ is a parallelogram as AM is parallel to XS and MS is parallel to AX. So $AM = XS = 2x$. Similarly $QZ = BM = \frac{4x}{3}$. Considering the base of triangle XYZ, $XS + SQ + QZ = 4$. So $2x + x + \frac{4x}{3} = 4$ and therefore $x = \frac{12}{13}$.

22. B $f(x) = x + \sqrt{x^2 + 1} + \dfrac{1}{x - \sqrt{x^2 + 1}} = \dfrac{(x + \sqrt{x^2 + 1})(x - \sqrt{x^2 + 1}) + 1}{x - \sqrt{x^2 + 1}}$. The numerator is $x^2 - (\sqrt{x^2 + 1})^2 + 1 = -1 + 1 = 0$. So $f(x) = 0$. Hence $f(2015) = 0$.

23. D Let a four-digit positive integer be expressed as $1000a + 100b + 10c + d$ where a, b, c and d are all different. In the 24 possible permutations of a, b, c and d, each of the four letters appears in each position six times. Adding all 24 numbers together gives $1000(6a + 6b + 6c + 6d) + 100(6a + 6b + 6c + 6d) + 10(6a + 6b + 6c + 6d) + 6a + 6b + 6c + 6d$. The total is therefore $1111 \times 6(a + b + c + d)$ which factorises to $2 \times 3 \times 11 \times 101(a + b + c + d)$. As $a + b + c + d < 101$, the largest prime factor of the sum is 101.

24. C There are five cards in Peter's set that are printed with an integer that has no prime factors in common with any other number from 1 to 25. The five numbers are 1 (which has no prime factors) and the primes 13, 17, 19 and 23. These cards cannot be placed anywhere in the row of N cards. One possible row is: 11, 22, 18, 16, 12, 10, 8, 6, 4, 2, 24, 3, 9, 21, 7, 14, 20, 25, 15, 5. So the longest row is of 20 cards.

25. C Repeatedly using the rule that $f(xy) = f(x) + f(y)$ allows us to write $f(500)$ as $f(2 \times 2 \times 5 \times 5 \times 5) = f(2) + f(2) + f(5) + f(5) + f(5) = 2f(2) + 3f(5)$. We are given values for $f(40)$ and $f(10)$ and from them we need to calculate the values of $f(2)$ and $f(5)$. Now $f(40)$ can be written as $f(2) + f(2) + f(10)$ so $20 = 2f(2) + 14$ and therefore $f(2) = 3$. Similarly $f(10) = f(2) + f(5)$ so $14 = 3 + f(5)$ giving $f(5) = 11$. So $f(500) = 2f(2) + 3f(5) = 2 \times 3 + 3 \times 11 = 39$.

For reasons of space, these solutions are necessarily brief. There are more in-depth, extended solutions available on the UKMT website, which include some exercises for further investigation:

http://www.ukmt.org.uk/

The answers

The table below shows the proportion of pupils' choices. The correct answer is shown in bold. [The percentages are rounded to the nearest whole number.]

Qn	A	B	C	D	E	Blank
1	3	7	4	**78**	5	4
2	**63**	25	1	4	1	5
3	15	**60**	11	4	4	7
4	6	**72**	8	3	1	11
5	**67**	3	5	4	5	15
6	1	1	2	1	**91**	3
7	10	**64**	6	6	4	10
8	1	3	5	**23**	45	22
9	14	**27**	7	6	24	22
10	3	3	5	**66**	6	17
11	7	15	**49**	13	10	7
12	**19**	14	20	3	4	40
13	2	6	4	3	**79**	7
14	13	5	6	6	**22**	48
15	4	10	**22**	9	22	32
16	**26**	13	8	7	5	41
17	8	4	**22**	13	4	49
18	5	4	7	**19**	9	55
19	**19**	3	10	6	5	56
20	5	7	3	4	**19**	62
21	2	4	**6**	2	2	84
22	4	**17**	6	4	6	64
23	2	3	4	**7**	2	82
24	4	6	**8**	4	3	75
25	2	2	**10**	5	3	77

SMC 2015: Some comments on the pupils' choice of answers as sent to schools in the letter with the results

The average mark this year was 57, somewhat lower than last year's 61. By itself, this has no great significance. When we look more closely at the responses to individual questions we see both reasons for encouragement, and for being concerned. The table included with your results will tell you how the responses of your students compare with the national distribution. We hope you will find the time to look at this information, and, in particular, that you will discuss with your pupils questions where they were not as successful as you might have hoped.

It was disappointing to see that in Question 2 a quarter of the students seemed to have thought that the given equation has just the one solution, $x = 5$, and missed the second solution, $x = -5$. By this stage in their mathematical development, students should have a firm understanding of number which includes negative numbers. They should expect quadratic equations to have two solutions (although not all of them do). If many of your pupils chose option B, please discuss with them the source of their error.

The comparatively low level of success with Question 4 is also worrying. Probably, most of the 18% of the students who chose a wrong option just made a wild guess without thinking about the geometry, but what are we to make of the fact than over 10% did not make an attempt at this question?

It is also a matter of concern that so many pupils left blank their answers to the two questions on geometry, Questions 12 and 14. As shown in the Extended Solutions [these may be downloaded from our website, www.ukmt.org.uk] there are several ways of solving each of these problems. To tackle them you need to have some geometrical facts at your fingertips. We would be interested to hear from teachers whose pupils had little success with these questions. Are the problems setters making wrong assumptions about the geometrical ideas that your pupils have met? Or, is it that pupils see the facts about tangents to circles and areas of triangles that the solutions depend on, but the present school curriculum fails to consolidate their understanding of them?

In contrast, the high level of success with Question 6 is pleasing, showing that when the students were willing to engage with a question, over 90% were capable of thinking through to a correct answer. There was also a high rate of success with the logic of Question 13. However, we note that neither of these questions requires anything much by way of technical skills.

The SMC marks

The profile of marks obtained is shown below.

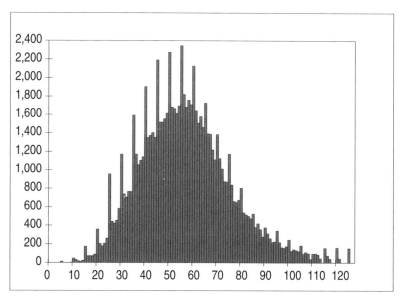

Bar chart showing the actual frequencies in the 2015 SMC

Since 2012, the UKMT has awarded certificates to the top 60% of SMC students. On this basis the cut-off marks were set at

GOLD – 82 or over   SILVER – 65 to 81   BRONZE – 50 to 64

Candidates who scored 104 or more were invited to take part in BMO 1 and those who scored from 86 to 103 were invited to take part in the Senior Kangaroo.

A sample of one of the certificates is shown below.

UK SENIOR MATHEMATICAL CHALLENGE

2015

of

received a

BRONZE CERTIFICATE

Chairman, United Kingdom Mathematics Trust

Institute
and Faculty
of Actuaries

THE UNITED KINGDOM SENIOR MATHEMATICAL CHALLENGE

The Senior Mathematical Challenge (SMC) is run by the UK Mathematics Trust. The SMC encourages mathematical reasoning, precision of thought, and fluency in using basic mathematical techniques to solve interesting problems. It is aimed at those in full-time education and with sufficient mathematical competence to undertake a post-16 course.

The problems on the SMC are designed to make students think. Most are accessible, yet still challenge those with more experience; they are also meant to be memorable and enjoyable.

Mathematics controls more aspects of the modern world than most people realise—from iPods, cash machines, telecommunications and airline booking systems to production processes in engineering, efficient distribution and stock-holding, investment strategies and 'whispering' jet engines. The scientific and industrial revolutions flowed from the realisation that mathematics was both the language of nature, and also a way of analysing—and hence controlling—our environment. In the last fifty years old and new applications of mathematical ideas have transformed the way we live.

All these developments depend on mathematical thinking—a mode of thought whose essential style is far more permanent than the wave of technological change which it has made possible. The problems on the SMC reflect this style, which pervades all mathematics, by encouraging students to think clearly about challenging problems.

The SMC was established as the National Mathematics Contest in 1961. In recent years there have been over 100,000 entries from around 2000 schools and colleges. Certificates are awarded to the highest scoring 60% of candidates (Gold : Silver : Bronze 1 : 2 : 3).

The UKMT is a registered charity. Please see our website www.ukmt.org.uk for more information. Donations to support our work would be gratefully received; a link for on-line donations is below.

www.donate.ukmt.org.uk

The Next Stages

Subject to certain conditions, candidates who obtained a score of 104 or over in the 2015 Senior Mathematical Challenge were invited to take the British Mathematical Olympiad Round One and those who scored from 86 to 103 were invited to take part in the Senior Kangaroo. The latter makes use of Kangaroo questions as well as a few others and is not a multiple choice paper but can be marked by character recognition as all the answers are three-digit numbers.

SENIOR 'KANGAROO' MATHEMATICAL CHALLENGE

Friday 27th November 2015

Organised by the United Kingdom Mathematics Trust

The Senior Kangaroo paper allows students in the UK to test themselves on questions set for the best school-aged mathematicians from across Europe and beyond.

RULES AND GUIDELINES (to be read before starting):

1. Do not open the paper until the Invigilator tells you to do so.

2. Time allowed: **1 hour**.

3. The use of rough paper is allowed; **calculators** and measuring instruments are **forbidden.**

4. **Use B or HB pencil only** to complete your personal details and record your answers on the machine-readable Answer Sheet provided. **All answers are written using three digits, from 000 to 999.** For example, if you think the answer to a question is 42, write 042 at the top of the answer grid and then code your answer by putting solid black pencil lines through the 0, the 4 and the 2 beneath.

   Please note that the machine that reads your Answer Sheet will only see the solid black lines through the numbers beneath, not the written digits above. You must ensure that you code your answers or you will not receive any marks. There are further instructions and examples on the Answer Sheet.

5. The paper contains 20 questions. Five marks will be awarded for each correct answer. There is no penalty for giving an incorrect answer.

6. The questions on this paper challenge you **to think**, not to guess. Though you will not lose marks for getting answers wrong, you will undoubtedly get more marks, and more satisfaction, by doing a few questions carefully than by guessing lots of answers.

Enquiries about the Senior Kangaroo should be sent to:
Maths Challenges Office, School of Maths Satellite,
University of Leeds, Leeds, LS2 9JT
Tel. 0113 343 2339
www.ukmt.org.uk

1. In a pile of 200 coins, 2% are gold coins and the rest are silver. Simple Simon removes one silver coin every day until the pile contains 20% gold coins. How many silver coins does Simon remove?

2. The value of the expression $1 + \cfrac{1}{1 + \cfrac{1}{1 + \cfrac{1}{5}}}$ is $\dfrac{a}{b}$, where a and b are integers whose only common factor is 1. What is the value of $a + b$?

3. The diagram shows a solid with six triangular faces and five vertices. Andrew wants to write an integer at each of the vertices so that the sum of the numbers at the three vertices of each face is the same. He has already written the numbers 1 and 5 as shown.

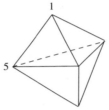

   What is the sum of the other three numbers he will write?

4. A box contains two white socks, three blue socks and four grey socks. Rachel knows that three of the socks have holes in, but does not know what colour these socks are. She takes one sock at a time from the box without looking. How many socks must she take for her to be certain she has a pair of socks of the same colour without holes?

5. The diagram shows two circles and a square with sides of length 10 cm. One vertex of the square is at the centre of the large circle and two sides of the square are tangents to both circles. The small circle touches the large circle. The radius of the small circle is $(a - b\sqrt{2})$ cm.

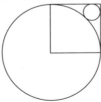

   What is the value of $a + b$?

6. The median of a set of five positive integers is one more than the mode and one less than the mean. What is the largest possible value of the range of the five integers?

7. The diagram shows a triangle ABC with area 12 cm². The sides of the triangle are extended to points P, Q, R, S, T and U as shown so that $PA = AB = BS$, $QA = AC = CT$ and $RB = BC = CU$.

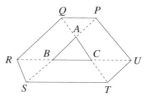

What is the area (in cm²) of hexagon $PQRSTU$?

8. A mob of 2015 kangaroos contains only red and grey kangaroos. One grey kangaroo is taller than exactly one red kangaroo, one grey kangaroo is taller than exactly three red kangaroos, one grey kangaroo is taller than exactly five red kangaroos and so on with each successive grey kangaroo being taller than exactly two more red kangaroos than the previous grey kangaroo. The final grey kangaroo is taller than all the red kangaroos. How many grey kangaroos are in the mob?

9. A large rectangle is divided into four identical smaller rectangles by slicing parallel to one of its sides. The perimeter of the large rectangle is 18 metres more than the perimeter of each of the smaller rectangles. The area of the large rectangle is 18 m² more than the area of each of the smaller rectangles. What is the perimeter in metres of the large rectangle?

10. Katherine and James are jogging in the same direction around a pond. They start at the same time and from the same place and each jogs at a constant speed. Katherine, the faster jogger, takes 3 minutes to complete one lap and first overtakes James 8 minutes after starting. How many seconds does it take James to complete one lap?

11. A ball is propelled from corner A of a *square* snooker table of side 2 metres. After bouncing off three cushions as shown, the ball goes into a pocket at B. The total distance travelled by the ball is $\sqrt{k}$ metres. What is the value of k?

(Note that when the ball bounces off a cushion, the angle its path makes with the cushion as it approaches the point of impact is equal to the angle its path makes with the cushion as it moves away from the point of impact as shown in the diagram below.)

12. Chris planned a 210 km bike ride. However, he rode 5 km/h faster than he planned and finished his ride 1 hour earlier than he planned. His average speed for the ride was x km/h. What is the value of x?

13. Twenty-five people who always tell the truth or always lie are standing in a queue. The man at the front of the queue says that everyone behind him always lies. Everyone else says that the person immediately in front of them always lies. How many people in the queue always lie?

14. Four problems were attempted by 100 contestants in a Mathematics competition. The first problem was solved by 90 contestants, the second by 85 contestants, the third by 80 contestants and the fourth by 75 contestants. What is the smallest possible number of contestants who solved all four problems?

15. The 5-digit number '$XX4XY$' is exactly divisible by 165. What is the value of $X + Y$?

16. How many 10-digit numbers are there whose digits are all 1, 2 or 3 and in which adjacent digits differ by 1?

17. In rectangle $JKLM$, the bisector of angle KJM cuts the diagonal KM at point N as shown. The distances between N and sides LM and KL are 8 cm and 1 cm respectively. The length of KL is $(a + \sqrt{b})$ cm. What is the value of $a + b$?

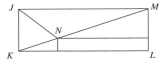

18. Numbers a, b and c are such that $\dfrac{a}{b + c} = \dfrac{b}{c + a} = \dfrac{c}{a + b} = k$.
How many possible values of k are there?

19. In quadrilateral $ABCD$, $\angle ABC = \angle ADC = 90°$, $AD = DC$ and $AB + BC = 20$ cm.

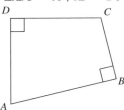

What is the area in cm^2 of quadrilateral $ABCD$?

20. The number $N = 3^{16} - 1$ has a divisor of 193. It also has some divisors between 75 and 85 inclusive. What is the sum of these divisors?

Further remarks

A solutions leaflet was provided.

SENIOR 'KANGAROO' MATHEMATICAL CHALLENGE

Friday 27th November 2015

Organised by the United Kingdom Mathematics Trust

SOLUTIONS

1. 180 The number of gold coins in the original pile is $0.02 \times 200 = 4$. These form 20% of the final pile. Therefore there are $4 \times 5 = 20$ coins left. Hence the number of silver coins Simon removes is $200 - 20 = 180$.

2. 28 The expression can be simplified in stages as follows:

$$1 + \cfrac{1}{1 + \cfrac{1}{1 + \cfrac{1}{5}}} = 1 + \cfrac{1}{1 + \cfrac{1}{\left(\frac{6}{5}\right)}} = 1 + \cfrac{1}{1 + \cfrac{5}{6}} = 1 + \cfrac{1}{\left(\frac{11}{6}\right)} = 1 + \frac{6}{11} = \frac{17}{11} = \frac{a}{b}.$$

Hence the value of $a + b$ is $17 + 11 = 28$.

3. 11 Let the three missing integers be x, y and z, as shown. Consider the 'top' three faces. Since the sum of the three numbers at the vertices of each face is the same, we have

$$1 + 5 + x = 1 + x + y = 1 + 5 + y$$

and hence $x = y = 5$. Therefore the sum of the numbers on a face is equal to $5 + 5 + 1 = 11$. But $x + y + z$ is equal to the sum of the numbers on a face. Hence the sum of the other three numbers that Andrew will write is 11.

4. 7 The first six socks Rachel takes out could consist of three different coloured socks and the three socks with holes in, in which case she would not have a pair of socks the same colour without holes in. However, whatever colour her next sock is, she must then complete a pair. Hence she must take seven socks to be certain of getting a pair of socks the same colour without holes in.

5. **50** Let O and P be the centres of the large and small circles respectively and label points Q and S as shown in the diagram. Let the radius of the small circle be r cm. Draw line PR so that R is on QS and PR is parallel to OS. Draw in line OQ. Since triangle OQS is right-angled and isosceles, $OQ^2 = 10^2 + 10^2$ by Pythagoras. Hence $OQ = 10\sqrt{2}$ cm. Similarly, since triangle PQR is right-

angled and isosceles, $PQ = r\sqrt{2}$ cm. Note that angle OQS = angle PQS = $45°$ so OPQ is a straight line. Therefore $10\sqrt{2} = 10 + r + r\sqrt{2}$. This has solution

$$r = \frac{10(\sqrt{2}-1)}{\sqrt{2}+1} = \frac{10(\sqrt{2}-1)(\sqrt{2}-1)}{(\sqrt{2}+1)(\sqrt{2}-1)} = \frac{10(2+1-2\sqrt{2})}{2-1} = 30 - 20\sqrt{2}.$$

Hence the radius of the small circle is $(30 - 20\sqrt{2})$ cm and the value of $a + b$ is $30 + 20 = 50$.

6. **7** Let the five integers be p, q, r, s and t with $p \leqslant q \leqslant r \leqslant s \leqslant t$. The median of the list is r and, since the mode is one less than the median, $p = q = r - 1$ and $r < s < t$. The mean is one more than the median and hence the total of the five integers is $5(r + 1)$. Therefore $r - 1 + r - 1 + r + s + t = 5r + 5$ and hence $s + t = 2r + 7$. Since the smallest possible value of s is $r + 1$, the maximum value of t is $r + 6$. Hence the largest possible value of the range of the five integers is $r + 6 - (r - 1) = 7$.

7. **156** Consider triangles ABC and AST. Angles CAB and TAS are equal because they are the same angle, $SA = 2BA$ and $TA = 2CA$. Hence triangles ABC and AST are similar. The ratio of their sides is $1 : 2$ and hence the ratio of their areas is $1^2 : 2^2 = 1 : 4$. Therefore the area of triangle AST is 4×12 cm^2 = 48 cm^2 and hence the area of $BSTC$ is $(48 - 12)$ cm^2 = 36 cm^2. In a similar way, it can be shown that each of the areas of $CUPA$ and

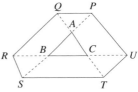

$AQRB$ is also 36 cm^2. Next consider triangles ABC and APQ. Angles BAC and PAQ are equal using vertically opposite angles, $AB = AP$ and $AC = AQ$. Hence triangles ABC and APQ are congruent (SAS) and so the area of triangle APQ is 12 cm^2. In a similar way, it can be shown that the each of areas of triangles BRS and CTU is also 12 cm^2. Hence the total area of hexagon $PQRSTU$ in cm^2 is $(3 \times 36 + 4 \times 12) = 156$.

8. **672** The first grey kangaroo has only one red kangaroo smaller than itself. Apart from that, each grey kangaroo can be grouped with two red kangaroos whose heights lie between its height and that of the previous grey kangaroo. The number of such groups is $(2015 - 2)/3 = 671$. Hence there are 672 grey kangaroos in the mob.

9. **28** Let the length of the original rectangle be x metres and let the height be y metres. Without losing any generality, assume the rectangle is sliced parallel to the height, as shown.

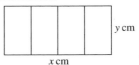

The information in the question tells us that

$$2x + 2y = 2\left(\frac{x}{4}\right) + 2y + 18 \text{ and that } xy = \left(\frac{x}{4}\right)y + 18. \text{ From the first equation, we}$$

have $\dfrac{3x}{2} = 18$ which has solution $x = 12$. Substitute this value into the second equation to obtain $12y = 3y + 18$, which has solution $y = 2$. Hence the perimeter of the large rectangle in metres is $2 \times 12 + 2 \times 2 = 28$.

10. **288** Katherine catches James after 8 minutes when she has jogged $\frac{8}{3}$ laps. In that time, James will have jogged one lap fewer so will have jogged $\frac{5}{3}$ laps. Therefore, James jogs $\frac{5}{3}$ laps in 8 minutes which is the same as 480 seconds. Hence he will jog $\frac{1}{3}$ of a lap in 96 seconds and so he jogs a whole lap in 288 seconds.

11. **52** A solution can be obtained by reflecting the square repeatedly in the cushion the ball strikes. The path of the ball is then represented by the line AB' in the diagram.

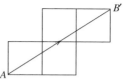

The length of the path can be calculated using Pythagoras Theorem. We have $(AB')^2 = (3 \times 2)^2 + (2 \times 2)^2$. Therefore $(AB')^2 = 36 + 16 = 52$ and so $AB' = \sqrt{52}$ metres and hence the value of k is 52.

12. **35** Chris's time for the ride when he rode at an average speed of x km/h was $\dfrac{210}{x}$ hours. His planned speed was $(x - 5)$ km/h when his time would have been $\dfrac{210}{x - 5}$ hours. The question tells us that he completed the ride 1 hour earlier than planned, so $\dfrac{210}{x - 5} - \dfrac{210}{x} = 1$. Therefore $210x - 210(x - 5) = x(x - 5)$ and hence $1050 = x^2 - 5x$. Thus $x^2 - 5x - 1050 = 0$ and hence $(x - 35)(x + 30) = 0$. Therefore, since x is positive, $x = 35$.

13. **13** Assume the man at the front of the queue is telling the truth and that everyone behind him always lies. However, then the person in third place in the queue would be telling the truth when he says that the person in second place always lies. This contradicts the original assumption and so the man at the front of the queue is lying. In this case, the man in second place is telling the truth, the man in third place is lying etc. Hence, every other person, starting with the first, is lying and so there are $1 + \frac{1}{2} \times 24 = 13$ people in the queue who always lie.

14. **30** The smallest number of contestants solving all four problems correctly occurs when the contestants who fail to solve individual problems are all distinct. In that case, the number failing to solve some question is $10 + 15 + 20 + 25 = 70$ and the number solving them all is $100 - 70 = 30$.

15. **14** First note that $165 = 3 \times 5 \times 11$. Hence, for '$XX4XY$' to be exactly divisible by 165, it must be exactly divisible by 3, 5 and 11. A number is divisible by 3 if and only if the sum of its digits is divisible by 3 so $3X + 4 + Y$ is divisible by 3 and hence $4 + Y$ is divisible by 3. A number is divisible by 5 if and only if its last digit is 5 or 0 so $Y = 5$ or 0. Since $4 + Y$ is divisible by 3 then $Y = 5$. A number is divisible by 11 if and only if the sum of its digits with alternating signs is divisible by 11 so $X - X + 4 - X + Y$ is divisible by 11. Hence $9 - X$ is divisible by 11 and so $X = 9$. Hence the value of $X + Y$ is $9 + 5 = 14$.

16. **64** Since adjacent digits differ by 1, each time the number has a digit that is a 1 or a 3, there is only one choice for the next digit as it must be a 2 whereas each time the number has a digit that is a 2, there are two choices for the next digit, namely 1 or 3. Consider all 10-digit numbers starting in a 1. There is only one choice for the second digit since it must be a 2, then two choices for the third digit, then one for the fourth etc. Altogether there are $1 \times 2 \times 1 \times 2 \times 1 \times 2 \times 1 \times 2 \times 1 = 16$ such numbers. Similarly there are 16 such numbers starting in 3. However, if we consider numbers starting in 2, there are two choices for the second digit then only one choice for the third then two for the fourth etc. Altogether there are $2 \times 1 \times 2 \times 1 \times 2 \times 1 \times 2 \times 1 \times 2 = 32$ such numbers. Hence there are $16 + 16 + 32 = 64$ such numbers with the required property.

17. 16

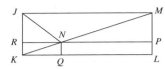

Let points P and Q be the points where the perpendiculars from N to ML and KL meet the lines and extend line PN so it meets JK at R, as shown in the diagram. Since JN is the bisector of angle MJK, angle $NJR = 45°$. Since angle JRN is $90°$, triangle JRN is isosceles and $JR = RN$. Let the length of RN be x cm. Hence the lengths of JR and PM are also x cm. Observe that triangles NKQ and MNP are similar since they have the same angles. Therefore $\dfrac{1}{x} = \dfrac{x}{8}$ and so $x = \sqrt{8}$ since x is positive. The length of KL is equal to the sum of the lengths of NP and NR. Therefore, the length of KL is $(8 + \sqrt{8})$ cm. Hence, the value of $a + b$ is 16.

18. 2 Consider the equation $\dfrac{a}{b+c} = \dfrac{b}{c+a}$. Multiply each side by $(b + c)(c + a)$ to get $a^2 + ac = b^2 + bc$ and so $a^2 - b^2 + ac - bc = 0$. Therefore $(a - b)(a + b + c) = 0$. Hence $a = b$ or $a + b + c = 0$. Similarly, if we consider the equations $\dfrac{b}{c + a} = \dfrac{c}{a + b}$ and $\dfrac{c}{a + b} = \dfrac{a}{b + c}$, then $b = c$ or $a + b + c = 0$ and $c = a$ or $a + b + c = 0$ respectively. Therefore, the possible values of k when all three equations are satisfied simultaneously occur when $a = b = c$, giving $k = \frac{1}{2}$, or when $a + b + c = 0$, giving $k = -1$. Hence there are two possible values of k.

19. 100 Let the lengths of BC, AB and AC be x, y and z centimetres respectively. Let the area of $\triangle ACD$ be U cm^2 and let the area of $\triangle ABC$ be V cm^2. Note that $\triangle ACD$ is one quarter of the square which has AC as an edge. Hence $U = \frac{1}{4}z^2$. Next, using Pythagoras, $z^2 = x^2 + y^2 = (x + y)^2 - 2xy = 20^2 - 4V$. Hence $U = \frac{1}{4}(400 - 4V) = 100 - V$. Therefore the area in cm^2 of $ABCD$ is $U + V = 100$.

(Note: *Since the answer to the problem is independent of x and y, one could observe that the given properties of quadrilateral ABCD are satisfied by a square of side 10 cm which has area 100 cm^2 and conclude that this is therefore the required answer.*)

20. 247 First factorise N twice using the difference of two squares i.e. $N = 3^{16} - 1 = (3^8 - 1)(3^8 + 1) = (3^4 - 1)(3^4 + 1)(3^8 + 1) = 80 \times 82 \times (3^8 + 1)$. This shows that both 80 and 82 are divisors of N in the required range. The question tells us that 193 is a divisor of N and, since 193 is prime, it must be a divisor of $3^8 + 1 = 81 \times 81 + 1 = 6562$. Now observe that $6562 = 2 \times 3281$ and that $3281 \div 193 = 17$. Therefore $N = 80 \times 82 \times 2 \times 17 \times 193$ or $N = (2^4 \times 5) \times (2 \times 41) \times 2 \times 17 \times 193$.

Next consider the integers from 75 to 85 inclusive to see which could be divisors of N. Because N has no prime factors of 3 or 7, we know that 75, 77, 78, 81 and 84 are not divisors of N while the initial argument established that 80 and 82 are divisors of N. Both 79 and 83 are prime and $76 = 4 \times 19$ so, since N does not have a prime factor of 79, 83 or 19, these must also be excluded. This only leaves 85 to be considered. Note that $85 = 5 \times 17$ and both 5 and 17 are prime factors of N so 85 is a divisor of N. Hence the divisors of N in the required range are 80, 82 and 85 with sum 247.

Certificates

These were awarded at two levels, Merit and Qualification.

Senior Kangaroo 2015

of

received a

CERTIFICATE of MERIT

Chairman, United Kingdom Mathematics Trust

THE UKMT SENIOR KANGAROO

The Senior Kangaroo is one of the follow-on rounds for the Senior Mathematical Challenge (SMC) and is organised by the UK Mathematics Trust (UKMT). Around 3,500 high-scoring students in the SMC are invited to participate in the Senior Kangaroo and to test themselves on questions set for the best school-aged mathematicians from across Europe and beyond.

The Senior Kangaroo is a one-hour examination comprising 20 questions; all answers are written using 3 digits, from 000 to 999. The problems involve amusing and thought-provoking situations which require the use of logic as well as mathematical understanding.

The UKMT is a registered charity.
For more information please see our website www.ukmt.org.uk
Donations to support our work would be gratefully
received and can be made by visiting
www.donate.ukmt.org.uk

Mathematical Olympiad for Girls

The UK Mathematical Olympiad for Girls (UK MOG) is held annually to identify students to engage in training for European Girls' Mathematical Olympiad (EGMO). Students who are not involved in training are still eligible for selection for the team.

The 2015 MOG paper was held on 29th September. The time allowed was $2\frac{1}{2}$ hours. The question paper and solutions follow with a prize-winner list.

United Kingdom Mathematics Trust
UK Mathematical Olympiad for Girls
Tuesday 29th September 2015

Instructions

1. Do not turn over until told to do so.

2. Time allowed: $2\frac{1}{2}$ hours.

3. Each question carries 10 marks. Full marks will be awarded for written solutions – not just answers – with complete proofs of any assertions you may make.

   Marks awarded will depend on the clarity of your mathematical presentation. Work in rough first, and then write up your best attempt.

4. Partial marks may be awarded for good ideas, so try to hand in everything that documents your thinking on the problem – the more clearly written the better.

   However, one complete solution will gain more credit than several unfinished attempts.

5. Earlier questions tend to be easier. Some questions have two parts. Part (a) introduces results or ideas useful in solving part (b).

6. The use of rulers and compasses is allowed, but calculators and protractors are forbidden.

7. Start each question on a fresh sheet of paper. Write on one side of the paper only.

   On each sheet of working write the number of the question in the top left-hand corner and your name, initials and school in the top right-hand corner.

8. Complete the cover sheet provided and attach it to the front of your script, followed by your solutions in question number order.

9. Staple all the pages neatly together in the top left-hand corner.

10. To accommodate candidates sitting in other time zones, please do not discuss the paper on the internet until 08:00 BST on Wednesday 30th September.

Enquiries about the Mathematical Olympiad for Girls should be sent to:
UKMT, School of Mathematics Satellite, University of Leeds, Leeds LS2 9JT
0113 343 2339 : enquiry@ukmt.org.uk : www.ukmt.org.uk

1. (a) Expand and simplify $(a - b)(a^2 + ab + b^2)$.

   (b) Find the value of

   $$\frac{2016^3 + 2015^3}{2016^2 - 2015^2}.$$

2. The diagram shows five polygons placed together edge-to-edge: two triangles, a regular hexagon and two regular nonagons.

   Prove that each of the triangles is isosceles.

3. A ladybird is going for a wander around a 10×10 board, subject to the following three rules (see the diagram).

   (i) She starts in the top left cell, labelled S.

   (ii) She only moves left, right or down, as indicated.

   (iii) She never goes back to a cell that she has already visited.

   In how many different ways can she reach the bottom row of cells, shaded grey?

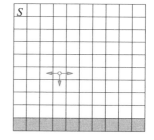

4. (a) A tournament has n contestants. Each contestant plays exactly one game against every other contestant. Explain why the total number of games is $\frac{1}{2}n(n - 1)$.

   (b) In a particular chess tournament, every contestant is supposed to play exactly one game against every other contestant. However, contestant A withdrew from the tournament after playing only ten games, and contestant B withdrew after just one game. A total of 55 games were played.

   Did A and B play each other?

5. (a) The integer N is a square. Find, with proof, all possible remainders when N is divided by 16.

   (b) Find all positive integers m and n such that

   $$m! + 76 = n^2.$$

   [The notation $m!$ stands for the factorial of m, that is, $m! = m \times (m - 1) \times \ldots \times 2 \times 1$. For example, $4! = 4 \times 3 \times 2 \times 1$.]

   Time allowed: $2\frac{1}{2}$ hours

Mathematical Olympiad for Girls: Solutions

These are polished solutions and do not illustrate the process of failed ideas and rough work by which candidates may arrive at their own solutions. Some of the solutions include comments, which are intended to clarify the reasoning behind the selection of a particular method.

The mark allocation on Mathematical Olympiad papers is different from what you are used to at school. To get any marks, you need to make significant progress towards the solution. This is why the rubric encourages candidates to try to finish whole questions rather than attempting lots of disconnected parts.

Each question is marked out of 10.

3 or 4 marks   roughly means that you had most of the relevant ideas, but were not able to link them into a coherent proof.

8 or 9 marks   means that you have solved the problem, but have made a minor calculation error or have not explained your reasoning clearly enough. One question we often ask is: if we were to have the benefit of a two-minute interview with this candidate, could they correct the error or fill the gap?

These solutions may be used freely within your school or college. You may, without further permission, post these solutions on a website that is accessible only to staff and students of the school or college, print out and distribute copies within the school or college, and use them in the classroom. If you wish to use them in any other way, please consult us.

---

1. (a) Expand and simplify $(a - b)(a^2 + ab + b^2)$.

   (b) Find the value of

$$\frac{2016^3 + 2015^3}{2016^2 - 2015^2}.$$

Commentary

The result in part (a) is called the difference of two cubes. Notice that part (b) involves a sum of two cubes in the numerator of the fraction. You will probably need to adapt the result of part (a) in order to use it in part (b).

One possibility in part (b) would be to do some calculations. However, this will be very time-consuming, so we try to find a quicker approach. We might try to simplify the fraction by factorising both the numerator and the denominator and looking for common factors.

To avoid writing out long numbers (and the risk of making numerical errors) it is a good idea to rewrite the expression using algebraic symbols. We will substitute the numbers back in at the end. This means that we are trying to simplify the fraction

$$\frac{m^3 + n^3}{m^2 - n^2}$$

where $m = 2016$ and $n = 2015$.

The denominator factorises as $(m - n)(m + n)$. (You might know this as the 'difference of two squares'.) In our case, we know that $m - n = 1$, so in fact the denominator is just $m + n$.

This is where part (a) can give us a useful suggestion. We know from (a) how to factorise $a^3 - b^3$. Can we do something similar to factorise $a^3 + b^3$?

There are various ways to see how to adapt part (a), including experimentation with changing signs. We find that

$$a^3 + b^3 = (a + b)\left(a^2 - ab + b^2\right).$$

This will be really helpful in simplifying the fraction, and then we can substitute the numbers back in.

The final expression still looks a little long to evaluate. Some clever use of factorising can simplify the calculation a little.

Solution

(a) Expanding out the brackets and simplifying, we find that

$$(a - b)\left(a^2 + ab + b^2\right) = a^3 + a^2b + ab^2 - a^2b - ab^2 - b^3$$

$$= a^3 - b^3.$$

(b) Let $m = 2016$ and $n = 2015$.

Using the factorisation

$$m^3 + n^3 = (m + n)\left(m^2 - mn + n^2\right),$$

and the difference of two squares $m^2 - n^2 = (m - n)(m + n)$, we may write the fraction as

$$\frac{(m + n)\left(m^2 - mn + n^2\right)}{(m - n)(m + n)} = \frac{m^2 - mn + n^2}{m - n}.$$

Since in our case $m - n = 1$, the value of this expression is

$$2016^2 - 2016 \times 2015 + 2015^2 = 2016\,(2016 - 2015) + 2015^2$$

$$= 2016 + 2015^2$$

$$= 4\,062\,241.$$

140

Alternative solution

(This solution does not use the result of part (a).)

Write $m = 2016$, $n = 2015$; then $m = n + 1$. Using the binomial expansion, we get

$$(n + 1)^3 = n^3 + 3n^2 + 3n + 1.$$

Therefore the fraction is

$$\frac{(n^3 + 3n^2 + 3n + 1) + n^3}{(n^2 + 2n + 1) - n^2} = \frac{2n^3 + 3n^2 + 3n + 1}{2n + 1}.$$

Using algebraic division, we obtain

$$n^2 + n + 1 = 2015^2 + 2015 + 1 = 4\,062\,241.$$

---

2. The diagram shows five polygons placed together edge-to-edge: two triangles, a regular hexagon and two regular nonagons.

   Prove that each of the triangles is isosceles.

Commentary

A triangle is isosceles if it has two sides of equal length. There are several regular polygons in this question, so it seems reasonable to start by identifying all lines of equal length.

If this does not complete the proof we can start looking at angles. If a triangle has two equal angles then it is isosceles.

We will almost certainly need to work out angles in a regular hexagon and a regular nonagon. We can do this in various ways. For example, we can find the sum of angles in a nonagon by splitting it into seven triangles (by drawing all the diagonals from one vertex). Alternatively, we can use the fact that the exterior angles of any polygon add up to $360°$; this means that in a regular n-sided polygon each exterior angle is $360° \div n$ so each interior angle is $180° - (360° \div n)$. We could also draw isosceles triangles with one vertex at the centre of the regular polygon. Either way, we find that each interior angle of a regular hexagon is $120°$ and each interior angle of a regular nonagon is $140°$.

It is a good idea to label some points on the diagram so you that can refer to various triangles and sides.

Our alternative solution uses properties of parallel lines and parallelograms. More precisely, it uses converses of two results about parallel lines and parallelograms.

The first result is about angles on parallel lines. If two parallel lines are intersected by a third line, then the interior angles (marked x and y in the diagram) add up to $180°$.

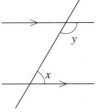

The converse of this result states that, if two lines are intersected by a third line so that angles x and y add up to $180°$, then the two lines are parallel.

The second result is about sides of a parallelogram. A parallelogram is defined as a quadrilateral with two pairs of parallel sides. One property of a parallelogram is that opposite sides are equal in length. One possible converse of this result is that, if a quadrilateral has one pair of equal and parallel sides, then it is a parallelogram.

You should note that converse statements are not always true. The two converse statements above are true and here you can use them without proof, although it is a good exercise to try to prove them.

Solution

Label some of the vertices, as shown in the diagram.

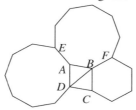

First we show that triangle ABD is isosceles.

Since the nonagons and the hexagon are regular and meet edge-to-edge we have

$$DA = AE = AB.$$

This means that triangle ABD is isosceles.

We now look at triangle BCD. From the regular polygons, we find that

$$BC = BF = AB,$$

but we do not know anything about sides CD and BD. So we calculate some angles. Each interior angle in a regular hexagon is $120°$ and each interior angle in a regular nonagon is $140°$. Therefore,

$$\angle DAB = 360° - 140° - 140°$$

$$= 80°$$

and

$$\angle ABC = 360° - 140° - 120°$$

$$= 100°.$$

Since we already know that the triangle ABD is isosceles, we can calculate

$$\angle ABD = \frac{180° - 80°}{2}$$

$$= 50°$$

and therefore

$$\angle DBC = 100° - 50°$$

$$= 50°.$$

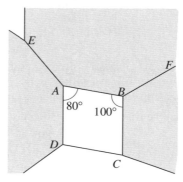

We cannot find directly any other angles in triangle *BCD*. However, triangle *BCD* is congruent to triangle *BAD* because

	$BC = AB$,	(from regular polygons)
	$BD = BD$,	(common side)
and	$\angle CBD = \angle ABD$	(each equals 50°)

Since triangle *BAD* is isosceles, so is triangle *BCD* (with $BC = CD$).

Alternative solution

Each interior angle in a regular hexagon is 120° and each interior angle in a regular nonagon is 140°. Therefore,

$$\angle DAB = 360° - 140° - 140°$$

$$= 80°$$

and

$$\angle ABC = 360° - 140° - 120°$$

$$= 100°.$$

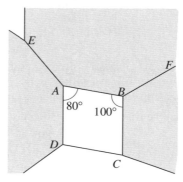

These two angles add up to 180° so, by the converse of internal angles on parallel lines, we find that AD and BC are parallel.

Since the nonagons and the hexagon are regular and meet edge-to-edge, we have

$$AD = EA = AB = BF = BC.$$

Hence AD and BC are equal and parallel. It follows that the quadrilateral $ABCD$ is a parallelogram. Therefore the sides AB and CD are equal.

But we already know that $AB = BC = DA$, so all four sides of $ABCD$ are in fact equal. Therefore the two required triangles are isosceles.

Note

The two triangles are in fact congruent, and the quadrilateral $ABCD$ is a rhombus.

---

3. A ladybird is going for a wander around a 10×10 board, subject to the following three rules (see the diagram).

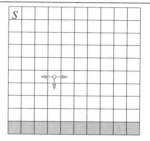

   (i) She starts in the top left cell, labelled S.

   (ii) She only moves left, right or down, as indicated.

   (iii) She never goes back to a cell that she has already visited.

   In how many different ways can she reach the bottom row of cells, shaded grey?

Commentary

One possible approach would be to try to list systematically all possible paths around the board. From the starting square the ladybird can either move down or right. If she goes down she then again has a choice of down or right; if she goes right she can continue to the right or go down, but cannot go left along the same level (because she is not allowed to return to a cell she has already visited).

While this method is certainly systematic, there are too many options to list. So we stop and think what the rules really mean for the ladybird's route around the board.

At any stage, the ladybird can move down a row. In order to reach the bottom, she will need to move down a row exactly nine times (remember that she cannot move up).

Within a row, she can move down from any of the ten cells. Rule (iii) says that she never goes back to a cell that she has already visited. This means that when she arrives at a row, she must move to the left or right or stay still, and then go down. She cannot go left for a bit then right for a bit, for example, or she would go back on herself.

This is a key observation. Imagine recording an accurate description of the ladybird's route through the chessboard. In principle, it might be a long sequence of steps to the left, steps to the right, and steps down. But we have seen that the rules mean that it is simpler than this. She takes a total of 9 steps down, and in between each step she navigates directly to the cell from which she will make the next step down. So to record her route precisely, it is enough to write a list of the nine cells from which she takes a step down — there is no ambiguity about her route in between those cells, she must just step down and then move directly to the next cell in the list. This gives us a much more manageable counting problem.

Solution

Once the ladybird (here called Ella) has reached the d th row she can move left or right, or not at all, to one of 10 cells in that row before her descent to the next row (unless she has already reached the last row).

Since Ella cannot go back on herself, there is only one way for her to reach any of the ten cells in the d th row.

For each of rows 1, 2, . . . , 9, Ella has 10 options for the point at which she descends. Therefore there are 10^9, that is, 1 000 000 000, ways for Ella to reach the bottom row of cells.

Note

Wherever Ella starts in the top row, the answer is the same.

Also, if the board is of shape $m \times n$ (that is, m rows, n columns) then Ella can reach the bottom row from anywhere in the top row in n^{m-1} different ways.

***

4. (a) A tournament has n contestants. Each contestant plays exactly one game against every other contestant. Explain why the total number of games is $\frac{1}{2}n(n-1)$.

   (b) In a particular chess tournament, every contestant is supposed to play exactly one game against every other contestant. However, contestant A withdrew from the tournament after playing only ten games, and contestant B withdrew after just one game. A total of 55 games were played.
   Did A and B play each other?

Solution

Part (a)

Commentary

There are quite a lot of ways of counting the number of games! We give some examples.

(i) We could consider each contestant in turn. The first contestant plays $n-1$ games (against every contestant other than herself). For the second contestant we have already counted the game against the first contestant, so she plays $n-2$ other games. Continuing this reasoning, we find that the total number of games is

$$(n-1) + (n-2) + \ldots + 2 + 1.$$

There are a good few ways of working out this sum.

One way is to compare the sum to its reverse. If we call the sum S, then we have both

$$(n - 1) + (n - 2) + \ldots + 2 + 1 = S,$$

and

$$1 + 2 + \ldots + (n - 2) + (n - 1) = S.$$

By adding corresponding terms, we get

$$(n - 1 + 1) + (n - 2 + 2) + \ldots + (2 + n - 2) + (1 + n - 1) = 2S.$$

The left-hand side of this equation is a sum of $n - 1$ bracketed terms, each of which is equal to n, so that sum is equal to $n(n - 1)$. Thus $S = \frac{1}{2}n(n - 1)$.

(ii) Yet another way is more geometrical. The sum S can be represented by a triangle of dots: one dot in the first row, two dots in a second, and so on. The diagram shows two such triangles fitted together to form a rectangle.

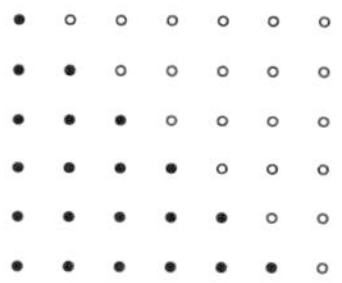

If there are $n - 1$ rows of dots, the rectangle has $n - 1$ rows and n columns, and hence contains $n(n - 1)$ dots in total. But the original sum represents half of this rectangle, so the result follows.

On the other hand, you may know about arithmetic series in general. The sum S is an arithmetic series with $n - 1$ terms, first term 1 and common difference 1. Therefore the sum is

$$\frac{n - 1}{2}\left[2 + (n - 2)\right] = \frac{1}{2}n(n - 1).$$

(iii) Finally, we can go about it differently. Instead of forming a sum, we can look at the number of ways to pair the contestants. We need to be careful not to count pairs twice. This is the solution we present below.

Contestants never play themselves but do play all the other $n - 1$ competitors. Therefore there are $n(n - 1)$ pairs (X, Y) such that X plays Y, with the contestants named in that order.

The game in which X plays Y is the same as that in which Y plays X however, so naming the contestants in order means that each game is counted twice. Therefore the total number of games is $\frac{1}{2}n(n - 1)$.

Part (b)

Commentary

We need to check whether it is possible to have a total of 55 games in the two cases: when A and B played each other, and when they did not.

One way to do this would be to count the number of games that do not involve A or B and then to add in the number of games played by A and by B. Another way would be to count the total number of games if A and B had played the whole tournament, and then to subtract the numbers of games missed by A and by B because they withdrew early.

In each case, we know that the total number of games played is 55. We do not know how many contestants there were at the start, so give this number a name (say m). We will get an equation involving m that we can then try to solve. We will also need to be careful to remember that A and B were scheduled to play each other, so we must not count that game twice.

Suppose that there are m contestants other than A and B. The number of games those m contestants played with each other is $\frac{1}{2}m(m-1)$.

There are an additional 10 games played by A. If those include a game between A and B, then there are no additional games played by B, so the total number of games played is

$$\tfrac{1}{2}m(m-1) + 10 = 55.$$

If B did not play A then there is one additional game played by B, so the total number of games is

$$\tfrac{1}{2}m(m-1) + 10 + 1 = 55.$$

In the first case, $m(m-1) = 90$, which is possible when $m = 10$. In the second case, $m(m-1) = 88$. The last equation has no integer solutions, since $m(m-1) \leqslant 72$ when $m \leqslant 9$ and $m(m-1) \geqslant 90$ when $m \geqslant 10$.

Thus A and B did play each other.

Note

There were 12 contestants at the start of the tournament.

---

5. (a) The integer N is a square. Find, with proof, all possible remainders when N is divided by 16.

   (b) Find all positive integers m and n such that

   $$m! + 76 = n^2.$$

   [The notation $m!$ stands for the factorial of m, that is, $m! = m \times (m-1) \times \ldots \times 2 \times 1$. For example, $4! = 4 \times 3 \times 2 \times 1$.]

Solution

Part (a)

Commentary

It seems reasonable to start by working out remainders of some square numbers; you may soon notice a pattern. However, we need to produce a general argument.

If a number n gives remainder r when divided by 16, we can write it as $n = 16k + r$.

The possible values of r are 0, 1, 2, ... ,15. For example, if n gives remainder

5 when divided by 16 then $n = 16k + 5$, so

$$n^2 = (16k + 5)^2 = 256k^2 + 160k + 25.$$

Notice that the first two terms are divisible by 16, so n^2 gives the same remainder as 25 when divided by 16.

We can repeat this calculation for each r from 0 to 15 to get the list of all possible remainders. It is worth noticing a slight shortcut: the remainders seem to repeat from $r = 8$. The solution below demonstrates why this is the case.

Write $N = n^2$ and $n = 8k + r$ where r, the remainder when n is divided by 8, is one of $0, 1, 2, \ldots, 7$. Then $N = (8k + r)^2 = 64k^2 + 16kr + r^2$, and this leaves the same remainder as does r^2 when divided by 16.

Those remainders R are shown in the following table.

r	0	1	2	3	4	5	6	7
R	0	1	4	9	0	9	4	1

Thus the possible remainders when N is divided by 16 are 0, 1, 4 and 9.

Part (b)

Commentary

Part (a) suggests that it may be helpful to look at remainders when dividing by 16. The possible remainders of n^2 are 0, 1, 4 and 9, and 76 gives remainder 12.

So $m!$ needs to give the remainder 4, 5, 8 or 13 when divided by 16.

Looking at some factorial numbers suggests that after a certain point, they are all divisible by 16. This is because 6! is a multiple of 16 and all further factorial numbers are multiples of 6! (e.g., $7! = 6! \times 7, 8! = 6! \times 7 \times 8$ and so on).

This means that m cannot be greater or equal to 6. We only need to check positive integers smaller than 6 to find all the solutions.

If $m \geqslant 6$ then $m!$ is a multiple of $6! = 720$, which itself is a multiple of 16. Therefore the remainder when $m! + 76$ is divided by 16 is the same as the remainder when 76 is divided by 16, which is 12. From part (a) we know, then, that $m! + 76$ cannot be a square if $m \geqslant 6$.

If m is 1, 2 or 3, then the remainders after division of $m! + 76$ by 16 are 13, 14 and 2 respectively, and so $m! + 76$ cannot be a square.

But if $m = 4$ then $m! + 76 = 24 + 76 = 100 = 10^2$, and if $m = 5$ then $m! + 76 = 120 + 76 = 196 = 14^2$. Therefore the only pairs (m, n) of positive integers such that $m! + 76 = n^2$ are $(4, 10)$ and $(5, 14)$.

Note

We could look at remainders on division by some other numbers. For example, a similar argument works if we look at division by 7. For $m \geqslant 7$, $m! + 76$ gives remainder 6 when divided by 7, and we can show that a square number cannot give this remainder.

The Mathematical Olympiad for Girls Prize Winners

The following contestants were awarded prizes:

Rose Blyth	Tonbridge Grammar School
Emma Brown	St Helen's School
Lydia Buckingham	Wellington School
Rosie Cates	Hills Road Sixth Form College
Sophie Crane	Pate's Grammar School
Louisa Cullen	Pocklington School
Siqi Fang	Culford School
Lara Gordon	Monmouth Comprehensive School
Caroline Harwin	Kendrick School
Katherine Horton	All Hallows Catholic School
Tomoka Kan	Westminster School
Kirsten Land	King's College London Mathematics School
Jackie Li	St. Paul's Girls' School
Sophie Maclean	Watford Grammar School for Girls
Sifa Poulton	The Grey Coat Hospital
Melissa Quail	Longsands Academy
Xinyu Shen	Winterbourne International Academy
Carys Siddle	King's College School, Wimbledon
Alevtina Studenikina	Cheltenham Ladies' College
Roan Talbut	The Perse School
Alice Vaughan-Williams	Nailsea School
Emma Vinen	Westminster School
Isobel Voysey	Westminster School
Lucy Wan	The Tiffin Girls' School
Jessica Wang	Watford Grammar School for Girls
Naomi Wei	City of London School for Girls
Leonie Woodland	The Stephen Perse Foundation
Catherine Wooller	BHASVIC
Ebony Zhang	The Perse School

British Mathematical Olympiads

Within the UKMT, the British Mathematical Olympiad Subtrust has control of the papers and everything pertaining to them. The BMOS produces an annual account of its events which, for 2015-2016, was edited by James Aaronson and Linden Ralph (of Trinity College, Cambridge). Much of this report is included in the following pages.

    United Kingdom Mathematics Trust

British Mathematical Olympiad

Round 1 : Friday, 27 November 2015

Time allowed *Three and a half hours.*

Instructions • *Full written solutions — not just answers — are required, with complete proofs of any assertions you may make. Marks awarded will depend on the clarity of your mathematical presentation. Work in rough first, and then write up your best attempt.*
Do not hand in rough work.

• *One **complete** solution will gain more credit than several unfinished attempts. It is more important to complete a small number of questions than to try all the problems.*

• *Each question carries 10 marks. However, earlier questions tend to be easier. In general you are advised to concentrate on these problems first.*

• *The use of rulers, set squares and compasses is allowed, but calculators and protractors are forbidden.*

• *Start each question on a fresh sheet of paper. Write on one side of the paper only. On each sheet of working write the number of the question in the top **left**-hand corner and your name, initials and school in the top **right**-hand corner.*

• *Complete the cover sheet provided and attach it to the front of your script, followed by your solutions in question number order.*

• *Staple all the pages neatly together in the top **left**-hand corner.*

• *To accommodate candidates sitting in other time zones, please do not discuss the paper on the internet until 8 am GMT on Saturday 28 November.*

Do not turn over until told to do so.

United Kingdom Mathematics Trust

2015/16 British Mathematical Olympiad
Round 1: Friday, 27 November 2015

1. On Thursday 1st January 2015, Anna buys one book and one shelf. For the next two years, she buys one book every day and one shelf on alternate Thursdays, so she next buys a shelf on 15th January 2015. On how many days in the period Thursday 1st January 2015 until (and including) Saturday 31st December 2016 is it possible for Anna to put all her books on all her shelves, so that there is an equal number of books on each shelf?

2. Let $ABCD$ be a cyclic quadrilateral and let the lines CD and BA meet at E. The line through D which is tangent to the circle ADE meets the line CB at F. Prove that the triangle CDF is isosceles.

3. Suppose that a sequence t_0, t_1, t_2, ... is defined by a formula $t_n = An^2 + Bn + C$ for all integers $n \geqslant 0$. Here A, B and C are real constants with $A \neq 0$. Determine values of A, B and C which give the greatest possible number of successive terms of the sequence which are also successive terms of the Fibonacci sequence. *The Fibonacci sequence is defined by $F_0 = 0$, $F_1 = 1$ and $F_m = F_{m-1} + F_{m-2}$ for $m \geqslant 2$.*

4. James has a red jar, a blue jar and a pile of 100 pebbles. Initially both jars are empty. A move consists of moving a pebble from the pile into one of the jars or returning a pebble from one of the jars to the pile. The numbers of pebbles in the red and blue jars determine the *state* of the game. The following conditions must be satisfied:

   a) The red jar may never contain fewer pebbles than the blue jar;

   b) The game may never be returned to a previous state.

   What is the maximum number of moves that James can make?

5. Let ABC be a triangle, and let D, E and F be the feet of the perpendiculars from A, B and C to BC, CA and AB respectively.

   Let P, Q, R and S be the feet of the perpendiculars from D to BA, BE, CF and CA respectively. Prove that P, Q, R and S are collinear.

6. A positive integer is called *charming* if it is equal to 2 or is of the form $3^i 5^j$ where i and j are non-negative integers. Prove that every positive integer can be written as a sum of different charming integers.

The British Mathematical Olympiad 2015-2016

The Round 1 paper was marked by volunteers in December. Below is a list of the prize winners.

Round 1 Prize Winners

The following contestants were awarded prizes:

Gold Medals

Jamie Bell	King Edward VI Five Ways School, Birmingham
Joe Benton	St Paul's School, Barnes, London
Clarissa Costen	Altrincham Grammar School for Girls, Cheshire
Jacob Coxon	Magdalen College School, Oxford
Lawrence Hollom	Churcher's College, Hampshire
Lucas Huysmans	Beaumont School, St Albans
Jeon Jongheon	Winchester College
Abdul Hadi Khan	Haileybury Almaty School, Kazakhstan
Kirsten Land	King's College London Mathematics School
Kyung Chan Lee	Garden International School, Malaysia
Warren Li	Eton College, Windsor
Yuyang Miao	Ruthin School, Denbighshire
Neel Nanda	Latymer School, London
Michael Ng	Aylesbury Grammar School
Philip Peters	Haberdashers' Aske's School for Boys, Herts
Thomas Pycroft	Whitchurch High School, Cardiff
Thomas Read	The Perse School, Cambridge
Edward Rong	Westminster School
Sam Watt	Monkton Combe School, Bath
Shenyang Wu	Anglo-Chinese School (Independent), Singapore
Harvey Yau	Ysgol Dyffryn Taf, Carmarthenshire
Renzhi Zhou	The Perse School, Cambridge

Silver medals:

Hugo Aaronson	St Paul's School, Barnes, London
Michal Adamkiewicz	Westminster School
Howard Au	Winchester College
Agnijo Banerjee	Grove Academy, Dundee
Callum Berry	Runshaw College, Leyland, Lancs
Lydia Buckingham	Wellington School, Somerset
Rosie Cates	Hills Road VI Form College, Cambridge
Alex Chen	Westminster School

Ewan Clementson	Queen Elizabeth Grammar School, Penrith
Siqi Fang	Culford School, Suffolk
Alexander Fruh	St Aloysius' College, Glasgow
Alex Harris	The Perse School, Cambridge
Katherine Horton	All Hallows Catholic School, Farnham, Surrey
Timothy Lavy	Magdalen College School, Oxford
Theo Lewy	Haberdashers' Aske's School for Boys, Herts
Jiaxuan Li	Ruthin School, Denbighshire
Arlen Liu	Dr Challoner's Grammar School, Amersham
Chris Liu	Winchester College
Diamor Marke	Wallington County Grammar School, Surrey
Edward Miller	Harris Westminster Sixth Form
Rohan Mitta	UWCSEA Dover Campus, Singapore
Joshua O'Reilly	Beeslack High School, Midlothian
Otto Pyper	Eton College, Windsor
Melissa Quail	Longsands Academy, St Neots, Cambs
Andrew Slattery	Winstanley College, Lancashire
Alex Song	Westminster School
Alan Sun	City of London School
Raghav Swaroop	King's College School, Wimbledon
Adrian Tang	West Island School (ESF), Hong Kong
Yuta Tsuchiya	Queen Elizabeth's School, Barnet
Kieran Woodcock	Ripon Grammar School, N. Yorks
Haiqi Wu	Cherwell College, Oxford
Chengran Yang	Loughborough Grammar School
Sechan Yun	The Perse School, Cambridge
Rayna Zhang	Ruthin School, Denbighshire

Bronze medals:

Rahul Arya	King George V School, Hong Kong
Thomas Baycroft	Notre Dame High School, Sheffield
Matthew Chaffe	Littleover Community School, Derby
Nathaniel Cleland	Gillingham School, Dorset
Piers Cole	Royal Grammar School, Guildford
Louisa Cullen	Pocklington School, nr York
Zhicheng Ding	Caterham School, Surrey
Stanley Dodds	Weydon School, Farnham, Surrey
Jacob Chevalier Drori	Highgate School, London
Reuben Green	Culloden Academy, Inverness
Xingtong He	Ruthin School, Denbighshire

Eddie Heyne	Wilson's School, Surrey
Anthony Hickling	Felsted School, Essex
Curtis Ho	Harrow School
Elizabeth Holdcroft	The Willink School, Reading
Charlie Hu	City of London School
Matthew Hutton	Royal Grammar School, Newcastle
Joseph Krol	Ermysted's Grammar School, N. Yorks
Yutao Kuang	St Marylebone CE School, London
Jacqueline Li	St Paul's Girls' School, Hammersmith
Mingdu Li	Fortismere School, London
Yinbai Li	Ruthin School, Denbighshire
Zijia Li	Westbourne School, Vale of Glamorgan
Hao Liang	Eton College, Windsor
Kaige Liu	RDFZ, Beijing
Xiao Ma	Ruthin School, Denbighshire
Jacob Mair	Burnham Grammar School, Slough
Muhammad Manji	Watford Grammar School for Boys
Shyam Patel	City of Leicester College
Mukul Rathi	Nottingham High School
Daniel Remo	Highgate School, London
Matthew Richmond	Hills Road VI Form College, Cambridge
Frederik Robinson	The Hollyfield School, Surbiton, Surrey
Benedict Randall Shaw	Westminster School
Bemin Sheen	Tiffin School, Kingston-upon-Thames
Alevtina Studenikina	Cheltenham Ladies' College
James Sun	Reading School
David Tao	Hampton School, Middlesex
Charles Thomas	St Paul's School, Barnes, London
Yuriy Tumarkin	Durham Johnston School
Naomi Wei	City of London Girls' School
Lennie Wells	St Paul's School, Barnes, London
Xiaoyu Weng	Ashbourne College, London
Ziming Xue	Anglo-Chinese School (Independent), Singapore
Ryuto Yamada	Winchester College
Alice Yang	Ellesmere College, Shropshire
Daniel Yue	King Edward's School, Birmingham
Tieze Zhang	Anglo-Chinese School (Independent), Singapore
Tingjun Zhang	Ashford School, Kent
Kaylie Zhu	Charterhouse, Godalming, Surrey

United Kingdom Mathematics Trust

British Mathematical Olympiad
Round 2: Thursday, 28 January 2016

Time allowed *Three and a half hours.*

Each question is worth 10 marks.

Instructions • *Full written solutions – not just answers – are required, with complete proofs of any assertions you may make. Marks awarded will depend on the clarity of your mathematical presentation. Work in rough first, and then draft your final version carefully before writing up your best attempt.*

*Rough work **should** be handed in, but should be clearly marked.*

• *One or two **complete** solutions will gain far more credit than partial attempts at all four problems.*

• *The use of rulers and compasses is allowed, but calculators and protractors are forbidden.*

• *Staple all the pages neatly together in the top **left**-hand corner, with questions 1, 2, 3, 4 in order, and the cover sheet at the front.*

• *To accommodate candidates sitting in other time zones, please do not discuss any aspect of the paper on the internet until 8 am GMT on Friday 29 January.*

In early March, twenty students eligible to represent the UK at the International Mathematical Olympiad will be invited to attend the training session to be held at Trinity College, Cambridge (31 March – 4 April 2016). At the training session, students sit a pair of IMO-style papers and eight students will be selected for further training and selection examinations. The UK Team of six for this summer's International Mathematical Olympiad (to be held in Hong Kong, China, 6-16 July 2016) will then be chosen.

Do not turn over until told to do so.

United Kingdom Mathematics Trust

2015/16 British Mathematical Olympiad
Round 2

1. Circles of radius r_1, r_2 and r_3 touch each other externally, and they touch a common tangent at points A, B and C respectively, where B lies between A and C. Prove that $16(r_1 + r_2 + r_3) \geqslant 9(AB + BC + CA)$.

2. Alison has compiled a list of 20 hockey teams, ordered by how good she thinks they are, but refuses to share it. Benjamin may mention three teams to her, and she will then choose either to tell him which she thinks is the weakest team of the three, or which she thinks is the strongest team of the three. Benjamin may do this as many times as he likes. Determine the largest N such that Benjamin can guarantee to be able to find a sequence T_1, T_2, ... , T_N of teams with the property that he knows that Alison thinks that T_i is better than T_{i+1} for each $1 \leqslant i \leqslant N$.

3. Let $ABCD$ be a cyclic quadrilateral. The diagonals AC and BD meet at P, and DA and CB produced meet at Q. The midpoint of AB is E. Prove that if PQ is perpendicular to AC, then PE is perpendicular to BC.

4. Suppose that p is a prime number and that there are different positive integers u and v such that p^2 is the mean of u^2 and v^2. Prove that $2p - u - v$ is a square or twice a square.

The British Mathematical Olympiad 2015-2016
Round 2

The second round of the British Mathematical Olympiad was held on Thursday 28th January 2016. Some of the top scorers from this round were invited to a residential course at Trinity College, Cambridge.

Leading Scorers

40	Neel Nanda	Latymer School, London
	Harvey Yau	Ysgol Dyffryn Taf, Carmarthenshire
39	Joe Benton	St Paul's School, Barnes, London
34	Warren Li	Eton College, Windsor
30	Lawrence Hollom	Churcher's College, Hampshire
	Kyung Chan Lee	Garden International School, Malaysia
29	Renzhi Zhou	The Perse School, Cambridge
27	David Tao	Hampton School, Middlesex
21	Alex Harris	The Perse School, Cambridge
20	Agnijo Banerjee	Grove Academy, Dundee
	Jamie Bell	King Edward VI Five Ways S., Birmingham
	Rosie Cates	Hills Road VI Form College, Cambridge
	Gurbir Johal	Barking Abbey School, Essex
	Moses Mayer	The British International S., Jakarta, Indonesia
	Michael Ng	Aylesbury Grammar School
	Philip Peters	Haberdashers' Aske's School for Boys, Herts
	Thomas Read	The Perse School, Cambridge
	Ziming Xue	Anglo-Chinese S. (Independent), Singapore
	Tingjun Zhang	Ashford School, Kent
	Ebony Zhang	The Perse School, Cambridge

Introduction to the BMO problems and full solutions

The 'official' solutions are the result of many hours' work by a large number of people, and have been subjected to many drafts and revisions. The contestants' solutions included here will also have been redrafted several times by the contestants themselves, and also shortened and cleaned up somewhat by the editors. As such, they do not resemble the first jottings, failed ideas and discarded pages of rough work with which any solution is started.

Before looking at the solutions, pupils (and teachers) are encouraged to make a concerted effort to attack the problems themselves. Only by doing so is it possible to develop a feel for the question, to understand where the difficulties lie and why one method of attack is successful while others may fail. Problem solving is a skill that can only be learnt by practice; going straight to the solutions is unlikely to be of any benefit.

It is also important to bear in mind that solutions to Olympiad problems are not marked for elegance. A solution that is completely valid will receive a full score, no matter how long and tortuous it may be. However, elegance has been an important factor influencing our selection of contestants' answers.

The 'Christopher Bradley Elegance Prize' was awarded to Warren Li (Eton College), Neel Nanda (Latymer School) and Alevtina Studenikina (Cheltenham Ladies' College), for particularly beautiful solutions of BMO2 problem 3.

BMO Round 1

Problem 1 (Proposed by Dan Griller)

On Thursday 1st January 2015, Anna buys one book and one shelf. For the next two years, she buys one book every day and one shelf on alternate Thursdays, so she next buys a shelf on 15th January 2015. On how many days in the period Thursday 1st January 2015 until (and including) Saturday 31st December 2016 is it possible for Anna to put all her books on all her shelves so that there is an equal number of books on each shelf?

Solution by the Editors:

2016 is a leap year so the total number of days in the two years is $365 + 366 = 731$. We split these days up by how many shelves Anna had on each day: for the first 14 days she had 1 shelf, for days 15 to 28 she had 2, and so on to days 729 to 731, when she had 53. We see that for $s \leqslant 52$ she had s shelves from days $14s - 13$ and $14s$ inclusive.

If at some time she has b books and s shelves, she can split her books equally among her shelves if and only if b is a multiple of s. Thus we count the number of multiples of s between $14s - 13$ to $14s$, for $s \leqslant 52$. (We can ignore the last three days when $s = 53$ since none of 729, 730 or 731 is a multiple of 53.) Note that s dividing $14s - k$ is equivalent to it dividing k, where k ranges from 0 to 13. Counting the number of such k for a given s:

s	1	2	3	4	5	6	7	8	...	13	14	...	52
Number of k	14	7	5	4	3	3	2	2	...	2	1	...	1

Number of $0 \leqslant k \leqslant 13$ which are multiples of s

Note that there is one value of k (namely $k = 0$) which all s divide, which is why the 1 continues all the way down to $s = 52$. Summing the bottom row, we find that the answer is

$$14 + 7 + 5 + 4 + 3 + 3 + 7 \times 2 + 39 \times 1 = 89.$$

Problem 2 (Proposed by Gerry Leversha)

Let *ABCD* be a cyclic quadrilateral and let the lines *CD* and *BA* meet at *E*. The line through *D* which is tangent to the circle *ADE* meets the line *CB* at *F*. Prove that the triangle *CDF* is isosceles.

Solution by Harvey Yau, Ysgol Dyffryn Taf

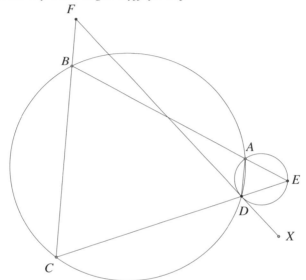

By angles in a cyclic quadrilateral,

$$\angle DCF = 180° - \angle DAB = \angle EAD.$$

By the alternate segment theorem,

$$\angle EAD = \angle XDE = \angle CDF,$$

so

$$\angle DCF = \angle EAD = \angle CDF,$$

so $\triangle CDF$ is isosceles.

160

Problem 3 (Proposed by Jeremy King)

Suppose that a sequence t_0, t_1, t_2, ... is defined by a formula $t_n = An^2 + Bn + C$ for all integers $n \geqslant 0$. Here A, B and C are real constants with $A \neq 0$. Determine values of A, B and C which give the greatest possible number of successive terms of the sequence which are also successive terms of the Fibonacci sequence. *The Fibonacci sequence is defined by $F_0 = 0$, $F_1 = 1$ and $F_m = F_{m-1} + F_{m-2}$ for $m \geqslant 2$.*

Solution by Bijal Shah, St Helen's School:

We let our quadratic be $Ax^2 + Bx + C$, and the Fibonacci sequence be F_m. We may assume that the first successive term of the sequence which is one of the successive terms of the Fibonacci sequence is t_0, since if it were t_k, we could consider the quadratic $A(x - k)^2 + B(x - k) + C$. If we can get 5 terms of the Fibonacci sequence, then

$$t_0 = C = F_{m-2}$$

$$t_1 = A + B + C = F_{m-1}$$

$$t_2 = 4A + 2B + C = F_m$$

$$t_3 = 9A + 3B + C = F_{m+1}$$

$$t_4 = 16A + 4B + C = F_{m+2}.$$

Now, $F_{m-2} + F_{m-1} = F_m$, so $3A + B - C = 0$. Similarly $4A - C = 0$ and $3A - B - C = 0$. From the first and last of these we see that $B = 0$, and then from the second we have $A = C = 0$. Thus there is no sequence of $t_0, \ldots, t_4$ which gives successive terms of the Fibonacci sequence, and so the greatest possible number of terms t_i which give successive terms in the Fibonacci sequence is 4, i.e. t_0, t_1, t_2, t_3.

Trying some values of t_0 we see that this is actually achievable when $t_0 = 2$, in which case $C = 2$ and $A = B = \frac{1}{2}$, and so our quadratic is

$$\frac{x^2}{2} + \frac{x}{2} + 2.$$

Problem 4 (Proposed by Dominic Rowland)

James has a red jar, a blue jar and a pile of 100 pebbles. Initially both jars are empty. A move consists of moving a pebble from the pile into one of the jars or returning a pebble from one of the jars to the pile. The numbers of pebbles in the red and blue jars determine the *state* of the game. The following conditions must be satisfied:

a) The red jar may never contain fewer pebbles than the blue jar;

b) The game may never be returned to a previous state.

What is the maximum number of moves that James can make?

Solution by Lucas Huysmans, Beaumont School:

Let n be the total number of pebbles in both jars at any given point in the game. When a move occurs, n either increases or decreases by 1, so n alternates between even and odd numbers (starting even).

Given r pebbles in the red jar (r an integer between 0 and 100) the range of valid values for b pebbles in the blue jar is

(i) $0 \leqslant b \leqslant r$ when $0 \leqslant r \leqslant 50$, and

(ii) $0 \leqslant b \leqslant 100 - r$ when $51 \leqslant r \leqslant 100$

by applying the conditions that $b \leqslant r$ and $b + r \leqslant 100$.

Let o and e be the number of times that n was odd and even respectively during a single game. Since n starts even and alternates between even and odd, we have either $e = o$ or $e = o + 1$.

We consider the number of odd states for each r and sum over r from 0 to 100. In the summation below we only list explicitly the number of states for $r = 0, 1, 2, 3, 4, \ldots, 49, 50, 51, 52, \ldots, 97, 98, 99, 100$. We obtain

$$0 + 1 + 1 + 2 + 2 + \ldots + 25 + 25 + 25 + 24 + \ldots + 2 + 2 + 1 + 1 + 0$$
$$= 2(1 + 2 + \ldots + 25) + 2(1 + 2 + \ldots + 24) + 25$$
$$= 25 \times 26 + 24 \times 25 + 25 = 25 \times 51 = 1275.$$

The total number of even states satisfies $e \leqslant o + 1 \leqslant 1276$. Thus the total possible number of states is at most $1275 + 1276 = 2551$. This is one more than the total number of moves, since the first state doesn't require a move to get to, but the other states do. So the maximum number of moves is 2550.

One strategy using this number of moves is as follows:

(i) If r is even and $b = 0$ place one pebble in the red jar if we can;

(ii) otherwise, if r is even but $b > 0$ remove one pebble from the blue jar;

(iii) otherwise, if b and r can both be larger then place one pebble in the blue jar;

(iv) otherwise $b = r$ (if $r \leqslant 50$) or $b = 99 - r$ (if $r > 50$), and we place one in the red jar.

162

Problem 5 (Proposed by Gerry Leversha)

Let ABC be a triangle, and let D, E and F be the feet of the perpendiculars from A, B and C to BC, CA and AB respectively.

Let P, Q, R and S be the feet of the perpendiculars from D to BA, BE, CF and CA respectively. Prove that P, Q, R and S are collinear.

Solution 1 by Shyam Patel, City of Leicester College:

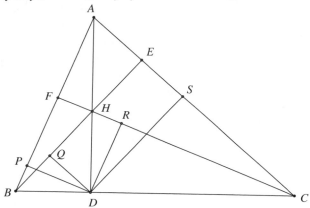

Note that AD, CF and BE are concurrent at H, the orthocentre. We also have

$$\angle ADB = \angle HDB = 90°$$
$$\angle CFB = \angle HFB = 90°$$

so $DHFB$ is cyclic. Applying Simson's theorem from D to $\triangle FHB$, we have that P, Q, R are collinear. Similarly, Q, R, S are collinear by applying Simson's theorem to $\triangle HCE$, again since D, C, E, H are concyclic.

Therefore P, Q, R and S are collinear.

Solution 2 by Warren Li, Eton College:

Note that AD, CF and BE are concurrent at H, the orthocentre.

Since $\angle HFB = \angle HDB = 90°$, H, F, B, D are concyclic; $\angle DPB = \angle DQB = 90°$, so P, B, D, Q are concyclic and $\angle FPD = \angle FRD = 90°$, so F, P, D, R are concyclic (in fact a rectangle). Therefore, using angles in the same segment,

$$\angle RPD = \angle RFD = \angle HFD = \angle HBD = \angle QBD = \angle QPD.$$

Since the angles RPD and QPD are equal, it follows that P, Q and R are collinear. Similarly we find that Q, R and S are collinear, so we are done.

Problem 6 (Proposed by Dominic Rowland)

A positive integer is called *charming* if it is equal to 2 or is of the form $3^i 5^j$ where i and j are non-negative integers. Prove that every positive integer can be written as a sum of different charming integers.

Solution by Katherine Horton, All Hallows Catholic School:

We first show that any charming number greater than 2 can be written as the sum of smaller, distinct charming numbers, or 'decomposed', and then show that this enables us to decompose any positive integer greater than 2. Note that $3 = 1 + 2$ and $5 = 2 + 3$, so we suppose there is a charming number greater than 5 which cannot be decomposed; we consider the smallest such number n. If n is a multiple of 5, i.e. $n = 3^a 5^{b+1}$ for some $a, b \geqslant 0$, we write

$$n = 3^a 5^{b+1} = 3^a 5^b + 3^{a+1} 5^b + 3^a 5^b$$

and noting that $2 < 3^a 5^b < n$ we can replace the last term in the sum with smaller, different charming numbers (since we assumed n was the smallest one we couldn't decompose). Thus we have a decomposition of n, as desired.

Otherwise n is not a multiple of 5, so $n = 3^{a+2}$ for some $a \geqslant 0$ (we have checked $n \leqslant 5$ above). Then

$$n = 3^{a+2} = 3^a + 3^{a+1} + 3^a 5^1$$

so again we can write it as a sum of smaller different charming numbers. So we are done for the first part.

For the second part, we suppose we can decompose some positive integer k, and try to find a decomposition for $k + 1$. For the smallest charming number not used in the decomposition sum, we add this to k and subtract the charming numbers used in its decomposition, so that the total is still k, but written with fewer terms. We continue this until at least one of 1 and 2 is not involved in the sum for k. If 1 is not involved we just add it to the sum to get a decomposition for $k + 1$; if 2 is not involved but 1 is then we replace the 1 with the 2 in the sum, and again find a decomposition for $k + 1$. Thus we are done.

BMO Round 2

Problem 1 (Proposed by Dominic Yeo)

Circles of radius r_1, r_2 and r_3 touch each other externally, and they touch a common tangent at points A, B and C respectively, where B lies between A and C. Prove that $16(r_1 + r_2 + r_3) \geqslant 9(AB + BC + CA)$.

All solutions proceed in a similar way to this one, first deriving relationships such as $AB^2 = 4r_1r_2$ and then using algebra to solve the problem.

Solution by Alex Harris, The Perse School:

Let A' be the foot of the perpendicular from O_2 to AO_1.

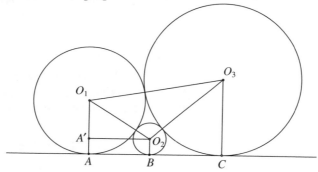

Since $A'O_2BA$ is a rectangle, $A'O_2 = AB$. Also $O_1A' = r_1 - r_2$ and $O_1O_2 = r_1 + r_2$. Hence, by Pythagoras' theorem,

$$AB^2 = (r_1 + r_2)^2 - (r_1 - r_2)^2$$

$$= 4r_1r_2.$$

Similarly,

$$AC^2 = 4r_1r_3$$

$$BC^2 = 4r_2r_3.$$

Furthermore, $AB + BC = AC$, so $\sqrt{r_1r_3} = \sqrt{r_1r_2} + \sqrt{r_2r_3}$. Hence, if we let $a = \sqrt{r_1}$ and $b = \sqrt{r_3}$, we learn that

$$\sqrt{r_2} = \frac{\sqrt{r_1r_3}}{\sqrt{r_1} + \sqrt{r_3}} = \frac{ab}{a + b}.$$

Thus, we are required to prove that

$$16\left(a^2 + b^2 + \left(\frac{ab}{a+b}\right)^2\right) \geqslant 9\left(2ab + \frac{2a^2b}{a+b} + \frac{2ab^2}{a+b}\right)$$

$$= 18\left(ab + \frac{ab(a+b)}{a+b}\right)$$

$$= 36ab,$$

or, in other words,

$$4\left((a^2 + b^2)(a+b)^2 + a^2b^2\right) \geqslant 9ab(a+b)^2.$$

Subtracting the right-hand side from the left-hand side, we get

$$4\left((a^2 + b^2)(a+b)^2 + a^2b^2\right) - 9ab(a+b)^2$$

$$= 4(a^2 + b^2 - 2ab)(a+b)^2 - ab\left((a+b)^2 - 4ab\right)$$

$$= (a-b)^2\left(4(a+b)^2 - ab\right)$$

$$= (a-b)^2\left(4a^2 + 7ab + 4b^2\right)$$

which is clearly nonnegative.

Problem 2 (Proposed by James Cranch)

Alison has compiled a list of 20 hockey teams, ordered by how good she thinks they are, but refuses to share it. Benjamin may mention three teams to her, and she will then choose either to tell him which she thinks is the weakest team of the three, or which she thinks is the strongest team of the three. Benjamin may do this as many times as he likes. Determine the largest N such that Benjamin can guarantee to be able to find a sequence $T_1, T_2, \ldots, T_N$ of teams with the property that he knows that Alison thinks that T_i is better than T_{i+1} for each $1 \leqslant i \leqslant N$.

This problem falls naturally into two parts; first showing that Benjamin can always find a list of length 10, and secondly showing that Alison can always stop Benjamin from finding a list of length 11.

Solution by Rosie Cates, Hills Road VI Form College:

We claim that $N = 10$ is maximal.

Proof that $N \geqslant 10$:

We are trying to prove that Benjamin can always find an ordered list of teams of length 10. Call a pair of teams t_x, t_y a problem pair if, no matter what he asks, Benjamin cannot tell which of t_x and t_y Alison believes is better.

Then, each team t_x may be a member of at most one problem pair: otherwise, if t_x, t_y and t_x, t_z are problem pairs, Benjamin should ask about t_x, t_y and t_z. In that case, Alison must tell Benjamin something about at least one of the pairs.

Observe that this means there can be at most 10 problem pairs. Suppose Benjamin names the teams in the problem pairs a_i and b_i for each problem pair. Each team is therefore given at most one name, and Benjamin can arbitrarily give any unnamed teams the rest of the names a_j and b_j for $j \leqslant 10$.

Notice that among teams $a_1, \ldots, a_{10}$, there are no problem pairs. Hence, Benjamin can put them in order, and so $N \geqslant 10$.

Proof that $N \leqslant 10$.

We are trying to give a strategy for Alison so that Benjamin can never find a list of 11 teams in order. Suppose that the teams are in order $c_1, c_2, \ldots, c_{20}$ with c_1 worse than c_2, and so on.

If Benjamin asks Alison a question involving c_{2i-1} and c_{2i} for $1 \leqslant i \leqslant 10$ along with c_j, then Alison will tell Benjamin either that c_j is the best or that c_j is the worst. In particular, she will never compare c_{2i-1} and c_{2i}. (She can say anything she wants to other questions.)

Then, in any list of length 11, by the pigeonhole principle there will be two teams of the form c_{2i-1} and c_{2i}. Benjamin cannot tell which of these teams is better, and so he cannot put this list in order. Hence, $N \leqslant 10$.

Problem 3 (Proposed by David Monk)

Let *ABCD* be a cyclic quadrilateral. The diagonals *AC* and *BD* meet at *P*, and *DA* and *CB* produced meet at *Q*. The midpoint of *AB* is *E*. Prove that if *PQ* is perpendicular to *AC*, then *PE* is perpendicular to *BC*.

Solution 1 *by Warren Li, Eton College*:

Let circle *APQ* meet *BC* at *X*, so $\angle AXQ = \pi/2$.

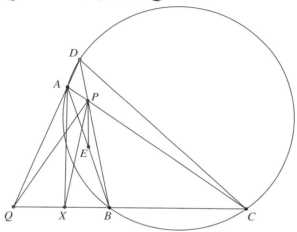

Now, *ABCD* is cyclic, so $\angle PAQ = \angle PBQ$. Also. since *APXQ* is cyclic, $\angle PAQ = \angle PXB$.

Hence, $\angle PXB = \angle PBQ$, so *PBX* is isosceles, and so *P* lies on the perpendicular bisector of *BX*.

Now, since *AX* and *BC* are perpendicular, and *E* is the midpoint of *AB*, *E* also lies on the perpendicular bisector of *BX*.

Therefore, *PE* is the perpendicular bisector of *BX*, so *PE* and *BC* are perpendicular, as required.

Solution 2 *by Neel Nanda, Latymer School*:

Reflect *A* in *P* to get *A'*.

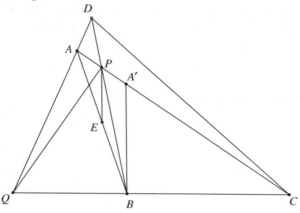

We have

$$\angle QA'P \;=\; \angle PAQ$$

$$=\; \pi - \angle DAC$$

$$=\; \pi - \angle DBC$$

$$=\; \angle QBP$$

and so *QBA'P* is cyclic. Hence, $\angle A'BQ = \pi/2$ as $\angle A'PQ = \pi/2$.

Now, $AA' = 2AP$ and $AB = 2AE$, and so triangles *AEP* and *ABA'* are similar. In particular, *A'B* and *PE* are parallel. Since *A'B* is perpendicular to *BC*, so must *PE* be.

Problem 4 (Proposed by Geoff Smith)

Suppose that p is a prime number and that there are different positive integers u and v such that p^2 is the mean of u^2 and v^2. Prove that $2p - u - v$ is a square or twice a square.

Solution 1 by Harvey Yau, Ysgol Dyffryn Taf:

Clearly we may assume that $p \neq 2$.

Observe that

$$(2p - u - v)(2p + u + v) = 4p^2 - u^2 - v^2 - 2uv$$
$$= \left(u^2 + v^2\right) - 2uv$$
$$= (u - v)^2.$$

Since $u^2 + v^2$ is even, u and v share the same parity and so $2p + u + v$ and $2p - u - v$ are even. This identity becomes

$$\left(\frac{2p - u - v}{2}\right)\left(\frac{2p + u + v}{2}\right) = \left(\frac{u - v}{2}\right)^2.$$

Hence, we have $\frac{1}{2}(2p - u - v) = qa^2$ and $\frac{1}{2}(2p + u + v) = qb^2$ for some q, a and b with q squarefree.

Since $2p + u + v > 0$, $q > 0$. Also,

$$q \left| \frac{2p + u + v}{2} + \frac{2p - u - v}{2} \right. = 2p.$$

If $p \mid q$, then $p \mid (u + v)$, so $p \mid \frac{1}{2}(u + v)$. However,

$$\left(\frac{u + v}{2}\right)^2 + \left(\frac{u - v}{2}\right)^2 = p^2$$

so $0 < \frac{1}{2}(u + v) < p$, which is a contradiction.

Hence, q is 1 or 2. If $q = 1$, then $2p - u - v = 2a^2$, which is twice a square. If $q = 2$, then $2p - u - v = (2a)^2$, which is square.

Solution 2 *by the Editors*:

First, we note that $2p - u - v > 0$ since $4p^2 = 2u^2 + 2v^2 > (u + v)^2$. Similar arguments to those of the previous solution show that p does not divide $u + v$.

Let $y = v - p$, $x = p - u$, $h = \text{GCD}(x, y)$, $x = Xh$ and $y = Yh$, so X and Y are coprime. Then it is easy to verify that

$$2p(x - y) = x^2 + y^2$$

$$2p(X - Y) = h(X^2 + Y^2).$$

Observe that $2p - u - v = x - y$, so we must prove that any odd prime divides $(x - y) = h(X - Y)$ an even number of times.

But, suppose q is an odd prime dividing $x - y$, which we may assume is not p. We have two cases:

- $q \nmid (X - Y)$. Then $q \nmid 2p(X - Y)$, so $q \nmid h$ which contradicts the assertion that $q \mid (x - y)$.
- $q \mid (X - Y)$. Then $X \equiv Y \neq 0$ modulo q, and so $q \nmid (X^2 + Y^2)$. Thus, if q^r is the highest power of q dividing $X - Y$, q^r must also be the highest power of q dividing h.

Since the first case cannot occur, we have q^r is the greatest power of q dividing $X - Y$ and h, and so q^{2r} is the highest power of q dividing $x - y$. Thus, the highest power of q dividing $2p - u - v$ is even for any odd prime q, and so, as $2p - x - y > 0$, it must be a square or twice a square.

Olympiad Training and Overseas Competitions

Each year UKMT hold several camps to select and prepare students for participation in the UK team at the International Mathematical Olympiad (IMO). Teams are also sent to other international events as part of the training process.

Oxford Training Camp August 2015

One of the first events of the UKMT year, Oxford Training Camp was held again at Queen's College Oxford. Twenty two students attended the camp which ran from 23rd to 28th August. Once more, our thanks go to Peter Neumann who organised and directed the very successful camp again.

Once again the academic programme of the camp was structured and quite intense. There were two lecture/tutorial courses in the morning, on Geometry and Number Theory, followed in the afternoon with presentations on a wide variety of topics including Graph Theory, Invariance Principle, Counting Strategies and Problem Solving. On the final morning the students sat a four and a half hour Olympiad style exam.

Students attending the Oxford Training Camp this year were: Rose Blyth (Tonbridge Grammar School), Georgie Bumpus (Moele Brace Science College), Alex Chen (Westminster School), Nathaniel Cleland (Gillingham School), Louisa Cullen (Pocklington School), Elizabeth Holdcroft (The Willink School), Katherine Horton (All Hallows Catholic School), Charlie Hu (City of London School), Phoebe Jackson (Moreton Hall School), Timothy Lavy (Magdalen College School), Ricky Li (Fulford School), Yuxin Liu (Roedean School), Asa McDermott (Judd School), Laurence Mayther (John Roan School), Yuji Okitani (Tapton School), Thomas Pycroft (Whitchurch High School), Melissa Quail (Longsands School), Benedict Randall Shaw (Westminster Under School), Yuriy Tumarkin (Durham Johnston School), Sean White (City of London School), Daniel Yue (King Edward's School), Siana Zhekova (Westminster Academy).

Hungary Camp 2015/16

Each year UKMT send a group of twenty students and a number of volunteers to Hungary over the New Year to train with the Hungarian IMO squad. As in previous years the group travelled out on 27th December and returned on 4th January. Thanks go to this year's volunteers, Dominic Yeo who led the team, Gabriel Gendler, and Kasia Warburton.

The UKMT students attending the camp this year were: Jamie Bell (King Edward VI Five Ways School), Joe Benton (St Paul's School), Lydia Buckingham (Wellington School), Rosie Cates (Hills Road VI Form College), Clarissa Costen (Altrincham Girls' Grammar School), Jacob

Coxon (Magdalen College School), Lawrence Hollom (Churcher's College), Katherine Horton (All Hallowes Catholic School), Lucas Huysmans (Beaumont School), Warren Li (Eton College), Neel Nanda (Latimer School), Michael Ng (Aylesbury Grammar School), Phil Peters (Haberdashers' Aske's), Thomas Pycroft (Whitchurch High School), Melissa Quail (Longsands Academy), Thomas Read (The Perse School), Alevtina Studenikina (Cheltenham Ladies' College), Sam Watt (Monkton Combe School), Harvey Yau (Ysgol Dyffryn Taf), Renzhi Zhou (The Perse School)

Romanian Master of Mathematics

The Romanian Masters of Mathematics was held this year between 23rd February and 29th February in Bucharest. The leader of the UK team was Alex Betts, with James Gazet as the deputy and Sally Anne Huk who attended as the Observer with Contestants. The team came second out of 20 teams in the RMM team competition this year, and individually gained two gold medals, two silver medals and an honourable mention.

The team consisted of: Joe Benton (St Paul's School), Rosie Cates (Hills Road Sixth Form College), Lawrence Hollom (Churcher's College), Warren Li (Eton College), Neel Nanda (Latymer School), Harvey Yau (Ysgol Dryffyn Taf).

Balkan Mathematical Olympiad

The UK continues to be invited as a guest nation to the Balkan Mathematical Olympiad, a competition for secondary school students which is organised annually by eleven countries in Eastern Europe on a rotation basis. In 2016 it was held in Tirana, Albania from 5th to 10th May.

This year the group was led by Dominic Yeo, with Gerry Leversha as deputy and Jill Parker accompanying the students. UKMT rules state that UK students can only attend this competition on a single occasion, thus giving an opportunity for as many students as possible to experience an overseas event. The team achieved two silver and four bronze medals at the event. This year the team was: Jamie Bell (King Edward VI Five Ways School), Rosie Cates (Hills Road VI Form College), Jacob Coxon (Magdalen College School), Michael Ng (Aylesbury Grammar School), Thomas Read (The Perse School), Renzhi Zhou (The Perse School).

The team leaders report for this can be found at

https://www.imo-register.org.uk/2016-balkan-report.pdf

Trinity Training Camp

The annual Trinity Training Camp was held at Trinity College, Cambridge, from 31st March to 4th April. UKMT are very grateful to Trinity College for its continuing support of this event.

This year, 22 students attended the camp, including all the candidates for the 2016 International Mathematical Olympiad (IMO) team, and younger students who have the potential to reach future international camps.

Students attending this year were: Connie Bambridge-Sutton (Reigate Grammar School), Agnijo Banerjee (Grove Academy), Jamie Bell (King Edward VI Five Ways School), Joe Benton (St Paul's School), Rosie Cates (Hills Road VI Form College), Jacob Coxon (Magdalen College School), Lawrence Hollom (Churcher's College), Charlie Hu (City of London School), Gurbir Johal (Barking Abbey School), Tomoka Kan (Westminster School), Ryan Lee (Magdalen College School), Warren Li (Eton College), Neel Nanda (Latymer School), Michael Ng (Aylesbury Grammar School), Thomas Read (The Perse School), Alex Song (Westminster School), Alevtina Studenikina (Cheltenham Ladies' College), James Sun (Reading School), Yuriy Tumarkin (Durham Johnston School), Naomi Wei ((City of London Girls' School), Harvey Yau (Ysgol Dryffyn Taf), Renzhi Zhou (The Perse School),

European Girls' Mathematical Olympiad (EGMO)

The 5th European Girls' Mathematical Olympiad was held in Busteni, Romania, between 10th and 16th April. From small beginnings in 2012 in Cambridge, UK, this event has grown to 39 countries in 2016, including 8 guest countries from outside Europe. This year the UK came 7th out of 39 teams participating at EGMO (6th out of the 31 official European teams). Each member of the team won a medal this year – achieving one gold medal, one silver medal and two bronze medals.

The UK team attending were: Rosie Cates (Hills Road Sixth Form College), Tomoka Kan (Westminster School), Alevtina Studenikina (Cheltenham Ladies' College), Naomi Wei (City of London School for Girls).

The Team leader was Jo Harbour and the deputy leader was Jenny Owladi.

Tonbridge Selection Camp

The final training camp before selection of the team of six for the IMO was this year held at Tonbridge School from Saturday 28th May to Wednesday 1st June.

Students participating were:

Joe Benton (St Paul's School), Rosie Cates (Hills Road Sixth Form College), Jacob Coxon (Magdalen College School, Oxford), Lawrence Hollom (Churcher's College, Hampshire), Warren Li (Eton College), Neel Nanda (Latymer School, London), Michael Ng (Aylesbury Grammar School)), Thomas Read (The Perse School, Cambridge), Harvey Yau (Ysgol Dyffryn Taf), Renzhi Zhou (The Perse School, Cambridge).

Staff at the camp were Geoff Smith, Joseph Myers, Dominic Yeo, Olga Smith, Jeremy King, Dan Crisan and Imre Leader.

The International Mathematical Olympiad

In many ways, a lot of the events and activities described earlier in this book relate to stages that UK IMO team members will go through before they attend an IMO. At this stage, it is worth explaining a little about the structure of the Olympiad, both for its own sake as well as to fit the following report into a wider context.

An IMO is a huge event and takes several years to plan and to execute. In 2016, teams from more than 100 countries went to Hong Kong to participate. A team consists of six youngsters (although in some cases, a country may send fewer). The focus of an IMO is really the two days on which teams sit the contest papers. The papers are on consecutive days and each lasts $4\frac{1}{2}$ hours. Each paper consists of three problems, and each problem is worth 7 marks. Thus a perfect score for a student is 42/42. The students are ranked according to their personal scores, and the top half receive medals. These are distributed in the ratios gold:silver:bronze = 1:2:3. The host city of the IMO varies from year to year. Detailed contemporary and historical data can be found at

http://www.imo-official.org/

However, whilst these may be the focus, there are other essential stages, in particular the selection of the problems and, in due course, the co-ordination (marking) of scripts and awarding of medals.

As stated, an IMO team is built around the students but they are accompanied by two other very important people: the Team Leader and the Deputy Leader (many teams also take Observers who assist at the various stages and some of these may turn out to be future Leaders). Some three or four days before the actual IMO examinations, the Team Leaders arrive in the host country to deal with the task of constructing the papers. Countries will have submitted questions for consideration over the preceding months and a short list of questions (and, eventually, solutions) are given to Team Leaders on arrival. The Team Leaders gather as a committee (in IMO parlance, the Jury) to select six of the short-listed questions. This can involve some very vigorous debate and pretty tough talking, but it has to be done! Once agreed, the questions are put into the papers and translations produced into as many languages as necessary, sometimes over 50.

At some stage, the students, accompanied by the Deputy Leader, arrive in the host country. As is obvious, there can be no contact with the Team Leader who, by then, has a good idea of the IMO papers! The Leaders and the students are housed in different locations to prevent any contact, casual or otherwise.

On the day before the first examination, there is an Opening Ceremony. This is attended by all those involved (with due regard to security).

Immediately after the second day's paper, the marking can begin. It may seem strange that students' scripts are 'marked' by their own Leader and Deputy. In fact, no actual marks or comments of any kind are put on the scripts themselves. Instead, having looked at scripts and decided what marks they think should be awarded, the Leader and Deputy have to justify their claim to others, called co-ordinators, who are supplied by the host country. Once all the marks have been agreed, sometimes after extremely protracted negotiation, the Jury decides where the medal boundaries should go. Naturally, this is a crucial part of the procedure and results in many tears as well as cheers.

Whilst the co-ordination of marks is going on, the students have time to relax and recover. There are often organised activities and excursions and there is much interaction and getting to know like-minded individuals from all corners of the world.

The grand finale is always the closing ceremony which includes the awarding of medals as well as speeches and numerous items of entertainment – some planned but others accidental.

57th International Mathematical Olympiad, Hong Kong, 6-16 July 2016, Report by Geoff Smith (UK Team Leader)

Dominic Yeo has taken the lead role in UK team training this year, and any reflected glory from the UK team's splendid performance at IMO 2016 in Hong Kong shines upon him. It makes sense to regard his report as the principal one for 2016, with mine containing a few incidental observations. Jill Parker was Observer with students, and I was UK team leader, sitting on the IMO Jury. As well as the official UK delegation, there were another couple of UKMT volunteers in Hong Kong. James Cranch and Joseph Myers are there as experienced anglo-phone co-ordinators, and Joseph has an extra brief to shadow IT specialist Matja Zeljko to build some redundancy into IMO computer support.

The British team was found through a selection process based on performances in test exams. They were

Joe Benton	St Paul's School, Barnes, London
Jacob Coxon	Magdalen College School, Oxford
Lawrence Hollom	Churcher's College, Petersfield, Hampshire
Warren Li	Fulford School, York
Neel Nanda	Latymer School, Edmonton, London
Harvey Yau	Ysgol Dyffryn Taf, Carmarthenshire, Wales

The reserves were

Rosie Cates	Hills Road VI Form College, Cambridge
Michael Ng	Aylesbury Grammar School
Thomas Read	The Perse School, Cambridge
Renzhi Zhou	The Perse School, Cambridge

Here are the results obtained by the UK students this year.

	P1	P2	P3	P4	P5	P6	Total	Medal
Joe Benton	7	7	2	7	2	1	26	Silver
Jacob Coxon	7	1	0	6	7	3	24	Silver
Lawrence Hollom	7	7	0	7	3	0	24	Silver
Warren Li	7	7	2	7	7	3	33	Gold
Neel Nanda	7	7	0	7	2	7	30	Gold
Harvey Yau	0	7	0	7	7	7	28	Silver
	35	36	4	41	28	21	165	

There are three problems to address on each of two consecutive days. Each exam lasts 4 hours 30 minutes. The cut-offs were 16 for bronze, 22 for silver and 29 for gold. The current IMO marks format became stable in 1981. This is the lowest gold cut, and the equal lowest silver cut, since then. This is evidence of the exceptional difficulty of this IMO, perhaps because of the technical complexity of the medium problems, numbers 2 and 5.

The Papers

Contestants have 4 hours 30 minutes to sit each paper. The three problems on each paper are each marked out of 7. It is intended that the three problems should be in increasing order of difficulty on each day.

Day 1

Problem 1 Triangle BCF has a right angle at B. Let A be the point on line CF such that $FA = FB$ and F lies between A and C. Point D is chosen such that $DA = DC$ and AC is the bisector of $\angle DAB$. Point E is chosen such that $EA = ED$ and AD is the bisector of $\angle EAC$. Let M be the midpoint of CF. Let X be the point such that $AMXE$ is a parallelogram (where $AM // EX$ and $AE // MX$). Prove that lines BD, FX, and ME are concurrent.

Problem 2 Find all positive integers n for which each cell of an $n \times n$ table can be filled with one of the letters I, M and O in such a way that:

- in each row and each column, one third of the entries are I, one third are M and one third are O; and
- in any diagonal, if the number of entries on the diagonal is a multiple of three, then one third of the entries are I, one third are M and one third are O.

Note: The rows and columns of an $n \times n$ table are each labelled 1 to n in a natural order. Thus each cell corresponds to a pair of positive integers (i, j) with $1 \leqslant i, j \leqslant n$. For $n > 1$, the table has $4n - 2$ *diagonals* of two types. A diagonal of the first type consists of all cells (i, j) for which $i + j$ is a constant, and a diagonal of the second type consists of all cells (i, j) for which $i - j$ is a constant.

Problem 3 Let $P = A_1 A_2 \ldots A_k$ be a convex polygon in the plane. The vertices A_1, A_2, ... , A_k have integral coordinates and lie on a circle. Let S be the area of P. An odd positive integer n is given such that the squares of the side lengths of P are integers divisible by n. Prove that $2S$ is an integer divisible by n.

Day 2

Problem 4 A set of positive integers is called *fragrant* if it contains at least two elements and each of its elements has a prime factor in common with at least one of the other elements. Let $P(n) = n^2 + n + 1$. What is the least possible value of the positive integer b such that there exists a non-negative integer a for which the set

$$\{P(a + 1), P(a + 2), \ldots, P(a + b)\}$$

is fragrant?

Problem 5 The equation

$$(x - 1)(x - 2)\ldots(x - 2016) = (x - 1)(x - 2)\ldots(x - 2016)$$

is written on the board, with 2016 linear factors on each side. What is the least possible value of k for which it is possible to erase exactly k of these 4032 linear factors so that at least one factor remains on each side and the resulting equation has no real solutions?

Problem 6 There are $n \geqslant 2$ line segments in the plane such that every two segments cross, and no three segments meet at a point. Geoff has to choose an endpoint of each segment and place a frog on it, facing the other endpoint. Then he will clap his hands $n - 1$ times. Every time he claps, each frog will immediately jump forward to the next intersection point on its segment. Frogs never change the direction of their jumps. Geoff wishes to place the frogs in such a way that no two of them will ever occupy the same intersection point at the same time.

(a)   Prove that Geoff can always fulfil his wish if n is odd.

(b)   Prove that Geoff can never fulfil his wish if n is even.

Extra Information

The word 'fragrant' refers to the meaning of 'Hong Kong', which is 'fragrant harbour'. The problems were proposed by Belgium, Australia, Russia, Luxembourg, Russia and the Czech Republic respectively. The authors were Art Waeterschoot, Trevor Tao, Alexandr Gaifullin, Gerhard Woeginger, Nazar Agakhanov & Ilya Bogdanov (so two authors for Problem 5) and Josef Tkadlec. The answer to the obvious question about the second composer is 'yes'.

Analysis of Results

Here are the countries ranked in the top 21 at IMO 2016. There were a total of 109 countries sending contestants.

United States of America (214); South Korea (207); China (204); Singapore (196); Taiwan (175); North Korea (168); Russia (165); United Kingdom (165); Hong Kong (161); Japan (156); Vietnam (151); Canada (148); Thailand (148); Hungary (145); Brazil (138); Italy (138); Philippines (133); Bulgaria (132); Germany (131); Indonesia (130); Romania (130).

This was the first ever top ten performance by the host territory, and the first top 20 performance by the Philippines. The UK team collectively scored 165 points, putting them joint top of Europe with Russia, the team with which we shared 7th place. This is the best UK performance since 1996 when the UK finished 5th.

Other continental champions were Africa: South Africa, Asia: Republic of Korea, Australasia: Australia, North America: USA and South America: Brazil.

Bitter local rivalries include:

- The annual Nordic knife fight, Sweden (1), Denmark (2), Norway (3), Iceland (4);
- The Baltic republic bar brawl finished, Lithuania (1), Estonia (2) and Latvia (3);
- The monarchy roll of honour (taking a liberal view of Grand Dukes,

Princes and elected Kings) is UK (1), Japan (2), Canada (3), Thailand (4), Australia (5), Sweden (6), Saudi Arabia (7), Netherlands (8), Spain (9), Belgium (10), New Zealand (11), Malaysia (12), Morocco (13), Denmark (14), Norway (15), Luxembourg (16), Cambodia (17), Jamaica (18) and Liechtenstein (19).

Other European countries which performed well were Hungary (14), Italy (16), Bulgaria (18) and Germany (19). Romania had, by their high standards, a modest year in position (20).

The results of Commonwealth and anglophone countries (taking an extremely relaxed interpretation of the word anglophone) were USA (1), Singapore (5), UK (7), Hong Kong (9), Canada (12), Philippines (17), Australia (25), India (34), Bangladesh (35), New Zealand (53), Malaysia (56), South Africa (58), Cyprus (63), Sri Lanka (66), Ireland (75), Nigeria (88), Trinidad and Tobago (88), Myanmar (96), Uganda (98), Kenya (99), Jamaica (102), Ghana (104) and Tanzania (106). Note that many of the teams ranked lower on this list did not send a full team of six students.

There was a fair amount of teasing about Brexit, and its supposed impact on team performance. This teasing mostly and mysteriously stopped after the IMO results were published. Spurred by this insolence, it can be reported that the medal count of the UK and that of the best six students of the rest of the European Union were equal; two golds and four silvers in each case. However, it must be admitted that the Rump European Union outscored the UK 178 to 165. The REU team consisted of Attila Gáspár of Hungary (35), Filippo Gianni Baroni (31) from Italy, and four participants chosen from a set of two Czechs, a French person, an Italian and two Swedes, all of whom scored 28 points.

Diary

This diary is a facetious summary of my personal experience at the IMO and is available on:

www.imo-register.org.uk/2016-report.pdf

Acknowledgements

This was a remarkably strong performance by a wonderful team. Sitting behind these young people is huge support, both in intellectual terms but also in terms of support from families and schools. There is also the UKMT infrastructure, and the army of volunteers and staff who create the competitions, publications, camps, mentoring and other activities which underpin the UK contribution to the IMO and other mathematics competitions. I must specifically thank Oxford Asset Management for their financial support for the IMO team. Their logo adorns the team blazer.

http://www.ukmt.org.uk/about-us/

UKMT Mentoring Schemes

This year's scheme has once again grown in both numbers and popularity. We are incredibly proud that these papers are currently being used by 1100 schools throughout the world. Bringing our future mathematicians, and their teachers, together to motivate and develop their love of all things Math! The mentoring materials, as ever, continue to be offered for free to all schools who register their interest with us. In addition we have over 250 mentees who are mentored individually by our group of enthusiastic volunteer mentors.

In addition to our volunteer mentors, we have had an amazing team of authors who work tirelessly on their individual schemes. Each volunteer or small team of volunteers writes a set of questions and solutions for the whole year. This takes a huge amount of time, to make the questions fresh, interesting and challenging.

Our schemes caters for pupils from years 7-13 (in England and Wales, and the equivalent years in Scotland and Northern Ireland). At Junior and Intermediate levels we encourage teachers to mentor their own pupils because regular contact is important at this stage, however we do also have a growing number of external mentors available at Intermediate level. At the Senior and Advanced levels, students are mentored by undergraduates, postgraduates and teachers who are familiar with problem-solving techniques. Any teacher who is willing to act a a mentor to their own pupils, using UKMT materials, is encouraged to do so. The UKMT schemes run from October through to May and anyone who is interested in either being a mentee, a mentor or using the sheets with their class is welcome to register by emailing mentoring@ukmt.org.uk at any time during the year. Teachers registering on the schemes go onto a mailing list to receive the monthly materials, which they can then use in any way they like with their own students, either individually or in class.

Junior Scheme

We have over 850 school mentors for this scheme level. The scheme is aimed at years 7-9 (although we do have the occasional year 6 pupil too), some of whom have completed the Junior Maths Challenge and are perhaps looking at our Junior Olympiad papers. Discussion points and hints are offered by the author to promote problem solving to pupils at an accessible level. The papers are written purposely to become more and more challenging as the year progresses.

Once a teacher has enrolled with us, we send out the most recent sheet each month. At this level, all pupils are mentored internally by their teachers who are welcome to use these resources in class. This is often a great way to stimulate the interest of a whole class, although increasingly, these papers are used by more and more pupils within an out of hours maths club.

Intermediate Scheme

The Intermediate scheme has over 800 registered users at school. It is aimed at those approximately in Years 9-11 who have done well in the Intermediate Maths Challenge and are preparing for Intermediate Olympiad papers or who have attended one of the UKMT National Mathematics Summer Schools. These sheets range in content from some questions which can be approached without any special techniques to others which require knowledge of more special areas, such as number theory. Our aim is to gradually introduce these techniques throughout the year and encourage mentees to ask questions or research the internet to find out more about these areas. Most pupils in this scheme are mentored by their teacher or work in small groups and maths clubs at school, however this year we did support 28 individual mentees with 13 volunteer mentors.

Senior Scheme

The senior materials are now shared with over 400 schools. This scheme is aimed at students in Years 11-13, with questions set at a quite challenging level. The level is aimed at those students who are taking BMO papers or who have outgrown the Intermediate Scheme. An important role of mentors at this level is to give encouragement to their mentees, as the questions are usually more taxing than anything they may confront at A-level, and each problem solved is a very distinct achievement which should give the student a good feeling of satisfaction. At this level it would be rare to expect the student to be able to complete all the problems on every paper. As well as being used by teachers with groups in schools, the senior scheme also provides external mentors who mentor students through the scheme. In 2015-16 our 86 volunteer Senior Mentors worked with nearly 200 mentees.

Advanced Scheme

Entry to the advanced level is by invitation only and this level is aimed at UK IMO squad members and others who have peaked on the Senior Scheme and their mentors have recommended them for promotion. The questions are very challenging and are mainly of interest to those who are aiming to be selected for the UK team in the International Mathematical Olympiad (IMO).This year we had a small group of 18 mentees working alongside 9 mentors.

182

Sample questions from 2015-2016
The following were the first questions on the October paper in each scheme this year.

Junior
If 17% of a number is 782, what is the number?

Intermediate
Four numbers, taken two at a time, give the sums 84, 88, 100, 100, 112, and 116. What are the four numbers?

Senior
The surface of a $10 \times 10 \times 10$ wooden cube is painted red. The cube is then cut into 1000 unit cubes. How many of these unit cubes have precisely two red faces?

Mentoring conference and dinner
In November 2015 the Mentoring Conference and dinner was held at Trinity College, Cambridge. This annual event is held, not only to give the volunteer mentors a training opportunity, and a chance to exchange ideas and advice, it is also a way to thank our volunteers for all their help throughout the year. This year our thanks go particularly to Imre Leader, Tim Gowers, and Vicky Neale for leading sessions and organising the event.

In conclusion...
The mentoring schemes are supported by Oxford Asset Management and we would like to thank them for their continuing support.

Our thanks must also go to all the volunteer mentors and question setters who have freely given so much time to make the schemes work and encourage the next generation of young mathematicians. Too numerous to name here (although they appear later in the list of volunteers), without them there would be no schemes at all. If you would like to find out more about becoming a mentor, contact the UKMT by email :

mentoring@ukmt.org.uk

UKMT Team Maths Challenge 2016

Overview

The Team Maths Challenge (TMC) is a national mathematics competition which gives pupils the opportunity to participate in a wide range of mathematical activities and compete against other pupils from schools in their region. The TMC promotes team working and, unlike the Junior, Intermediate and Senior Challenges, students work in groups and are given practical tasks as well as theoretical problems to add another dimension to mathematics.

The TMC is designed for teams of four pupils in:

- Y8 & Y9 (England and Wales)
- S1 & S2 (Scotland)
- Y9 & Y10 (Northern Ireland)

with no more than two pupils from the older year group.

Sample TMC material is available to download from the TMC section of the UKMT website (www.tmc.ukmt.org.uk) for use in school and to help teachers to select a team to represent their school at the Regional Finals.

Report on the 2016 TMC

The fourteenth year of the competition saw yet another record number of participating schools. Entries were received from 1770 teams, of which 1650 turned up to take part at one of 70 Regional Finals.

As usual, competition details and entry forms were sent to schools in early October and made available on the UKMT website, which also provided up-to-date information on Regional Final venues and availability of places, as well as past materials for the use of schools in selecting and preparing their team of four. Schools also received a copy of the winning poster from the 2015 National Final, originally created by The Perse School (Cambridge) and professionally reproduced by Arbelos.

Each team signed up to participate in one of the 70 Regional Finals, held between late February and the end of April at a widely-spread set of venues. Each Regional Final comprised four rounds which encouraged the teams to think mathematically in a variety of ways. The Group Round is the only round in which the whole team work together, tackling a set of ten challenging questions. In the Crossnumber the team splits into two pairs; one pair gets the across clues and the other pair gets the down clues. The two pairs then work independently to complete the Crossnumber using logic and deduction. For the Shuttle, teams compete against the clock to answer a series of questions, with each pair working on different questions and the solution of each question dependent on the previous answer. The final round of the day, the Relay, is a fast and lively race involving much movement to answer a series of questions in pairs. Each Regional Final was run by a regional lead coordinator with support from an assistant coordinator and, at some venues, other local helpers. The teachers who accompanied the teams were fully occupied too – they were involved in the delivery and marking of all of the rounds.

TMC National Final

Eighty-eight teams (the winners from each Regional Final plus a few runners-up) were invited to the National Final on 20th June, which was again held at the Lindley Hall, part of the prestigious Royal Horticultural Halls, in Westminster, London. As usual, the four rounds from the Regional Finals also featured at the National Final except that the Group Round became the Group Circus: a similar round but with the inclusion of practical materials for use in solving the questions. In addition, the day began with the Poster Competition, which is judged and scored separately from the main event. The Poster theme for 2016 was 'Folding', inspiring some intricate designs among the entries, which were all exhibited down the side of the hall throughout the day for the perusal of the participants as well as the judges.

The following schools, coming from as far north as Perth and as far south as Guernsey, participated at the National Final:

Abbey Grange CE Academy, Leeds	Durham Johnston School
Backwell School, North Somerset	Elizabeth College, Guernsey
Bacup & Rawtenstall Grammar School, Lancs	Forest School, London
Beaconsfield High School, Buckinghamshire	Friends' School Lisburn
Beverley Grammar School, East Yorks	Fullbrook School, Surrey
Birkdale School, Sheffield	Glasgow Academy
Boston Grammar School, Lincs	Hampton School, Middlesex
Bottisham Village College, Cambridgeshire	Hereford Cathedral School
Bournemouth School	Howell's School, Cardiff
Bradford Grammar School	Ixworth Free School, Suffolk
Brighton College	Judd School, Tonbridge, Kent
Cargilfield Preparatory, Edinburgh	King Edward VI Grammar School, Chelmsford
Caroline Chisholm School, Northants	King Edward VI High Sch. for Girls, Birmingham
Charterhouse, Godalming, Surrey	King Edward's School, Bath
Cheltenham Ladies' College, Gloucs	Kings' School, Winchester
Colchester Royal Grammar School	Kingston Grammar School, Surrey
Colyton Grammar School, Devon	Lancaster Royal Grammar School
Comberton Village College, Cambridgeshire	Liverpool Blue Coat School
Davenies School, Buckinghamshire	Loughborough Grammar School
Devonport High School for Boys, Plymouth	Macmillan Academy, Middlesbrough

Magdalen College School, Oxford
Manchester Grammar School
Manchester High School for Girls
Merchant Taylors' School, Middlesex
Millfield School, Somerset
Netherhall School, Cambridge
Newquay Tretherras, Cornwall
Norwich School
Nottingham High School
Oundle School, Northants
Parmiter's School, Watford
Queen Elizabeth Grammar School, Penrith
Queen Ethelburga's College, N. Yorks
Queen Mary's Grammar School, Walsall
Radley College, nr Abingdon
Royal Grammar School, Newcastle
Rugby School
School of St Helen and St Katharine, Abingdon
Sir Roger Manwood's School, Kent
Sir Thomas Picton School, Haverfordwest
Skipton Girls' High School, N. Yorks
St Bede's Prep School, Eastbourne
St Edmund Arrowsmith RC High S., Lancashire
St Edward's CoE Academy, Leek, Staffs

St Gerard's School, Bangor, Gwynedd
St Leonard's School, Fife
St Louis Middle School, Bury St Edmunds
St Olave's Grammar School, Kent
St Paul's Girls' School, Hammersmith
St Thomas More Catholic High School, Crewe
Strathallan School, Perth and Kinross
Sutton Grammar School for Boys, Surrey
Tapton School, Sheffield
Taunton School (Lower School)
The Grange School, Cheshire
The Perse School, Cambridge
The Portsmouth Grammar School
The Ridgeway School, Swindon
The Stephen Perse Foundation, Cambridge
The Tiffin Girls' School, Kingston-upon-Thames
Tonbridge School, Kent
Ulverston Victoria High School, Cumbria
University College School, London
Warwick School
West Kirby Grammar School, Wirral
West Park School, Derby
Westminster Under School, London
Wheatley Park School, Oxon

After a hard-fought competition, the Team Maths Challenge 2016 trophy went to Westminster Under School (London), retaining their 2015 title, while the Poster Competition was won by Sutton Grammar School.

The team responsible for producing another set of excellent and engaging materials were Martin Perkins, Jenny Ramsden, Madeleine Copin and Beth Ashfield (the checkers of the questions), Dean Bunnell and Keith Cadman (Group Round), Peter Ransom (Crossnumber), Karl Hayward-Bradley and David Crawford (Shuttle), Ann Ault and Sue Essex (Relay), Andrew Jobbings, Peter Neumann, Fraser Heywood and Colin Campbell (Poster Competition).

As usual, thanks are due to a great number of people for ensuring another successful year of the TMC: the team of volunteers (listed at the back of this book) who generously give up their time to write, check and refine materials, run Regional Finals (with a helping hand from family members in a few cases!) and readily carry out countless other jobs behind the scenes; the staff in the UKMT office in Leeds for the way in which the competition is administered (particularly Nicky Bray who has responsibility for the central coordination of the competition, assisted by Shona Raffle-Edwards and Jo Williams, with additional support from Gerard Cummings and Sara Liptrot) and the team of packers for their efficient and precise preparation and packing of materials; the teachers who continue to support the competition and take part so willingly, some of whom also undertake the significant task of organising and hosting a Regional Final at their own school and, of course, the pupils who participate so enthusiastically in the competition at all levels. Our thanks also go to additional contacts at schools and other host venues responsible for organising and helping with Regional Finals (listed at the back of this book).

TMC Regional Finals Material

Each of the 70 Regional Finals held across the UK involved four rounds:

1.	Group Round	2.	Crossnumber
3.	Shuttle	4.	Relay Race

Group Round
Teams are given a set of 10 questions, which they should divide up among themselves so that they can answer, individually or in pairs, as many as possible in the allotted time.

Question 1

Starting at the time shown on the twelve-hour clock, how many times over a twelve-hour period is the angle between the minute hand and the hour hand equal to 90°?

[6]

Question 2
(a) In a particular kite, the smallest angle is a quarter of the angle opposite to it. The angle between a long side and a short side of the kite is 115°. What is the smallest angle in this kite?

[3]

(b) In another kite, the smallest angle is also a quarter of the angle opposite to it. The angle between a long side and a short side of this kite is five times its smallest angle. What is the smallest angle in this kite?

[3]

Question 3

(a) Find the value of

$$\frac{1 \times 2 \times 3 \times 4 \times 5 \times 6 \times 7 \times 8}{1 + 2 - 3 + 4 - 5 + 6 + 7 + 8}.$$

[3]

(b) Find the value of

$$2^5 + 2^6 + 2^7 + 2^8 + 2^9 + 2^{10}.$$

[3]

Question 4

| square | rectangle | rhombus | kite | parallelogram | trapezium |

Write down the names of some of the quadrilaterals listed above so that, between them, they contain the vowels

| a, e, i, o and u |

at least once each and have, in total, the minimum possible number of letters.

[6]

Question 5

In a competition, teams A, B and C play against each other once only.
Team A beats both teams B and C whilst team B draws with team C.
In total, team A scores 11 goals, team B scores no goals and team C scores 3 goals.

How many different sets of scores are possible?

[6]

Question 6

A sum of money is shared equally between five people.
Sunita, Lauren and Maisie each spend half of their share. Florence spends one third of her share. Thomas spends a quarter of his share. There is then £700 left out of the original sum of money.

How much money did each of the five people receive as their share at the start?

[6]

188

Question 7

All of the odd integers from 1 to 999 inclusive are added up.

What is the total?

[6]

Question 8

Charlie is leading in a race. He is 81 metres in front of Sam who is in last place. Jon is between Charlie and Sam. Jon is 40 metres from the finish line and is twice as far away from Sam as he is from Charlie.

How far has Sam left to run?

[6]

Question 9

The digits of three consecutive two-digit integers greater than 20 have a sum of 27. Two of these integers are prime numbers.

(a) Find a set of three consecutive integers with these properties.

[3]

(b) Find another set of three consecutive integers with these properties.

[3]

Write down your sets of integers in ascending order.

Question 10

When a 1 is placed after a five-digit integer the result is three times as large as when a 1 is placed before it.

What is the five-digit integer?

[6]

Crossnumber

Teams are divided into pairs, with one pair given the across clues and one pair given the down clues. Each pair answers as many questions as possible on the grid, showing their answers to the supervising teacher who either confirms or corrects them. The correct version is then shown to both pairs. The sole communication permitted between the two pairs is to request, via the supervising teacher, for a particular clue to be solved by the other pair.

Across:

1.	A triangular number that is also a square	(2)
2.	A factor of 22 Across	(2)
4.	A multiple of the sum of its digits	(3)
7.	A factor of 2016	(3)
8.	A multiple of 18 Across	(5)
10.	24 Across plus 11 Down	(2)
12.	$88^2 + 33^2$	(4)
14.	A prime number whose digits are consecutive primes in order	(4)

17. An angle, in degrees, of an isosceles triangle that contains a 62° angle (2)
18. The sum of its digits is six (5)
22. 23 Across + 20 Down + 19 Down (3)
23. A cube that is the sum of three consecutive cubes (3)
24. x where $x + 11$ Down $= 3x - 79$ (2)
25. Square root of 20 Down (2)

Down:

1. A factor of 2016 (3)
3. $12^2 + 33^2$ (4)
4. 3 Down + 10 × 14 Across (5)
5. 1 Across minus 2 (2)
6. A factor of 2016 (2)
9. A multiple of the sum of its digits (3)
11. A cube (2)
12. The sum of two squares in two ways (2)
13. 4 Down + 12 Across (5)
15. The sum of the digits in this number's column is ten (3)
16. A triangular number also a square (4)
19. The number of primes that are less than fifty (2)
20. A square that becomes a cube when four is added to it (3)
21. A multiple of 25 Across (2)

Shuttle

Teams are divided into pairs, with one pair given Questions 1 and 3 (along with the record sheet on which to record their answers) and the other pair given Questions 2 and 4. The first pair works on Question 1 and then passes the answer to the students in the other pair who use it to help them answer Question 2, for which they can first carry out some preparatory work. This continues with the second pair passing the answer to Question 2 back to the first pair and so on until a full set of answers is presented for marking. Bonus points are awarded to all teams which present a correct set of answers before the 6-minute whistle, then the other teams have a further 2 minutes in which to finish. Four of these shuttles are attempted in the time given.

A1   Calculate

$$555 + 777 + 888$$

Pass on the *sum of the digits* of your answer.

A2   *T is the number you will receive*
k is a positive number that satisfies the equation

$$k^2 = T^2 + 8^2.$$

Pass on the value of k.

A3   *T is the number you will receive*
A linear sequence is

$$6, \ 10, \ 14, \ 18, \ 22, \ \dots \ .$$

Pass on the value of the $(4T)$th term of the sequence.

A4   *T is the number you will receive*
One angle in a quadrilateral is $T°$.
The remaining three angles are in the ratio $1 : 2 : 3$.
Write down the size of the smallest angle, in degrees.

B1

> Michael has *n* sweets.
> James has twice as many sweets as Michael.
> Kelly has three more sweets than James.

In total they have 43 sweets.
Pass on how many sweets Michael has.

B2   *T is the number you will receive*

> $8 \times 15 \times 16 \times 30 \times T = 40 \times 12 \times 24 \times 20 \times K.$

Pass on the value of *K*.

B3   *T is the number you will receive*
The value of

> $$\frac{T}{63} - \frac{T}{64}$$

can be written as a fraction $\frac{A}{B}$, written in its lowest terms.
Pass on the value of $A \times B$.

B4   *T is the number you will receive*
Lynn thinks of a number. She then performs these calculations in order:

> * add 3
> * multiply by 5
> * subtract 13
> * multiply by 2
> * add 6
> * divide by 10.

She gets the answer *T*.
Write down the value of Lynn's original number.

C1 A set of five positive integers has mean 9, median 8 and mode 7.
Pass on the largest possible integer in the set.

C2 *T is the number you will receive*
The area of triangle *ABC* is T cm^2 less than the area of trapezium *PQRS*.

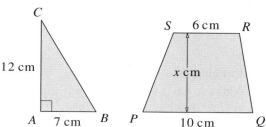

Pass on the value of *x*.

C3 *T is the number you will receive*
Ben's class were surveyed to find out if they liked English, Maths, both, or neither.
Out of the 30 pupils:

> 17 people said they liked Maths;
> 14 people said they liked English; and
> T people said they liked neither Maths nor English.

Pass on the number of pupils in Ben's class who liked *both* Maths and English.

C4 *T is the number you will receive*
A large crate has dimensions 2 m × 2 m × 1 m.
Write down how many boxes with dimensions
10 cm × Tcm × 5 cm will fit into the crate.

D1 X is a positive integer.

$$X^2 = 8^2 - 7^2 + 6^2 - 5^2 + 4^2 - 3^2 + 2^2 - 1^2.$$

Pass on the value of X.

D2   *T is the number you will receive*
H is the Highest Common Factor of 240 and $108T$.
Pass on the value of H.

D3   *T is the number you will receive*
Miss Watkins has a set of stickers, each of which is either red, green or blue, to give out to her class.

The ratio of red stickers to green stickers is 4 : 3.
The ratio of green stickers to blue stickers is 2 : 3.

Miss Watkins has T red stickers.
Pass on the number of blue stickers she has.

D4   *T is the number you will receive*
In the diagram, lines XA and DY are parallel and lines AB and BC are perpendicular.
Angle BAX equals $T°$ and angle CDY equals $2T°$.

Write down the size, in degrees, of *reflex* angle DCB.

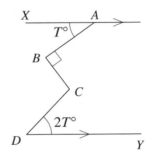

Relay

The aim here is to have a speed competition with students working in pairs to answer alternate questions. Each team is divided into two pairs, with each pair seated at a different desk away from the other pair and their supervising teacher.

One member of Pair A from a team collects question A1 from the supervising teacher and returns to his/her partner to answer the question together. When the pair is certain that they have answered the question, the runner returns to the front and submits their answer. If it is correct, the runner is given question B1 to give to the other pair (Pair B) from their team. If it is incorrect, Pair A then has a second (and final) attempt at answering the question, then the runner returns to the front to receive question B1 to deliver to pair B. The runner then returns, empty handed, to his/her partner. Pair B answers question B1 and a runner from this pair brings the answer to the front, as above, then takes question A2 to Pair A. Pair A answers question A2, their runner returns it to the front and collects question B2 for the other pair, and so on until all questions are answered or time runs out. Thus the A pairs answer only A questions and the B pairs answer only B questions. Only one pair from a team should be working on a question at any time and each pair must work independently of the other.

A1   What is the area of the shaded triangle?

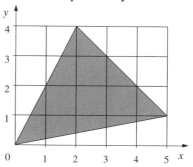

A2   What is the product of the smallest two-digit triangular number and the largest two-digit prime number?

A3   Each of five pupils has a different number of pens in their pencil cases. The mean is 6.4 pens.

What is the highest possible number of pens in a pencil case?

A4   In one week Sonja works for $17\frac{1}{2}$ hours at £8.40 an hour and then 8 hours at £9.00 per hour.

25% of this gross wage is deducted for tax, etc.

What is left per week?

A5 What is the size of the smallest angle in this triangle?

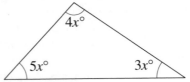

A6 An odd three-digit number less than 200 has digit product 4.
What is the number?

A7 On a map with scale 1:50 000, the path Martha is going to walk is 4 cm long.
She walks at 4 km per hour.
In minutes, how long will it take her?

A8 The diagram shows the pattern of square slabs that form a patio.

The area of the patio is 5.67 square metres.

What is the perimeter?

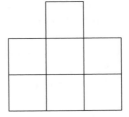

A9 A mathematical grandmother allows her six grandchildren equal shares of her dog-walking for 2016. Art does all his share first, starting on 1 January.
What is the date when Bert takes over from Art?

A10 Amid is planning to take part in a long-distance cycle race.
His training route is 49 km long, as shown.

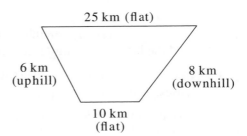

He cycles at an average speed of 30 km per hour along the flat, 24 km per hour uphill and 40 km per hour downhill.
How many minutes does he take to cover one circuit?

A11 A train left the station at 10:16, twenty-three minutes late. The driver was not able to make up any of the time and so the train took the same length of time as usual to reach the next station, that is, 89 minutes.

At what time should the train have arrived if it was on time?

A12

> Let t be the number of edges of a triangle.
> Let q be the number of edges of a quadrilateral.
> Let p be the number of edges of a pentagon.
> Let d be the number of edges of a decagon.
> Let e be the number of even prime numbers.
> Let s be the smallest prime number.

Calculate $d^2(tqp + e) + s$.

A13 In the United Kingdom a pint is 20 fluid ounces, while in the USA a pint is 16 fluid ounces.

The fluid ounce has the same volume in both countries, and there are 8 pints in a gallon.

My car averages 60 miles per gallon in England.

How many miles per gallon can I expect it to do in similar conditions in America?

A14 The following two equations are plotted on a graph.

$$y = 4 - 3x$$

$$y = 2x - 1$$

At what point do the two lines intersect?

A15 Rachel, Nicky and Shona buy a large packet of popcorn.

Rachel eats $\frac{1}{4}$ of the packet and passes it to Nicky, who eats $\frac{1}{5}$ of the remainder before passing it to Shona who eats $\frac{1}{6}$ of what is left.

What fraction of the packet remains for them to pass on to Steve?

B1 Jane puts her hand into an opaque bag containing seven pairs of gloves. There are four red pairs and three green pairs. In each pair the left glove is different to the right glove. Jane pulls out one glove at a time.

How many must she pull out to be certain of a pair?

B2 Which three-digit number is not a prime, is palindromic and has the sum of its digits equal to seven?

B3 To celebrate the maths club's 150th birthday Dr Smith has ordered 168 commemorative items. To pay for this he has included, in his order, a number of items for sale. Of the order, $\frac{1}{3}$ are mugs to be given free to the members and $\frac{1}{2}$ are ties which will be given to helpers and staff. The rest of the items will be sold.

How many items were for sale?

B4 The following two equations are plotted on a graph.

$$y = 3x - 3$$

$$y = 2x$$

At what point do the two lines intersect?

B5 A cuboid has a square base and is $1\frac{1}{2}$ times as high as it is wide. The shortest edges are 12 cm long.

What is the volume of the cuboid?

B6 Mrs Christie invested £80 000 while Mr Dickens invested £60 000. They shared the profits of £23 800 in the ratio of their investments.

How much profit did Mr Dickens receive?

B7 What is the largest angle of this triangle?

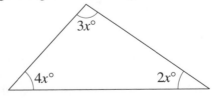

B8 A 10 lb turkey needs to be cooked by 19:30 and the oven takes 20 minutes to heat up to the right temperature. The cooking time is then 20 minutes per pound.

What is the latest time at which the oven can be turned on?

B9   Harry pays £85 deposit on a bike, then £85.50 per month until he
        pays for the bike in full. The bike costs £854.50.
        For how many months did Harry pay until he owned the bike?

B10   Joshua averages 34 marks in nine tests. His average mark for the
        first five tests is 37 and in the last five his average is 32 marks.
        What was his score for the fifth test?

B11   Great-granny GG takes one a day of each of two types of tablet, A
        and B. Tablet A is in packs of 30, tablet B in packs of 25.
        GG starts new packets of both on 1 July.
        On what date will she next start new packets of both?

B12   What is the product of the smallest two-digit prime number and
        the largest two-digit Fibonacci number?

B13   Peter and Alan are sitting facing each other on opposite sides of a
        desk. Peter uses a calculator, and an example of how his calculator
        displays its answers is shown below.

        For one question, Peter's calculator shows the answer 2016.
        Alan sees a different number, since the calculator is upside-down
        for him.
        What is the difference between their two numbers?

B14   Mike runs eight laps of the school track at 66 seconds per lap and
        Jane runs the eight laps in 9 minutes and 4 seconds at a steady
        speed.
        What is the difference in their average times for one lap?

B15   Charlie bought 200 shirts at £4.50 each and increased that by 60%
        to calculate the selling price.
        He sold 101 shirts and, to sell the rest, he offered them at 3 for the
        price of 2.
        How much profit, in pence, did he make on each of the last 99
        shirts?

TMC National Final Material

At the National Final, the Group Round is replaced by the Group Circus.

Group Circus

Teams move around a number of stations (eight at the 2016 National Final) to tackle a variety of activities, some of which involve practical materials.

Station 1

A friend has a box with four balls in it - two are red, one is black and one is white. She takes two balls out at random and shows me that one of them is red.

What is the probability that both of them are red?

Station 2

You are provided with two large squares (one red and one blue) divided into 16 congruent small squares, like the one shown below.

(a) Cut the large red square into three pieces, just one of which is a square, and rearrange them to make an 8 × 2 rectangle, without gaps or overlaps. Cuts may only be made along grid lines and *you are allowed* to turn pieces over.

(b) Cut the large blue square into five pieces, one of which is a square and the other four are congruent, and rearrange them to make an 8 × 2 rectangle, without gaps or overlaps. Cuts may only be made along grid lines and *you are not allowed* to turn pieces over.

Station 3

Three buses, numbered 117, 127 and 137, arrived together at my local bus station at 05:43.

The number 117 buses then arrive at this bus station every 18 minutes.

The number 127 buses then arrive at this bus station every 12 minutes.

The number 137 buses then arrive at this bus station every 14 minutes.

What will be the next time that three buses numbered 117, 127 and 137 arrive together at my local bus station?

Station 4

You are provided with two hexagons each divided into six triangles (like the one shown below) and the number cards 1, 3, 5, 7 and 9.

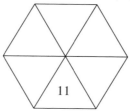

(a) Place one of the number cards 1, 3, 5, 7, and 9 in each triangle on one hexagon so that the sum of the numbers in any three adjacent triangles is prime. The number 11 is already in place. Show your solution to the supervising teacher.

(b) Using the second hexagon find a second solution to the task given in part (a) and show it to your supervising teacher. Your second solution must not be a reflection of the first one.

Station 5

The number of days in a non-leap year is equal to the sum of two squares.

(a) Find two squares which give one solution.

(b) Find two other squares which give a second solution.

The number of days in a leap year is equal to the sum of two cubes and one square.

(c) Find these three numbers.

Station 6

You are provided with a 7 × 7 grid of squares and nine cards with arrows on them, as shown below.

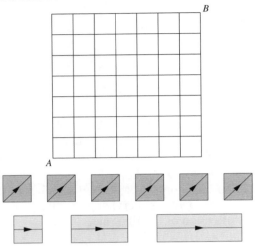

Place the cards so that:

(i) the arrows form a continuous route starting at corner *A* of the grid and ending at corner *B*;

(ii) all of the cards are used;

(iii) the cards do not overlap;

(iv) no part of a card lies outside the grid;

(v) the edges of each card are parallel to the lines of the grid.

Station 7

(a) A rectangle has a perimeter of 38 cm and an area of 48 cm².
What are the dimensions of the rectangle?

(b) An equilateral triangle has a perimeter of 48 cm. The area of the triangle can be written in the form $a^2\sqrt{b}$ cm², where a and b are single-digit numbers.
What are the values of a and b?

Station 8

How many different answers can be obtained using only the digits 1, 2, 3 and 4 each, in any order, together with a single × sign?

For example, 31 × 24 and 2 × 413 give two of the answers.

The numbers you use as factors in the calculations must all be integers.

Crossnumber

Across:

1.	7 Across minus 11 Down	(3)
3.	The square root of $23^3 + 24^3 + 25^3$	(3)
5.	A palindromic number whose digits have a sum of 33	(5)
7.	The difference between two consecutive Fibonacci numbers	(3)
8.	A number less than 3 Down	(3)
10.	A multiple of 18 Down	(4)
13.	The largest two-digit factor of 2 Down	(2)
15.	43 plus the square root of 12 Down	(2)
17.	$4 + 10 \times 12^2$	(4)
20.	21 Down minus a cube	(3)
22.	$n^n + 1$ for some n	(3)
23.	A factor of 5 Across	(5)

24. The mean of 14 Down and 1 Across (3)

25. 4994 minus 19 Down (3)

Down:

1. A palindromic number whose digits have a sum of 41 and which consists of two different digits (5)

2. 88×77 (4)

3. A number greater than 8 Across (3)

4. A square that is 8 Across $\times 3 - 102$ (3)

6. A Fibonacci number that is a multiple of 13 (3)

9. 15 Across $\times 11 + 11$ down (3)

11. A multiple of 19 (3)

12. A square (3)

14. A multiple of 13 Across (3)

16. $5^5 + 4^5 + 7^5 + 4^5 + 8^5$ (5)

18. A factor of 10 Across (3)

19. The product of its digits is 432 (4)

20. The mean of 20 Down and 21 Down (3)

21. A power of 2 (3)

Shuttle

A1 Pass on the value of:

$$-12 \times (11 - 10 - 9) \div (7 - 6 - 5) + 4 \times (-3) \times (-2 - 1).$$

A2 *T is the number that you will receive.*

The median of a set of five different positive integers is T.
The mean of the same set of integers is $\frac{T}{2}$ greater than the median.
Pass on the value of the largest possible integer in the set.

A3 *T is the number that you will receive.*

$3(T - 8)x = 2T(x + 2) - 4(2 - 9x)$
Pass on the value of x.

A4 *T is the number that you will receive.*

A pot of paint contains enough paint to cover an area of $1800 \ \text{cm}^2$.
Write down how many pots of paint are needed to cover the surface of a cuboid with dimensions $\frac{T}{2}$ cm by $\frac{T}{3}$ cm by $\frac{T}{4}$ cm.

B1 50 Year 9 pupils were asked whether they have a bicycle or a skateboard.

> 25 said they have a bicycle,
> 20 said they have a skateboard, and
> twice as many said they have neither as said they have both.

Pass on the number of people who said they have a bicycle but not a skateboard.

B2 *T is the number that you will receive.*

Lewis has a bag containing $(T + 1)$ counters, 8 of which are red. He takes out two counters, one after the other, without replacement.
The probability that both of Lewis's counters are red is $\frac{p}{q}$, a fraction in its lowest terms.
Pass on the value of $q - 3p$.

B3   *T is the number that you will receive.*

The diagram shows triangle *ACD*. The point *B* lies on *AC* so that
AB = *AD* and *DB* = *BC*. Angle *DAB* = *T*°.

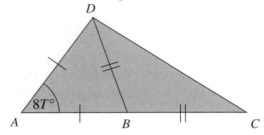

Pass on the size in degrees of angle *BCD*.

B4   *T is the number that you will receive.*

An arithmetic sequence starts 136, 128, 120, 112 …
Write down the value of the (10*T*)th term.

C1 $2\frac{3}{4} \times 4\frac{5}{6} \div 6\frac{7}{8} = \dfrac{a}{b}$

$\dfrac{a}{b}$ is a fraction in its lowest terms.
Pass on the value of $2b - a$.

C2   *T is the number that you will receive.*

The shape below consists of 12 cubes of side $\frac{1}{2}T$ cm.

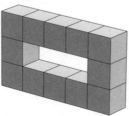

The total surface area is *A* cm².
Pass on the value of $\frac{1}{2}A$.

C3 *T is the number that you will receive.*

Evan has two shades of purple paint:

- Paint A contains red and blue paint in the ratio 1 : 3.
- Paint B contains red and blue in the ratio 2 : 3.

He makes a new shade, *Evanescence*, by mixing paints A and B together in the ratio $1 : (T - 1)$.
The ratio of red to blue paint in *Evanescence* is $a : b$, written in its lowest terms.
Pass on the value of $b - a$.

C4 *T is the number that you will receive.*

Tia's age is T times her age in T years' time minus T times her age T years ago.
Write down Tia's age.

D1 The prime factorisation of 999000 can be written as
$$2^a \times 3^b \times 5^c \times d,$$
where a, b and c are whole numbers, and d is a prime number.
Pass on the value of $d - abc$.

D2 *T is the number that you will receive.*

Evie travels a distance of T km at an average speed of x km per hour. She then travels a further $\frac{3}{2}T$ km at an average speed of $\frac{1}{2}x$ km per hour.
The whole journey takes 8 hours.
Pass on the value of x.

D3 *T is the number that you will receive.*

Jennifer has built some pyramids with T-sided polygons as their base, and some prisms with T-sided polygons as their base.

In total there are 70 edges and 44 vertices on the 3D-shapes.

Pass on the total number of 3D-shapes Jennifer has built.

D4 *T is the number that you will receive.*

A blue panther runs 20% more slowly than a black panther, but $4T\%$ more quickly than a pink panther.
A black panther runs $B\%$ more quickly than a pink panther.
Write down the value of B.

Relay

A1 Place the numbers *A*, *B* and *C* in decreasing order of size.

> | $A = \frac{7}{8}$ | $B = 0.86$ | $C = 87\%$ |

A2 What is the **next** year with digits having the same median and range as the digits of this year, 2016?

A3 A wheel makes 840 revolutions in one hour.

How long does it take in minutes, at the same rate, to complete 28 revolutions?

A4 Fifty people were stopped in the street and asked if they watched TV or listened to the radio that day.

Eight said they did neither, forty-one watched TV and six listened to the radio.

How many watched TV and also listened to the radio?

A5 A large tin has 100 sweets in it. The first person in a long queue takes 1, the second 2, the third 3, with each person taking one more sweet than the person before them.

How many sweets are left when the next person cannot take their number of sweets?

A6 The sign in a railway carriage lists the stops:

> Havant, Cosham, Portchester, Fareham, Swanwick and Southampton.

What is the median number of letters in the station names?

A7 *a*, *b*, *c* and *d* represent the numbers 2, 3, 4 and 5, but not necessarily in that order.

What is the smallest fraction with numerator (*a* + *d*) and denominator (*b* + *c*)?

A8 The fair offers a special ticket of £12 for an evening pass allowing unlimited rides. Alternatively each ride will cost £1 per person.

Four friends, Bert, Carol, Del and Eve each buy the special ticket. Carol and Eve go on 18 rides each and Bert and Del go on 9 and 14 respectively.

Altogether how much did they save by buying the special tickets?

A9   The points A (2, 1), B (5, 3), C (3, 6) and D form a square.
The square is reflected in the line $x = 4$.
What are the coordinates of the image of point D?

A10   A hiker practising compass work walks a distance of 24 metres on a bearing of 050° then 32 metres on a bearing of 140°.
Finally she returns in a straight line to her starting point.
What **total** distance has she walked?

A11   The trapezium $PQRS$ is plotted on a graph.
PQ is parallel to SR.
The trapezium has one line of symmetry,

$P = (0, 0)$	$Q = (3, 0)$	$R = (5, 5)$

What is the area of the trapezium?

A12   An official document needed the date written in the form dd/mm/yyyy.
On the 26 January this year I noticed that 4 digits were each used twice.
How many days later is the **last date** for which this happens again this year?

A13   Ann buys wool in a shop which charges her £6 for 10 balls. Sue gets her wool in a shop where £7.80 is the cost of 12 balls.
They use the same number of balls of wool to knit identical jumpers.
One of them spent 20p less than the other on the wool that she used.
How many balls of wool did they use between them?

A14   A tap is dripping constantly at 12 ml per 30 seconds. This continues until detected three hours later and stopped.
How much water was wasted in the three hours?

A15   A book containing 390 puzzles is printed with two puzzles on each page. It took Nick 17 minutes, on average, to complete one page.
How long, in hours and minutes, did it take Nick to complete the puzzle book?

B1   A rectangle with length 20 cm and width 16 cm has the same perimeter as a square.
What is the area of the square?

B2 A big box contains 100 sweets.

The first person takes one sweet, the next two, and so on, each taking twice as many as the one before.

How many sweets are left when the next person cannot take her full share?

B3 *a*, *b*, *c* and *d* represent the numbers 2, 3, 4 and 5, but not necessarily in that order.

What is the largest fraction with numerator $(a + b)$ and denominator $(c + d)$?

B4 On the first day of each month Joshua receives £7.60 pocket money. On his birthday, on 29 February, he is given a 5 % increase.

How much will he receive this year in pocket money?

B5 An office joker arranges for the office clock to run backwards from midnight on 31 March.

What time does the clock show when the manager enters the office at 08.37 on April Fool's Day (1 April)?

Use a 24-hour clock.

B6 Thirty-five students were asked to sign up for at least one of the three sports at the club. 24 signed up for squash and 16 for badminton. All the badminton players also signed up for squash. One squash player signed up for table tennis. None of the students signed up for all three.

How many students signed up for table tennis?

B7 A square *ABCD* of side 3 cm is rotated 90 degree clockwise about the point *A*, then 90 degree clockwise about the point *C*, then 90 degree clockwise about the point *B*, and finally 90 degree clockwise about the point *D*.

How far is the vertex *A* from its original position?

B8 The trapezium *ABCD* has area 16 cm^2.

AB is parallel to *DC*.

$A = (1, 1)$	$B = (3, 1)$	$C = (6, 5)$

What are the coordinates of *D*?

B9 A passenger pays for his £3.72 bus ticket and receives some change from the driver. No paper money is used by either.

What is the smallest possible number of coins used in the transaction?

B10 When 63 is divided by a positive integer x the remainder is 3.

What is the total of all the possible values of x?

B11 A new ride at the fair is a roundabout in the shape of a pentagon, with identical seats at the vertices.

In how many different ways can five friends sit around the roundabout?

B12 The swimming teacher has four sessions on Monday with between 6 and 9 students per session. She charges £18 per person for each session.

What is the difference between the least and the most she would receive for 10 Mondays?

B13 The sign in a railway carriage lists the stops:

Barnham, Chichester, Bosham, Southbourne, Emsworth and Havant.

What is the median number of letters in the station names?

B14 Kenneth began drawing a net of a square based pyramid. He got as far as drawing a rectangle x by $2x$ and dividing it into two identical squares, one of which is the base of the pyramid. One triangular face was drawn by joining the midpoint of the shorter side of the rectangle to the vertices of the base of the pyramid. The other equal triangular faces were then drawn.

What is the area of the complete net?

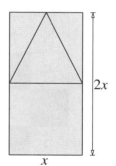

B15 Sara is practising her compass-work before an expedition in the New Forest.

She walks 84 paces on a bearing of 041°.

She then walks 35 paces on a bearing of 311°.

Finally, she walks 50 paces directly towards her starting point.

How many paces is she away from her starting point?

Solutions from the Regional Finals

Group Round Answers

1. 22
2. (a) 26; (b) 24
3. (a) 2016; (b) 2016
4. trapezium, rhombus

5. 7

6. 240
7. 250 000
8. 94
9. 59, 60, 61; 71, 72, 73
   (in either order)
10. 42 857

Crossnumber

3 [1]	6	■	1 [2]	1 [3]	■	2 [4]	4	3 [5]
3	■	6 [6]	■	2 [7]	2	4	■	4
6 [8]	6 [9]	3	0	3	■	8 [10]	0	■
■	4	■	■	3	■	0	■	2 [11]
8 [12]	8	3 [13]	3	■	2 [14]	3	5 [15]	7
5	■	3	■	1 [16]	■	■	0	■
■	5 [17]	6	■	2 [18]	2	1 [19]	0	1 [20]
2 [21]	■	3 [22]	5	2	■	5	■	2
2 [23]	1	6	■	5 [24]	3	■	1 [25]	1

Shuttle

A1	6
A2	10
A3	162
A4	33

B1	8
B2	2
B3	2016
B4	2015

C1	14
C2	7
C3	8
C4	10 000

D1	6
D2	24
D3	27
D4	243

Relay

A1	9 square units	B1	8 gloves
A2	970	B2	232
A3	22 pens	B3	98
A4	£164.25	B4	(3, 6)
A5	45°	B5	2592 cm^2
A6	141	B6	£10 200
A7	30 minutes	B7	80°
A8	10.8 metres	B8	15:50
A9	2nd March	B9	9 months
A10	97 minutes	B10	39
A11	11:22	B11	28 November
A12	6102	B12	979
A13	48 miles per gallon	B13	7086
A14	(1, 1)	B14	2 seconds
A15	$\frac{1}{2}$	B15	30 pence

Solutions from the National Final

Group Circus

1. 0.2 or $\frac{1}{5}$ or equivalent

2. (a)

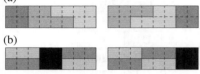

(b)

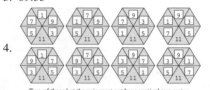

Others are possible.

3. 09:55

4.

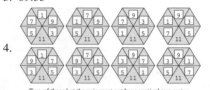

Two of these but the pair must not have vertical symmetry.

5. (a) 169 or 13^2, 196 or 14^2
   (b) 4 or 2^2, 361 or 19^2
   (c) 125 or 5^3, 216 or 6^3, 25 or 5^2

6.

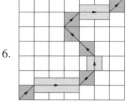

Just one example

7. (a) 16cm × 3cm
   (b) $a = 8, b = 3$

8. 36

Crossnumber

¹8	1	²6			³2	0	⁴4	
8		⁵7	8	⁶3	8	7		4
⁷9	8	7		7		⁸1	⁹8	1
8		¹⁰6	¹¹1	7	¹²4		8	
¹³8	¹⁴8		7		8		¹⁵6	¹⁶5
	8		¹⁷1	¹⁸4	4	¹⁹4		4
²⁰1	0	²¹1		4		²²2	5	7
2		²³2	6	1	2	9		4
²⁴8	4	8				²⁵6	9	8

Shuttle

A1	12
A2	62
A3	120
A4	6

B1	20
B2	9
B3	27
B4	-2016

C1	1
C2	6
C3	2
C4	8

D1	10
D2	5
D3	6
D4	55

Relay

A1	$A\,C\,B$
A2	2061
A3	2 minutes
A4	5
A5	9 sweets
A6	7.5 or $7\frac{1}{2}$ or $\frac{15}{2}$
A7	$\frac{5}{9}$
A8	£11
A9	(8, 4)
A10	96 metres
A11	25 square units
A12	315 days
A13	8
A14	4.32 litres
A15	55 hours 15 minutes

B1	324 cm^2
B2	37 sweets
B3	$\frac{9}{5}$
B4	£95.00
B5	15.23
B6	12
B7	6 cm
B8	(0, 5)
B9	5
B10	162
B11	24
B12	£2160
B13	7.5 or $7\frac{1}{2}$ or $\frac{15}{2}$
B14	$3x^2$ square units
B15	41 paces

UKMT and Further Maths Support Programme
Senior Team Maths Challenge 2016

Overview

The Senior Team Maths Challenge is now entering into its 10th year and continues to grow in size and popularity. The 2015-16 competition comprised of over 1200 schools competing in 63 Regional Finals held across the United Kingdom; a higher number of competing teams than ever before.

Each team is made up of four students from years 11, 12 and 13 (max two year 13 students per team) and the Regional Competition consists of 3 Rounds; The Group Round, the Crossnumber and the Shuttle. For the Group Round, 10 questions are answered by each team in 40 minutes, while the Crossnumber involves each team solving a mathematical version of a crossword by splitting in two to work on the 'Across' and the 'Down' clues. The competition finishes with the Shuttle, which consists of sets of four linked questions, answered in pairs against a timer.

National Final

The culmination of the competition is at the National Final in February, where the top 86 teams were invited to the Royal Horticultural Halls in London to compete for the title of 'National Champions'. Yet again, it was an exciting finale, at which the high level of energy and enthusiasm throughout the day created a wonderful celebration of mathematics.

Congratulations to all the schools who took part in the STMC National Final. These schools were:

Abingdon School	Nottingham High School
Alton College	Oakham School
Altrincham GS for Girls	Ockbrook School
Ashford School	Pocklington School
Atlantic College	Queen Elizabeth Sixth Form Coll
Backwell School	Queen Elizabeth's Boys' School
Birkdale School	Queen Mary's Grammar School
Bourne Grammar	Queen's College
Bournemouth School	Reading School
Caistor Grammar School	Reigate Grammar School
Caterham School	Robert Gordon's College
Charterhouse School	Royal Grammar School
City of London School	Royal Grammar School Guildford

Culford School

Devonport High School for Boys

Dr Challoner's Grammar School

Dulwich College

Durham Johnston Comprehensive

Dyffryn Taf School

Exeter Mathematics School

Franklin College

Friend's School Lisburn

Gillingham School

Guernsey Grammar School

Hampton School

Harris Westminster Sixth Form

Harrow School

Hills Road Sixth Form College

James Allen's Girls' School

Katharine Lady Berkeley's School

King Edward VI GS, Chelmsford

King Edward VI School

King Edward's School

King's College London Maths School

Lancaster Royal GS

Leicester Grammar School

Lime House School

Littleover Community School

Loughborough Grammar School

Marymount International School

Merchiston Castle School

Myton School

Northgate High School

Rugby School

Ruthin School

Rydal Penrhos School

Shrewsbury School

South Cheshire College

Southbank International School

St Edward's College

St Helen's School

St Mary's School, Calne

St Olaves Grammar School

Stamford School

Stonyhurst College

Strathallan School

Tapton School

The Grammar School at Leeds

The High School of Glasgow

The King Edward VI Academy

The King's School Macclesfield

The Priory Academy LSST

The Royal Grammar School

Tiffin School

Tonbridge School

Torquay Boys' Grammar School

Truro School

University College School

Wales High School

Westcliff HS for Boys Academy

Westminster School

Winstanley College

Wolverhampton Girls' High School

For 2015-16 we had a three way tie for first place from King Edward's School, Birmingham, Ruthin School and Westminster School. The Poster Competition winners were Backwell School.

The National Final consisted of the Group Round, the Crossnumber and the Shuttle with the addition of a Poster Competition at the start of the day. Teams were required to answer questions on 'Kirkman's schoolgirl problem and Steiner systems' and set these in the form of an attractive poster. Thanks to Peter Neumann, Colin Campbell, Fraser Haywood, Alexandra Hewitt and Andrew Jobbings for their hard work in preparing the materials and judging the posters. The Poster Competition did not contribute to the overall result of the National Final but a poster based on the work of the winning team has been professionally produced and printed. This will be sent to all of the schools that took part in the competition.

Thanks

As with all UKMT competitions, grateful thanks are due to all of the volunteers who wrote questions, acted as checkers for the materials produced, ran Regional Finals alongside FMSP coordinators and who helped on the day at the National Final.

The checkers of the questions were: Heather Reeve (Lead Checker), Alan Slomson, Jenny Ramsden and Martin Perkins.

The Round Rulers, who oversaw the materials for each round, were: Charles Oakley (Group round), Peter Hall (Crossnumber), Katie Ray (Shuttle) and James Cranch (Starter questions).

The writers of the questions were: Kerry Burnham, Tony Cheslett, David Crawford, Karen Fogden, James Hall, Steve Mulligan, Dennis Pinshon and Alexandra Randolph.

As ever, many thanks to everyone involved for making 2015-16 another successful year.

Regional Group Round

1   What is the largest odd number that is a factor of

$$\frac{2014 \times 2015 \times 2016}{2013 - 2014 + 2015 - 2016 + 2017} ?$$

[6 marks]

2   A second hand car dealership use boards with a four-digit digital display to show the price of their cars.

A new salesman accidentally rotated all the price signs by 180° when he placed them on the car windscreens. An example of such a rotation is shown below.

On one car, the result of the rotation represented a reduction from the intended sale price of the car of £3603. What was the intended sale price of the car?

[6 marks]

3 Consider the following crossnumber.

ACROSS   DOWN
2. A square   1. A square
4. A square   3. A square

There are four ways of completing the crossnumber using non-zero digits.

What is the greatest possible total of the six single digits in the completed grid?

[6 marks]

4 The nth term of a sequence is u_n. The sequence is defined by $u_1 = 1$ and, for each positive integer n,

$$u_{n+1} = \begin{cases} u_n + 1 & \text{if } n \text{ is odd,} \\ u_n + n & \text{if } n \text{ is even.} \end{cases}$$

What is the value of u_{100}?

[6 marks]

5

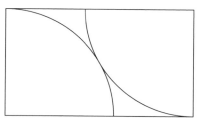

Two quarter circles, each of radius 2 units, fit inside a rectangle. The centres of the circles are opposite corners of the rectangle. What is the area, in square units, of the rectangle?

[6 marks]

6 The graph of the equation $y = x^2 - 2x$ is reflected in the line $y = 1$. The image has the equation $y = ax^2 + bx + c$. What is the value of $a + b + c$?

[6 marks]

7   In the diagram, *ABCD* is a square of area one square unit. The three additional points are defined as follows:

E lies on the line *BC* with the ratio of lengths *BE* : *EC* = 2 : 1,
F lies on the line *CD* with the ratio of lengths *CF* : *FD* = 1 : 2,
G lies on the line *DA* with the ratio of lengths *DG* : *GA* = 2 : 1.

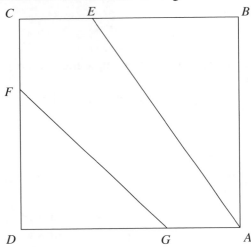

What is the area of the pentagon *AECFG*? Give your answer as a fraction in its lowest terms.

[6 marks]

8   Each of the ten different letters in *TEAM REGIONAL* stands for a different single-digit integer.

LOG is 123 and *MMM*, *MMA* and *MAT* are three consecutive integers in ascending order.

What is the value of *G* + *O* + *A* + *L*?

[6 marks]

9   Albert has forgotten the four-digit code for his padlock.

Each digit may have any value from 0 to 9 (inclusive), and digits may be repeated.

Albert recalls that:

> the first two digits form a prime number (leading zeros are allowed);
>
> the second and third digits form a two-digit square; and
>
> the third and fourth digits form a two-digit prime.

He tries 0253, but that does not work. Including 0253, how many codes are possible for Albert to try?

[6 marks]

10   Hexadecimal is a base 16 number system.

The six extra digits required are provided by letters, whose meanings are given in the following table.

Base 16	A	B	C	D	E	F
Decimal	10	11	12	13	14	15

For example, the hexadecimal number

$$\textbf{221B} = \textbf{2} \times 16^3 + \textbf{2} \times 16^2 + \textbf{1} \times 16 + \textbf{11} \times 1$$

is equivalent to the decimal number 8731.

It is claimed that

> Only **ACE** people understand hexadecimal.

Suppose that ACE is a hexadecimal number and not an adjective.

How many people are claimed to understand hexadecimal?

Give your answer in decimal form.

[6 marks]

Regional Final Crossnumber

Across

4	The number of possible arrangements of the letters in the word FINAL	(3)
6	The product of the cube of six and the cube of five	(5)
8	The sum of 11 Across, 20 Down and 21 Down	(3)
9	Eleven less than 5 Down × 4	(4)
11	A number which, when multiplied by 12 Across, is 28 less than twice 6 Across	(3)
12	The value of $n^3 + n^2 + n + 4$ where n is an integer	(3)
14	A square	(3)
15	A ninth of the square of 13 Down	(3)
16	A number which is 113 more than twice 14 Down	(4)
18	The value of yx^3, where x and y are the solutions to $\frac{4\ \text{Across}}{24}x + \frac{6\ \text{Across}}{1000}y = 150$, $\frac{1\ \text{Down}}{16}x + \frac{13\ \text{Down}}{3}y = 139$	(3)
22	A number whose digits are the first five numbers from the Fibonacci sequence (but not in order)	(5)
23	Eight times the fifth three-digit prime number	(3)

Down

1   The largest possible angle, in degrees, in an isosceles triangle with an exterior angle of 154°   (3)

2   The value of $n^3 - 2n^2 + 5n$, where n is an integer   (3)

3   The interior angle, in degrees, of a regular polygon   (3)

5   The largest prime factor of 22 Across   (4)

7   A number less than 5 Down   (4)

10   The value of $x(4y^2 + x) + 10$, where x and y are the solutions to $\frac{4 \text{ Across}}{24}x + \frac{6 \text{ Across}}{1000}y = 150, \frac{1 \text{ Down}}{16}x + \frac{13 \text{ Down}}{3}y = 139$ (3)

11   A square   (3)

12   A perfect number   (2)

13   The value of $2^5 + 0^1 + 1^0 + 6^2$ (2)

14   Eight more than a square   (4)

17   The number of possible arrangements of the letters in the word RHOMBUS   (4)

19   The product of eleven and the sum of all the prime factors of 2015   (3)

20   Twice 12 Across   (3)

21   Ten less than the interior angle, in degrees, in a regular polygon with $\sqrt[3]{6}$ Across sides   (3)

A1 The diagram shows an isosceles triangle *ABC* with *AC* = *BC*.

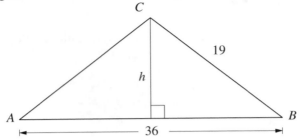

Pass on the value of the *square* of the height *h*.

A2 *T is the number that you will receive.*

The diagram shows a circle centre
O and a triangle *OPQ*.
The points *P* and *Q* lie on the
circle.
Pass on the value of *x*°.

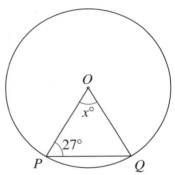

A3 *T is the number that you will receive.*

The shape shown is made from three
identical sectors with radius $\frac{1}{4}T$ and
angle $(T + 13)°$.
The perimeter can be expressed in the
form $a + b\pi$, where *a* and *b* are
integers.
Pass on the value of $a + b$.

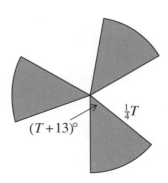

A4   *T is the number that you will receive.*

A point is initially in the position with coordinates $\left(\frac{1}{9}T, 7\right)$.
It is then reflected in the line $y = x$.
After this, it is translated 5 units to the right and 9 units vertically upwards.
The final position is (a, b).
Write down the final position (a, b).

B1   The equation

$$(2x + 1)(x + 3) = x^2 + 17x = 6$$

has solutions $x = a$ and $x = b$.
Pass on the value of $a + b$.

B2   *T is the number that you will receive.*

In the solutions to the simultaneous equations

$$6x = 2y + (3T + 6)$$
$$3x^2 + 2xy = 189$$

$x = a$ and $y = b$.
Pass on the value of $a + b$.

B3   *T is the number that you will receive.*

The diagram shows a trapezium *ABCD*.

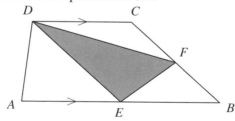

The point E lies on AB so that $AE = EB = DC$.
The point F is the midpoint of BC.
The area of the trapezium is $(7T - 1)$ cm^2.
Pass on the area in cm^2 of triangle *DEF*.

B4   *T is the number that you will receive.*

T years ago, Steve was $T - 1$ times as old as Karl.
In $\frac{1}{3}T$ years from now, Steve will be twice as old as Karl.
Write down the sum of their ages now.

C1   In the diagram, *AB* is parallel to and equal to *DC*.

The lines *AB* and *BC* are tangents to the circle.

Pass on the size of angle *ABC* in degrees.

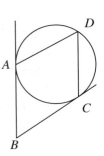

C2   *T is the number that you will receive.*

Two cylinders *A* and *B* are similar.
Cylinder *A* has surface area 108 cm^2
and volume *V* cm^3.
Cylinder *B* has surface area 48 cm^2
and volume 2*T* cm^3.
Pass on the sum of the digits of *V*.

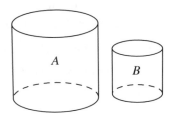

C3   *T is the number that you will receive.*

A bag contains red and blue counters.
Adding *T* − 1 red counters to the original bag would make the ratio of red counters to blue counters 2 : 1.
Adding *T* + 1 blue counters to the original bag would make the ratio of red counters to blue counters 1 : 4.
Pass on the number of counters originally in the bag.

C4   *T is the number that you will receive.*

The diagram shows the lines $y = 3x$, $y = \frac{1}{3}x$ and $x + y = 2T$.

Write down the area of the triangle enclosed by these three lines.

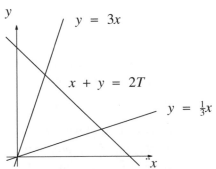

D1   The operation ✪ is defined by

$$x \text{✪} y = \frac{x + y}{x - y}.$$

Pass on the value of 9 ✪ (16 ✪ 12).

D2   *T is the number that you will receive.*

A bag contains n discs.

There are $T - 3$ red discs, $\frac{1}{2}T$ blue discs and the rest are yellow.

I choose a disc from the bag but do not replace it; I then choose another disc.

The probability that I choose either 2 red discs or 2 blue discs is $\frac{8}{33}$.

Pass on the value of n.

D3   *T is the number that you will receive.*

I have two solids: a sphere of radius T cm and a cylinder of height 10 cm and radius R cm.

The surface area of the sphere is twice the total surface area of the cylinder.

Pass on the value of R.

{*Note*: The surface area of a sphere with radius r is $4\pi r^2$.}

D4   *T is the number that you will receive.*

The expression

$$T^{-\frac{2}{3}} + (2T)^{-\frac{3}{2}} + 27^{-\frac{2}{3}}$$

can be written as $\frac{a}{b}$, where a and b are positive integers that have no common factors except 1.

Write down the fraction $\frac{a}{b}$.

Group Round answers

1.	63 441	**6.**	3
2.	6562	**7.**	$\frac{4}{9}$
3.	35	**8.**	15
4.	2501	**9.**	26
5.	$4\sqrt{3}$	**10.**	2766

Crossnumber: Completed grid

[1] 1	■	[2] 1	■	[3] 1	■	■	[4] 1	[5] 2	0
[6] 2	7	0	0	0	■	[7] 1	■	0	■
8	■	0	■	[8] 8	8	8	■	8	■
■	■	■	■	■	■	[9] 8	3	1	[10] 3
[11] 2	0	6	■	[12] 2	[13] 6	2	■	■	1
2	■	■	[14] 2	8	9	■	[15] 5	2	9
[16] 5	[17] 5	3	7	■	■	■	■	■	■
■	0	■	[18] 1	3	[19] 5	■	[20] 5	■	[21] 1
■	4	■	2	■	[22] 3	1	2	1	5
[23] 9	0	4	■	■	9	■	4	■	8

Shuttle answers

A1	**37**
A2	**32**
A3	**54**
A4	**(12,15)**

B1	**10**
B2	**4**
B3	**9**
B4	**36**

C1	**60**
C2	**9**
C3	**10**
C4	**100**

D1	**8**
D2	**12**
D3	**8**
D4	$\frac{217}{576}$

1   A right-angled triangle has hypotenuse of length 2080 and a shorter side of length 2016. The third side has length 2^n. What is the value of n?

[6 marks]

2   (a) What is the least positive integer which leaves remainder 1 when divided by 7 and remainder 2 when divided by 11?

[3 marks]

   (b) What is the least positive integer which leaves remainder 1 when divided by 7, remainder 2 when divided by 11 and remainder 3 when divided by 13?

[3 marks]

3   *ABCD* is a square with side length 1. A semi-circle with diameter *CD* is drawn on the interior of *ABCD* as shown. The point *E* on *DA* is such that line *BE* is a tangent to the semi-circle.

What is the area of the triangle *ABE*?

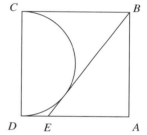

[6 marks]

4   Anya, Boris, Chiara and Derek played 'two-a-side' football in the park. In each round one team, made up of two attackers, tries to score a goal. The other team, made up of one defender and one goalkeeper, tries to stop them. They played a series of rounds with each round ending after a goal was scored. The player who scored the goal became the goalkeeper in the next round with the other positions determined at random.

When they stopped playing, Anya had been the goalkeeper nine times, Boris had not been the goalkeeper in thirteen of the rounds, Chiara had not been the goalkeeper in fourteen of the rounds and Derek had been an attacker in sixteen rounds but never played as defender.

   (a) How many rounds were played altogether?   [3 marks]
   (b) Who scored the goal in the sixth round?   [3 marks]

5   A rectangular piece of paper has its corners at A, B, C and D. The length of CD is 12 cm. The paper is folded so that the corner that was at A now coincides with C to form the pentagon $B'CDEF$, as shown. The length of EF is 15 cm.

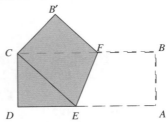

What is the perimeter of the pentagon $B'CDEF$, in cm?

[6 marks]

6

a	b	c
d	e	f
g	h	i

The letters a to i represent the numbers 1 to 9 in some order. Each letter represents a different number such that:

$a + b + c > d + e + f > g + h + i$;

e is a prime factor of g;

$f > a$;

$b + g = h$;

$i \neq 1$.

Find the values of a, b, c, d, e, f, g, h and i. Give your answer in the form '$abcdefghi$'.

[6 marks]

7   (a)   Ernie is celebrating his 18th birthday today. He notices his age is a factor of 2016.

In what year is the next time that his age on his birthday is a factor of the year?

[3 marks]

(b)   Frida and Graham (both younger than 80 years in age) realise that if they write their two-digit ages next to each other (Frida's first), they form a four-digit square. Graham realises that they will be able to achieve a similar feat in exactly 17 years' time.

How old is Frida?

[3 marks]

8   Incapability Green has a set of five square lawns around two seating areas that are right-angled triangles in shape and two triangular flowerbeds. One of the seating areas is bounded by a square pond and the two smallest lawns.

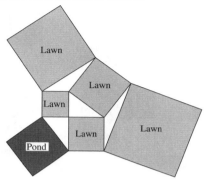

The total area of the five lawns is 2016 m². What is the area of the pond in m²?

[6 marks]

9   (a)   Using the digits 0, 1, 2, 3, 4 and 5 no more than once each, how many five-digit even numbers can be formed?

[3 marks]

(b)   What is the sum of all four-digit integers whose digits are all odd numbers?

[3 marks]

10   A two-digit Keith number '*ab*' is a number that appears in the sequence generated from the recurrence relation:

$$u_{n+2} = u_{n+1} + u_n \text{ for } n \geqslant 1$$
$$u_1 = a, \qquad u_2 = b.$$

For example, 14 is a Keith Number since 14 appears in the sequence 1, 4, 5, 9, 14, 23, ... In fact, 14 is the first Keith Number.

The third Keith number is 28.

Coincidentally, the fourth Keith Number is the sum of the second and third Keith numbers.

What is the fourth Keith number?

[*Note*: Mike Keith introduced Keith numbers in 1987; he was an American mathematician and software designer.]

[6 marks]

Across

1. The value of u^2, where u and v are the solutions to
$$\frac{21 \text{ Across}}{5}u + \frac{12 \text{ Down}}{25}v = 478, \quad \frac{5 \text{ Down}}{25}u + \frac{3 \text{ Across}}{125}v = 1740 \qquad (3)$$

3. $\left(\sqrt[3]{21 \text{ Across}} \times \sqrt[3]{12 \text{ Down}}\right)$ (4)

6. The obtuse angle, in degrees, between the lines $y = x$ and $y = (\tan 60°)x$ (3)

8. N more than the sum of the interior angles, in degrees, of a regular polygon with N sides   (4)

10. $\sqrt{12 \text{ Down} \times 9 \text{ Down}}$ (3)

11. The value of p^{p-1} where p is a prime number   (3)

13. Nine more than a square   (4)

16. A number such that the sum of all six digits in its row is a multiple of nine   (4)

19. Larger than a fifth of 7 Down (3)

21. A cube (3)

22. Four less than the sum of a square and three times the lowest common multiple of 12 Down and 21 Across (4)

23. The sum of 600 and the smallest three-digit factor of 18 Down (3)

24. A value of $r^2 + (6 \text{ Across})r + 21$ where $r < 13$ is a positive integer (4)

25. The integer part of $\dfrac{4000}{\sqrt{9 \text{ Down}}}$ (3)

Down

2. Larger than 1 Across × 5 (3)

3. The difference between 3 Across times ten and 18 Down (5)

4. N^2 more than the sum of the interior angles, in degrees, of a regular polygon with N sides (4)

5. The value of $3z^2$, where $z = 4\sqrt{11 \text{ Across}} \times 3\sqrt{21 \text{ Across}}$ (4)

7. The product of the second two-digit prime and the third odd square (3)

9. The value of v^2, where u and v are the solutions to $\dfrac{21 \text{ Across}}{5}u + \dfrac{12 \text{ Down}}{25}v = 478, \quad \dfrac{5 \text{ Down}}{25}u + \dfrac{3 \text{ Across}}{125}v = 1740$ (3)

12. $\dfrac{9}{125}$ of 20 Down (3)

14. The integer part of $\dfrac{\sqrt{2000}}{\sqrt{1 \text{ Across}}}$ (3)

15. The value of $10e + f + 22$ where $e = 13$ Across and $f = 11$ Across (5)

17. A prime factor of 8 Across (3)

18. The value of $\dfrac{5(a^2 - 29a + 154)}{a - 7}$ where $a = 12$ Down (4)

19. The obtuse angle, in degrees, between the lines $x = 2$ and $y = (\tan 60°)x$ (3)

20. The value of p^p where p is a prime number (4)

22. A number so that the sum of all six digits in its column is two more than a multiple of nine (3)

Shuttle

A1 p and q are two different primes greater than 25.

Pass on the least possible value of $p + q$.

A2 *T is the number that you will receive.*

The digit sum of 78 is 15 because $7 + 8 = 15$.

Pass on the number of positive integers less than $T + 36$ which have a digit sum of 14.

A3 *T is the number that you will receive.*

A circle has an area of $T\pi$.

Pass on the area of the largest square which can be drawn inside the circle.

A4 *T is the number that you will receive.*

Four identical circles are touching inside a rectangle, as shown.

The radius of each circle is $\dfrac{T}{10}$.

Write down the perimeter of the rectangle in the form $a + b\sqrt{c}$ where a and b are integers and c is a prime number.

B1 The expression

$$\frac{5!}{6} \times \frac{5}{4!} \div \frac{4}{3!} - \frac{3}{2!} + \frac{1!}{2}$$

can be simplified to the fraction $\dfrac{a}{b}$, where a and b are positive integers with no common factors.

Pass on the value of $a + b$.

[*Note*: $n!$ stands for the *factorial* of n, that is,
$n \times (n - 1) \times (n - 2) \times \ \dots \ \times 2 \times 1$.]

B2 *T is the number that you will receive.*

Simplify $\sqrt{8} + \sqrt{108} \div \sqrt{6} + \sqrt{6} \times \sqrt{3T}$ into the form $a\sqrt{b}$, where a is an integer and b is a prime number.

Pass on the value of a.

B3   *T is the number that you will receive.*

An irregular octagon has three of its *exterior* angles each equal to $2T°$ and another four each equal to $(3T - 5)°$.
The largest *interior* angle of the octagon is $A°$.
Pass on the value of A.

B4   *T is the number that you will receive.*

The volume of a large vase is 500 cm³ and its surface area is $(T + 40)$ cm².
The volume of a similar vase is 108 cm³ and its surface area is A cm².
Write down the value of A.

C1   In the pentagon *ABCDE*, *AB* is parallel to *DC*, $\angle DEA = \angle ABC$ and $\angle CDE$ is 40° larger than $\angle EAB$.
Also, $\angle EAB$ is twice as large as $\angle DEA$.

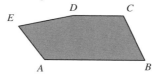

Pass on the size, in degrees, of $\angle BCD$.

C2   *T is the number that you will receive.*

A is the number of positive integers strictly less than $\dfrac{T}{2}$ that are cubes.

B is the number of positive integers strictly less than $\dfrac{T + 1}{3}$ that are triangular numbers.

C is the number of positive integers strictly less than $\dfrac{T}{4}$ that are primes.

Pass on the value of $A + B + C$.

C3 *T is the number that you will receive.*

x	A	B
T	1	5
$T + 5$	2	4
$T + 10$	3	3
$2T$	4	2
50	5	1

When the frequencies are given by column A, the mean value of x is X greater than the mean value of x when the frequencies are given by column B.

Pass on the value of X.

C4 *T is the number that you will receive.*

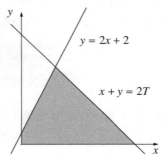

Write down the area of the shaded region.

D1 The point $(1, 2)$ is reflected in the line $y = 5 - x$ and its image is the point (a, b).

The point (a, b) is then rotated $90°$ anticlockwise about the point $(2, 2)$ and its image is the point (c, d).

Pass on the value of $a + b + c + d$.

D2   *T is the number that you will receive.*

p and *q* are distinct integers which are the solutions of a quadratic equation of the form

$$x^2 - ax + T^2 = 0$$

where *a* is some number.

Pass on the least possible value of the difference between *p* and *q*.

D3   *T is the number that you will receive.*

O is the centre of the circle and *B*, *D* and *E* lie on the circle.

Lines *BC* and *DC* are tangents to the circle and *OE* is parallel to *BC*.

$\angle BCD = 2T° + 10°$.

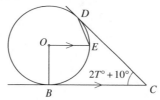

Pass on the size, in degrees, of $\angle CDE$.

D4   *T is the number that you will receive.*

ABCD is a trapezium in which *AB* is parallel to *DC*. The sides *AD* and *DC* are both of length $(T - 1)$ cm. $\angle DAB = 30°$ and $\angle ABC = 45°$.

Write down the area of the trapezium, in cm², in the form $a + b\sqrt{c}$ where *a* and *b* are integers and *c* is a prime number.

Group Round answers

1.	9	6.	719 628 453
2.	(a) 57 (b) 211	7.	(a) 2025 (b) 17
3.	$\frac{3}{8}$ or 0.375 or equivalent	8.	288
4.	(a) 17 (b) Anya	9.	(a) 312 (b) 3 471 875
5.	46	10.	47

Crossnumber: Completed grid

Shuttle answers

A1	60
A2	5
A3	10
A4	$14+2\sqrt{3}$

B1	25
B2	20
B3	160
B4	72

C1	116
C2	20
C3	10
C4	146

D1	10
D2	15
D3	25
D4	$360+72\sqrt{3}$

Other aspects of the UKMT

As well as the Maths Challenges, the UKMT is involved in other events and activities.

Enriching Mathematical Thinking
UKMT Teacher Meetings 2016

Six teacher meetings were held this year: Belfast (W5, Belfast), Cambridge (CMS, University of Cambridge), Cardiff (Cardiff City Hall), Edinburgh (University of Edinburgh), Greenwich (University of Greenwich) and Leeds (University of Leeds).

Around 300 teachers attended the one-day events. Each meeting featured three sessions with lunch and refreshment breaks and delegates received a resource pack and CPD certificate to take back to the classroom.

NRICH (www.nrich.maths.org.uk) gave sessions at all six meetings and we are grateful to Charlie Gilderdale, Alison Kiddle and Becky Warren for the excellent quality of these sessions and the accompanying resources.

Colin Wright captured the imagination of the audience with his session on *'Maths in a Twist: Mobius Strips'* at Belfast and Leeds, Katie Steckles got the delegates discussing *'Topology, Shape and Problem Solving'* at Greenwich and Cambridge, Matt Parker got the audience working with paper and scissors to discover *'The Magic of Mathematics'* at Cardiff and Ben Sparks talked energetically about *'The Creation of Number'* at Edinburgh.

UKMT volunteers led a session at each event demonstrating the mathematical thinking behind the questions used in the UKMT Challenges and how UKMT materials can be used to stimulate classroom interest. The 2016 speakers were Lizzie Kimber, Gerry Leversha, Steven O'Hagan, Steve Mulligan, Stephen Power, and Dominic Rowland.

We are very grateful to our host venues and to all UKMT volunteers who assisted with these events.

Mathematical Circles

The Mathematical Circles developed from two trial events in spring 2012. Following on from the success of these we have since significantly expanded the programme.

Local schools are invited to select two students from Year 10 (or S3 in Scotland) to send to the two-day events, which are comprised of mathematically demanding work through topics such as geometry, proof and modular arithmetic. Students have the opportunity to discuss mathematics and make new friends from other schools around their region. Our thanks go to the following people who ran the 2015-16 events, and to the schools who supported these:

Exeter, Exeter Mathematics School, run by Kerry Burnham

Glasgow, Govan High School, run by Dorothy Winn

Gloucester, Wycliffe School, run by Mark Dennis

Leeds, University of Leeds, run by Alan Slomson

London West, St Pauls School, run by Dominic Rowland

Manchester, University of Manchester, run by Alan Slomson

Rickmansworth, Royal Masonic School, run by Sue Cubbon

Wells, Wells Cathedral School, run by Susie Jameson

Weymouth, All Saints School, run by Tony Gardiner

Winchester, St Swithun's School, run by Stephen Power

Thanks are also given to those people who ran sessions (a list of which is given in the Volunteers section of the Yearbook).

Mathematical Circles are being held throughout the next academic year. If you would like to find out more about how you can become involved in the Mathematical Circles, either through your school hosting an event or by supporting us in running a session, please do contact us at enquiry@ukmt.org.uk.

Primary Team Maths Resources

In recognition and support of the growing number of secondary schools organising and hosting local team maths events for their feeder schools, UKMT developed a set of Primary Team Maths Resources (PTMR) intended for use at such events. The first ever PTMR were made available free of charge in spring 2012. At the start of each calendar year, a new set of material has since been made available.

Schools may choose to use the materials in other ways, e.g. a primary school may use the materials to run a competition for their own Year 5 and 6 pupils (and equivalent), or a secondary school may use the materials as an end of term activity for their Year 7 pupils.

The PTMR include more materials than would be needed for any one competition, allowing schools to pick and choose those most appropriate for their purposes. Some of the rounds are familiar from the UKMT Team Challenges (the Group Round, Crossnumber, Relay and Mini Relay) and the material includes some new rounds (the Logic Round, Make a Number, Open Ended Questions, and Speed Test).

The 2016 PTMR and full instructions for suggested use is available by contacting the UKMT via email at enquiry@ukmt.org.uk. Further details including sample and past materials can be found on our website at http://www.ukmt.org.uk/team-challenges/primary-team-maths-resources/

Best in School Events

Since 2007, the UKMT has partnered with the Royal Institution to invite top scoring IMC candidates to attend RI masterclass celebration events, held in the summer term. These events give students from Year 9 and S3, and sometimes Year 12, the opportunity to attend inspiring lectures, meet mathematicians from their local area, and have a go at 'hands-on' mathematics.

In 2016, these events took place in Bath, Edinburgh, Liverpool, London (Year 9 and Year 12 events), Newcastle, and Plymouth.

Website – www.ukmt.org.uk

Visit the UKMT website for information about all the UKMT activities, including the Maths Challenges, team events, latest UKMT news and newsletters, contact details, and to purchase publications and past papers.

There are online resources featuring past questions from the Challenges, mentoring questions, and sample Primary Team Maths Challenge materials. Also links to sponsors, supporters and other mathematical bodies providing further resources for young mathematicians.

Other similar bodies overseas

The UKMT has links of varying degrees of formality with several similar organisations in other countries. It is also a member of the World Federation of National Mathematics Competitions (WFNMC). What follows is a brief description of some of these other organisations. Some of the information is taken from the organisations' web sites but a UK slant has been applied.

"Association Kangourou sans Frontières"

http://www.aksf.org/

The obvious question is: why Kangaroo? The name was given in tribute to the pioneering efforts of the Australian Mathematics Trust. The Kangaroo contest is run by local organisers in each country under the auspices of the 'Association Kangourou sans Frontières', which was founded by a small group of countries in 1991. There are now over 50 countries involved and more than six million participants throughout Europe and beyond, from the UK to Mongolia and from Norway to Cyprus.

In the UK in 2016, over 7000 children in the years equivalent to English Years 9, 10 and 11 took part in the 'Cadet' and 'Junior' levels of the Kangaroo competition, as a follow-up to the Intermediate Maths Challenge. Four representatives of the UK Mathematics Trust, Andrew Jobbings, Paul Murray, Rachel Greenhalgh and David Crawford, attended the meeting in Sweden, at which these Kangaroo papers were constructed.

The main objective of the Kangaroo, like all the competitions described in this section, is to stimulate and motivate large numbers of pupils, as well as to contribute to the development of a mathematical culture which will be accessible to, and enjoyed by, many children and young people. The Association also encourages cross-cultural activities; in some countries, for example, prize-winners are invited to attend a mathematics 'camp' with similar participants from other nations.

The Australian Mathematics Trust

www.wfnmc.org

For over twenty-five years, the Australian Mathematics Competition has been one of the major events on the Australian Education Calendar, with about one in three Australian secondary students entering each year to test their skills. That's over half a million participants a year.

The Competition commenced in 1978 under the leadership of the late Professor Peter O'Halloran, of the University of Canberra, after a successful pilot scheme had run in Canberra for two years.

The questions are multiple-choice and students have 75 minutes in which to answer 30 questions. There are follow-up rounds for high scorers.

In common with the other organisations described here, the AMC also extends its mathematical enrichment activities by publishing high quality material which can be used in the classroom.

Whilst the AMC provides students all over Australia with an opportunity to solve the same problems on the same day, it is also an international event, with most of the countries of the Pacific and South-East Asia participating, as well as a few schools from further afield. New Zealand and Singapore each enter a further 30,000 students to help give the Competition an international flavour.

World Federation of National Mathematics Competitions – WFNMC

www.amt.canberra.edu.au/wfnmc.html

The Federation was created in 1984 during the Fifth International Congress for Mathematical Education.

The Federation aims to provide a focal point for those interested in, and concerned with, conducting national mathematics competitions for the purpose of stimulating the learning of mathematics. Its objectives include:

- Serving as a resource for the exchange of information and ideas on mathematics competitions through publications and conferences.
- Assisting with the development and improvement of mathematics competitions.

- Increasing public awareness of the role of mathematics competitions in the education of all students and ensuring that the importance of that role is properly recognised in academic circles.
- Creating and enhancing professional links between mathematicians involved in competitions around the world.

The World Federation of National Mathematics Competitions is an organisation of national mathematics competitions affiliated as a Special Interest Group of the International Commission for Mathematical Instruction (ICMI).

It administers a number of activities, including

- The Journal *Mathematics Competitions*
- An international conference every four years.
- David Hilbert and Paul Erdős Awards for mathematicians prominent on an international or national scale in mathematical enrichment activities.

The UKMT sent two delegates, Tony Gardiner and Bill Richardson, to the WFNMC conference in Zhong Shan in 1998 and provided support for several delegates who attended ICME 9 in Tokyo in August 2000, at which the WFNMC provided a strand.

In August 2002, the WFNMC held another conference, similar to the one in 1998. The venue for this was Melbourne, Victoria. On this occasion, the UKMT provided support for two delegates: Howard Groves and Bill Richardson.

In July 2006, WFNMC 5 was held in the UK at Robinson College, Cambridge. This event was a tremendous success with around 100 delegates from many parts of the world.

In July 2008, WFNMC had a strand at ICME 11 in Mexico. UKMT was represented by Bill Richardson.

In July 2010, WFNMC 6 was held in Riga. The UKMT was represented by Howard Groves, Dean Bunnell, David Crawford and James Welham.

In July 2014, WFNMC 7 was held in Colombia. The UKMT was represented by David Crawford.

Lists of volunteers involved in the UKMT's activities

UKMT officer bearers

Chair:	Professor Chris Budd
Secretary:	Dr Alan Eames-Jones
Treasurer:	Dr David Crawford

The Council

Mrs Anne Baker	Professor John Brindley
Professor Chris Budd (from April 2016)	Dr Colin Campbell
Dr Katie Chicot	Dr James Cranch
Dr David Crawford	Mr Robert Cresswell
Mr Alex Crews (to April 2016)	Dr Ceri Fiddes (to April 2016)
Mrs Karen Fogden	Mr James Gazet (from April 2016)
Mr Karl Hayward-Bradley (to April 2016)	Professor Frances Kirwan
Dr Gerry Leversha (from April 2016)	Prof. Adam McBride (to April 2016)
Mr Steve Mulligan	Dr Vicky Neale (from November 2015)
Miss Jenny Ramsden	Mr Bill Richardson (Vice-Chair)
Professor Alastair Rucklidge	Dr Geoff Smith (Vice-Chair)

Members of the Trust who are not on the Council or members of a Subtrust

The Mathematical Association	The Royal Institution	Mr Dennis Archer
Mr Richard Atkins	Dr Roger Bray	Mr Dean Bunnell
Dr Don Collins	Dr Diane Crann	Mr G de Sainte Croix
Dr Alan Eames-Jones	Dr Tony Gardiner	Mr Terry Heard
Mrs Margaret Jackson	Mrs Susie Jameson-Petvin	Dr Andrew Jobbings
Dr Vinay Kathotia	Mr Graham Keniston-Cooper	
Mrs Patricia King	Professor Tom Körner	Mr Nick Lord
Mr Tony Mann	Mr Dennis Orton	Mr Peter Ransom
Dr Adrian Sanders	Dr Sara Santos	Prof. Bernard Silverman
Dr John Silvester	Mr Robert Smart	Dr Brian Stewart
Mr Peter Thomas	Mr Alex Voice	Mr James Welham
Mr Brian Wilson	Ms Mary Wimbury	

The Subtrusts

British Mathematical Olympiad Subtrust

Dr Geoff Smith (Chair)

Dr James Cranch	Dr Ceri Fiddes	Mr James Gazet
Dr Vesna Kadelberg (Secretary)	Professor Imre Leader	Dr Joseph Myers
Dr Vicky Neale	Mr Dominic Yeo	

246

Team Maths Challenge Subtrust

Mr Steve Mulligan (Chair)

Mr Karl Hayward-Bradley

Miss Pam Hunt (Statistician)

Mr Martin Perkins (Treasurer)

Mr Alex Crews

Mr Fraser Heywood

Dr Peter Neumann (Secretary)

Mrs Heather Reeve

Challenges Subtrust

Mr Bill Richardson (Chair)

Professor John Brindley (Treasurer)

Mrs Karen Fogden

Mr Carl James

Professor Adam McBride

Mrs Mary Read

Miss Jenny Ramsden (Secretary)

Dr Alan Slomson

Mrs Anne Baker

Dr David Crawford

Mr Howard Groves

Dr Calum Kilgour

Mr Paul Murray

Mr Stephen Power

Professor Chris Robson

Enrichment Subtrust

Dr Vicky Neale (Chair)

Mrs Mary Teresa Fyfe (Secretary)

Miss Jenny Ramsden

Dr Katie Chicot

Mr Stephen Power

Dr Alan Slomson

Other Committees

Finance and General Purposes Committee

Professor Chris Budd

Dr Alan Eames-Jones

Professor Adam McBride (to April 2016)

Mr Bill Richardson

Mrs Rachel Greenhalgh (UKMT Director)

Dr David Crawford

Professor Frances Kirwan (to April 2016)

Mr Stephen Mulligan

Dr Geoff Smith

Mr Graham Keniston-Cooper (Observer)

Nominations Committee

Dr Katie Chicot (Chair)

Mrs Mary Teresa Fyfe

Professor Chris Budd

Mr Stephen Mulligan

Publications Committee

Dr Gerry Leversha (Chair)

Mr Nick Lord

Mr James Gazet

Mr Mark Strutt

Investment Committee

Mr Graham Keniston-Cooper (Chair)

Mrs Rachel Greenhalgh

Professor Adam McBride

Dr David Crawford

Mr Paul Jeffreys

Members of the BMOS Extended Committee

Robin Bhattacharyya (Loughborough GS)
Mary Teresa Fyfe (ex Hutchesons' GS)
Ben Green (Trinity College, Cambridge)
Jeremy King (Tonbridge School)
Gerry Leversha (ex St Paul's School)
David Monk (ex Edinburgh University)
Peter Neumann (Queen's Coll., Oxford)
Adrian Sanders (ex Trinity College, Camb.)
Alan West (ex Leeds University)

Philip Coggins (ex Bedford School)
James Gazet (Eton College)
Andrew Jobbings (Arbelos)
Patricia King (ex Benenden School, Kent)
Adam McBride (Uni. of Strathclyde)
Joseph Myers (CodeSourcery)
Alan Pears (ex King's College, London)
Zhivko Stoyanov (University of Bath)
Brian Wilson (ex Royal Holloway, London)

BMOS Markers

James Aaronson (Trinity Coll, Cambridge)
Natalie Behague (Trinity Coll, Cambridge)
Robin Bhattacharrya (Loughborough GS)
Sam Cappleman-Lynes (Trin. Coll, Cam.)
James Cranch (University of Sheffield)
Ceri Fiddes (Millfield School)
Daniel Griller (Hampton School)
Karl Hayward-Bradley (Wellington Coll.)
Tim Hennock (Jane Street Capital)
Daniel Hu (Trinity Coll, Cambridge)
Freddie Illingworth (Trinity Coll, Cam.)
Andrew Jobbings (Arbelos)
Sahl Khan (Trinity Coll, Cambridge)
Gordon Lessells (University of Limerick)
Sam Maltby (New Vision)
David Mestel (Trinity Coll, Cambridge)
Joseph Myers (CodeSourcery, Inc)
David Phillips (Trinity Coll, Cambridge)
Linden Ralph (Trinity Coll, Cambridge)
Paul Russell (Churchill Coll., Cambridge)
Karthik Tadinada (St Paul's School)
Jerome Watson (Bedford School)

Ben Barrett (Trinity Coll, Cambridge)
Alexander Betts (Trinity Coll, Cambridge)
Florence Cappleman-Lynes (Trin. Coll, Cam.)
Philip Coggins (ex Bedford School)
Tim Cross (KES, Birmingham)
Richard Freeland (Trinity Coll, Cam.)
Stuart Haring (Haberdashers' Aske's Boys S.)
Adrian Hemery (St Paul's School)
Maria Holdcroft (Queen's Coll, Oxford)
Ina Hughes (University of Leeds)
Ian Jackson (Tonbridge School)
Vesna Kadelburg (Stephen Perse Found.)
Jeremy King (Tonbridge Sch)
Gerry Leversha (ex St Paul's School)
Matei Mandache (Trinity Coll, Cambridge)
Jordan Millar (Trinity Coll, Cambridge)
Roger Patterson (Sevenoaks School)
Eve Pound (Cambridge)
Dominic Rowland (St Paul's School)
Geoff Smith (Uni. of Bath)
Kasia Warburton (Trinity Coll, Cambridge)

MOG Markers

Emily Bain (Cambridge)
Natalie Behague (Trinity Coll, Cambridge)
Andrew Carlotti (Trinity Coll, Cambridge)
Philip Coggins (ex Bedford Sch)
James Cranch (University of Sheffield)
Tim Cross (King Edward's Birmingham)
Paul Fannon (The Stephen Perse Found.)
Richard Freeland (Trinity Coll, Cambridge)
Gabriel Gendler (Trinity Coll, Cambridge)
Adam Goucher (Trinity Coll, Cambridge)
Daniel Hu (Trinity Coll, Cambridge)
Magdalena Jasicova (Cambridge)
Andrew Jobbings (Arbelos)
Vesna Kadelburg (Stephen Perse Found.)
Sam Maltby (New Vision)
Matei Mandache (Trinity Coll, Cambridge)
David Mestel (Trinity Coll, Cambridge)
Joseph Myers (CodeSourcery, Inc.)
Vicky Neale (University of Oxford)
Peter Neumann (ex Queen's Coll, Oxford)
Sylvia Neumann (Oxford)
Martin Orr (University College London)
Roger Patterson (Sevenoaks School)
David Phillips (Trinity Coll, Cambridge)
Linden Ralph (Trinity Coll., Cambridge)
Katya Richards (Trinity Coll, Cambridge)
Kasia Warburton (Trinity Coll, Cambridge)
Jerome Watson (Bedford School)
Joanna Yass (St Catherine's Coll, Cambridge)

Markers for IMOK and JMO

Anne Baker	(Conyers School, Stockton-on-Tees)	IMOK
Dean Bunnell	(ex Queen Elizabeth GS, Wakefield)	IMOK / JMO
Magdalena Burrows	(Kent)	IMOK
Valerie Chapman	(Northwich)	IMOK
Daniel Clark	(University of Oxford)	IMOK
Philip Coggins	(ex Bedford School)	IMOK / JMO
James Cranch	(University of Sheffield)	IMOK / JMO
David Crawford	(Leicester Grammar School)	IMOK / JMO
Tim Cross	(KES, Birmingham)	IMOK
Sue Cubbon	(St Albans, Herts)	IMOK
Wendy Dersley	(Southwold)	IMOK
David Forster	(Oratory School)	IMOK
Mary Teresa Fyfe	(Hutchesons' Grammar School, Glasgow)	IMOK / JMO
Carol Gainlall	(Park House School, Newbury)	IMOK / JMO
Gwyn Gardiner	(ex King Edward's School, Birmingham)	JMO
Tony Gardiner	(Birmingham)	IMOK / JMO
Michael Griffiths	(Warrington)	IMOK
Howard Groves	(ex RGS, Worcester)	JMO
James Hall	(Harrow School)	IMOK
Stuart Haring	(Haberdashers' Aske's Boys Sch)	IMOK
Hugh Hill	(Winchester College)	IMOK
Maria Holdcroft	(Queen's College, Oxford)	IMOK

Ian Jackson	(Tonbridge School)	IMOK
Carl James	(Leicester Grammar School)	IMOK
Susie Jameson-Petvin	(Wells Cathedral School)	IMOK
Andrew Jobbings	(Arbelos, Shipley)	IMOK / JMO
David Knipe	(Cambridge)	IMOK
Gerry Leversha	(ex-St Paul's School)	IMOK
Nick Lord	(Tonbridge School)	IMOK
Sam Maltby	(Sheffield)	IMOK / JMO
Matthew Miller	(Germany)	IMOK
Linda Moon	(The Glasgow Academy)	IMOK
Phil Moon	(The High School of Glasgow)	IMOK
Joseph Myers	(CodeSourcery, Inc.)	IMOK
Peter Neumann	(The Queen's College, Oxford)	IMOK
Sylvia Neumann	(Oxford)	IMOK
Steven O'Hagan	(Hutchesons' Grammar School,Glasgow)	IMOK / JMO
Roger Patterson	(Sevenoaks School)	IMOK
Jenny Perkins	(Torbridge High School, Plymouth)	IMOK / JMO
David Philips	(St Albans)	IMOK / JMO
Eve Pound	(Cambridge)	IMOK
Stephen Power	(St Swithuns School, Winchester)	IMOK / JMO
Catherine Ramsay	(Hutchesons' Grammar School)	IMOK / JMO
Jenny Ramsden	(High Wycombe)	IMOK / JMO
Christine Randall	(Southampton)	IMOK
Alexandra Randolph	(North London Collegiate School)	IMOK
Peter Ransom	(Southampton)	IMOK / JMO
Chris Robson	(ex University of Leeds)	IMOK
Fiona Shen	(Queen Ethelburga's College, York)	IMOK / JMO
Alan Slomson	(University of Leeds)	IMOK / JMO
Anne Strong	(St Anne's School, Guernsey)	IMOK
Alex Voice	(Westminster Abbey Choir School, London)	JMO
Christopher Walker	(Cumnor House School)	IMOK
Paul Walter	(Highgate School, London)	IMOK
David Webber	(University of Glasgow)	JMO
Rosie Wiltshire	(Wootton Bassett School)	IMOK / JMO

Problems Groups

There are currently eight groups. The first being the BMO Setting Committee.

Jeremy King (Chair) (Tonbridge School)

Alexander Betts (Trinity College, Cambridge) Daniel Griller (Hampton School)

Paul Jefferys (ex Trinity College, Cambridge) Gerry Leversha (ex St Paul's School)

Dominic Rowland (St Paul's School)   Geoff Smith (University of Bath)

The other seven groups have overlapping membership. There is one group for each and the chair is shown in []: the Senior Mathematical Challenge (S) [Karen Fogden]; the Junior and Intermediate Mathematical Challenges (I&J) [Howard Groves]; the Junior Mathematical Olympiad (JMO) [Mary Teresa Fyfe]; the IMOK Olympiad papers [Andrew Jobbings]; the Intermediate Kangaroo (IK) [David Crawford and Paul Murray]; Senior Kangaroo (SK) [Carl James] and the Junior Kangaroo (JK) [David Crawford]. Those involved are listed below.

Steve Barge	(Sacred Heart Catholic College)	S
Dean Bunnell	(ex Queen Elizabeth GS, Wakefield)	S / IMOK / JMO
James Cranch	(University of Sheffield)	IMOK
David Crawford	(Leicester Grammar School)	JK / IK / I&J
Karen Fogden	(Henry Box School, Witney)	S / I&J / JMO
Mary Teresa Fyfe	(Hutchesons' GS, Glasgow)	S / IMOK / JMO
Carol Gainlall	(Park House School, Newbury)	I&J
Tony Gardiner	(Birmingham)	I&J / IMOK / JMO
Nick Geere	(Kelly College)	S
Michael Griffiths	(Warrington)	S / IMOK
Howard Groves	(ex RGS, Worcester)	S / I&J / IMOK / JMO
James Hall	(Harrow School)	IMOK
Jo Harbour	(Wolvercote Primary School)	JMO
Carl James	(Leicester Grammar School)	SK
Andrew Jobbings	(Arbelos, Shipley)	S / I&J / IMOK / JMO
Calum Kilgour	(St Aloysius College)	JMO
Gerry Leversha	(ex St Paul's School)	IMOK
Paul Murray	(Lord Williams School, Thame)	I&J / JMO / IK
Steven O'Hagan	(Hutchesons' GS, Glasgow)	JMO
Andy Parkinson	(Beckfoot School, Bingley)	IMOK
Stephen Power	(St. Swithun's School, Winchester)	IMOK
Catherine Ramsay	(Glasgow)	JMO
Alexandra Randolph	(North London Collegiate School)	JMO
Mary Read	(The Lady Eleanor Holles School)	IMOK
Lionel Richard	(Hutchesons' GS, Glasgow)	S
Fiona Shen	(Queen Ethelburga's College	S
Alan Slomson	(University of Leeds)	S / I&J
Alex Voice	(Westminster Abbey Choir School)	I&J / JMO

It is appropriate at this stage to acknowledge and thank those who helped at various stages with the moderation and checking of these papers: Adam McBride, Peter Neumann, Stephen Power, Jenny Ramsden and Chris Robson.

Summer School Staff

Summer School for Girls – August 2015

Oana Adascalitei	Natalie Behague	Beverley Detoeuf
Victor Flynn	Sam Ford	Robert Gray
Howard Groves	Liza Hadley	Vinay Kathotia
Zoe Kelly	Lizzie Kimber	Frances Kirwan
James Munro	Vicky Neale	Claire Rebello
Alan Slomson	Geoff Smith	

Oxford Summer School – August 2015

Beverley Detoeuf	Sue Cubbon	Richard Freeland
Maria Holdcroft	Andrew Jobbings	Vincent Knight
Vicky Neale	Martin Orr	Hannah Roberts
Dominic Rowland	Alan Slomson	Geoff Smith

Leeds Week 1 – July 2016

Katie Chicot	Tony Gardiner	Fraser Heywood
Jack Hodkinson	Andrew Jobbings	Calum Kilgour
Lizzie Kimber	Steven O'Hagan	Catherine Ramsay
Alan Slomson	Mairi Walker	Dorothy Winn

Leeds Week 2 – July 2016

Robin Bhattacharyya	Michael Bradley	Oliver Feng
James Gazet	Imre Leader	Gerry Leversha
Georgina Majury	Charlotte Squires-Parkin	Paul Russell

TMC event coordinators, writers (W) and checkers (C)

Patricia Andrews	Beth Ashfield (C)	Ann Ault (W)
Martin Bailey	Anne Baker	Bridget Ballantyne
Andrew Bell	Zillah Booth	Elizabeth Bull
Dean Bunnell (W)	Kerry Burnham	Keith Cadman (W)
Colin Campbell (W)	Madeleine Copin (C)	Elaine Corr
James Cranch	David Crawford (W)	Rosie Cretney
Alex Crews	Mark Dennis	Geoffrey Dolamore
Sue Essex (W)	Sheldon Fernandes	Jackie Fox

Roy Fraser
Karl Hayward-Bradley (W)
Sue Hughes
Andrina Inglis
Pat Lyden
Steve Mulligan
Pauline Noble
Valerie Pinto
Peter Price
Wendy Rathbone
John Slater
Anne Strong
Rosie Wiltshire

Helen Gauld
Terry Heard
Sally Anne Huk
Andrew Jobbings (W)
Cara Mann
Helen Mumby
Martin Perkins (C)
Vivian Pinto
Jenny Ramsden (C)
Heather Reeve
Alan Slomson
Penny Thompson

Peter Hall
Fraser Heywood (W)
Pam Hunt
Tricia Lunel
Matthew Miller
Peter Neumann (W)
Dennis Pinshon
Stephen Power
Peter Ransom (W)
Valerie Ridgman
Graeme Spurr
Ian Wiltshire

Additional local helpers and organisers at TMC host venues

Anthony Alonzi
Sharon Austin
Helena Benzinski
Nigel Brookes
Maxine Clapham
Ladi Dariya
Nina Edgley
Nia Innes
George Kinnear
Helen Martin
Marijke Molenaar
Colin Reid
John Robinson
David Shemoon
Richard Stakes
Rachel Tindal
Richard Walter

Morag Anderson
Russell Baker
Will Bird
David Brooks
Rebecca Cotton-Barratt
Andrew Davies
Charlotte Fine
Georgie Introna
Rajmin Mahabir
David McNally
Heather Morgan
Duncan Rhodes
Andrew Rogers
Jodie Sheppard
Gerald Telfer
Sam Twinam
Liz Ward

Tess Andrew
Alec Barnes
Richard Bradshaw
Helen Burton

Wendy Dersley
Nishma Gohil
Beth Kellham
Claire Maher
Iain Mitchell
Julie Mundy
Peter Richmond
Amelia Rood
Amanda Smallwood
Paul Thomas
Danny Walker
Phillip Watson

Emma Atkins
David Bedford
Frank Bray
Joseph Carthew
Colin Crawford
Ruth Earl
Stephen Hope
Alice Keys
Neil Maltman
Jen Moat
Damian Murphy
Michael Roberts
Ann Rush
Dominic Soares
Annette Thompson
Jo Walker
Tim Whalley

STMC coordinators and regional helpers
[also involved in the writing (W) and checking (C) of materials where indicated]

Hugh Ainsley
Gillian Baker
Andrew Bell
Kerry Burnham (W)
Tony Cheslett (W)
Alex Crews
Karen Fogden (W)
James Hall (W)
Terry Heard
Sally Anne Huk
John Lardner
Charlie Oakley (W)
Lorna Piper
Alexandra Randolph (W)
Valerie Ridgman
Anne Strong
Ian Wiltshire

Patricia Andrews
Matthew Baker (W)
Zillah Booth
Colin Campbell
David Crawford (W)
Laura Daniels
Helen Gauld
Peter Hall (W)
Fraser Heywood
Pam Hunt
Pat Lyden
Martin Perkins (C)
Stephen Power
Katie Ray (W)
John Slater
Penny Thompson
Rosie Wiltshire

Ann Ault
Phillip Beckett
Dean Bunnell
Valerie Chapman
Rosie Cretney
Sue Essex
Douglas Hainline
Paul Healey
Alexandra Hewitt
Andrina Inglis
Peter Neumann
Dennis Pinshon (W)
Jenny Ramsden (C)
Heather Reeve (C)
Alan Slomson (C)
Neil Turner

Maths Circles Speakers and Event Leaders (L)

Tarig Abdelgadir
John Berry
Sarah Cassidy
Katie Chicot
James Cranch
Ceri Fiddes
Gwyn Gardiner
Hugh Hill
Gerry Leversha
Gihan Marasingha
Peter Neumann
Catherine Ramsey
Alistair Rucklidge
Geoff Smith
Bart Vlaar

Pat Andrews
Abi Bown
Valerie Chapman
Philip Coggins
Sue Cubbon (L)
Mary Teresa Fyfe
James Hall
Susie Jameson-Petvin (L)
Danielle Lewis
Adam McBride
Tim Paulden
Peter Ransom
John Slater
Susan Sturton
Claire Willman

James Beltrami
Kerry Burnham (L)
Tony Cheslett
Madeleine Copin
Mark Dennis (L)
Tony Gardiner (L)
Paul Healey
Andrew Jobbings
Kevin Lord
Vicky Neale
Stephen Power (L)
Dominic Rowland (L)
Alan Slomson (L)
Krasi Tsaneva-Atanasova
Dorothy Winn (L)

254

We thank the following schools and universities for hosting Maths Circles events

All Saints School, Weymouth

Govan High School, Glasgow

St Paul's School, London

University of Leeds, Leeds

Wells Cathedral School, Wells

Exeter Mathematics School, Exeter

Royal Masonic School, Rickmansworth

St Swithun's School, Winchester

University of Manchester, Manchester

Wycliffe School, Gloucester

BMOS Mentoring Schemes

Advanced Mentoring Sheets: Richard Freeland

Senior Sheets: Freddie Illingworth & Maria Holdcroft

Intermediate Sheets: Andrew Jobbings, David Phillips & Zoe Kelly

Junior Sheets: John Slater

Advanced external mentors:

James Aaronson	Andrew Carlotti	Richard Freeland
Adam Goucher	Tim Hennock	Freddie Illingworth
Henry Liu	Jordan Millar	Joseph Myers

Senior external mentors:

Olivia Aaronson	Oana Adascalitei	Anne Andrews
Andrea Antoniazzi	Sam Banks	Katriona Barr
Jamie Beacom	Philip Beckett	Natalie Behague
Don Berry	Ruth Carling	Nicholas Chee
Andrea Chlebikova	Xenatasha Cologne-Brookes	Gabriel Craciun
Rosie Cretney	Samuel Crew	John Cullen
Pawel Czerniawski	Jan Dangerfield	Natasha Davey
John Dixon	Chris Eagle	Chris Ellingham
Robin Elliott	Oliver Feng	John Fernley
Nicole Few-Durnall	Mary Teresa Fyfe	James Gazet
Gabriel Gendler	Julian Gilbey	Esteban Gomezllata Marmolejo
James Hall	Danny Hamilton	Paul Healey
Adrian Hemery	Fraser Heywood	Edward Hinton
Maria Holdcroft	Ina Hughes	Mihail Hurmuzov
Michael Illing	Susie Jameson-Petvin	Sahl Khan
Andrew Kirk	Mark Knapton	Robert Lasenby
Jasmina Lazic	Gerry Leversha	Michael Lipton
Daniel Low	Chris Luke	Matei Mandache
Gareth McCaugham	Harry Metrebian	Radhika Mistry

Vicky Neale
Keith Porteous
Jerome Ripp
Jack Shotton
Oliver Thomas
Perry Wang
Catherine Wilkins
Brian Zhang

Pavlena Nenova
Peter Price
Julia Robson
Ben Spells
Paul Voutier
Kasia Warburton
Daniel Wilson

Peter Neumann
Katya Richards
Roberto Rubio
Stephen Tate
Benjamin Walker
Mark Wildon
Dorothy Winn

Intermediate external mentors:

Alice Ahn
Jamie Frost
David Phillips
Alan Slomson
George Welsman

Bernard Connolly
Zoe Kelly
Oliver Sieweke
Hugo Strauss

Andrew Jobbings
Roger Kilby
Ian Slater
Alasdair Thorley

UKMT Publications

The books published by the UK Mathematics Trust are grouped into series.

The *YEARBOOKS* series documents all the UKMT activities, including details of all the challenge papers and solutions, lists of high scorers, accounts of the IMO and Olympiad training camps, and other information about the Trust's work during each year.

1. 2015-2016 Yearbook

This is our 18th Yearbook, having published one a year since 1998-1999. Edited by Bill Richardson, the Yearbook documents all the UKMT activities from that particular year. They include all the challenge papers and solutions at every level; list of high scorers; tales from the IMO and Olympiad training camps; details of the UKMT's other activities; and a round-up of global mathematical associations.

Previous Yearbooks are available to purchase. Please contact the UKMT for further details.

PAST PAPERS

1. *Ten Years of Mathematical Challenges 1997 to 2006*

Edited by Bill Richardson, this book was published to celebrate the tenth anniversary of the founding of UKMT. This 188-page book contains question papers and solutions for nine Senior Challenges, ten Intermediate Challenges, and ten Junior Challenges.

The *HANDBOOKS* series is aimed particularly at students at secondary school who are interested in acquiring the knowledge and skills which are useful for tackling challenging problems, such as those posed in the competitions administered by the UKMT.

1. *Plane Euclidean Geometry: Theory and Problems*,
   AD Gardiner and CJ Bradley

An excellent book for students aged 15-18 and teachers who want to learn how to solve problems in elementary Euclidean geometry. The book follows the development of Euclid; contents include Pythagoras, trigonometry, circle theorems, and Ceva and Menelaus. The book contains hundreds of problems, many with hints and solutions.

2. *Introduction to Inequalities*, CJ Bradley

Introduction to Inequalities is a thoroughly revised and extended edition of a book which was initially published as part of the composite volume 'Introductions to Number Theory and Inequalities'. This accessible text aims to show students how to select and apply the correct sort of inequality to solve a given problem.

3. *A Mathematical Olympiad Primer*, Geoff C Smith

This UKMT publication provides an excellent guide for young mathematicians preparing for competitions such as the British Mathematical Olympiad. The book has recently been updated and extended and contains theory including algebra, combinatorics and geometry, and BMO1 problems and solutions from 1996 onwards.

4. *Introduction to Number Theory*, CJ Bradley

This book for students aged 15 upwards aims to show how to tackle the sort of problems on number theory which are set in mathematics competitions. Topics include primes and divisibility, congruence arithmetic and the representation of real numbers by decimals.

5. *A Problem Solver's Handbook*, Andrew Jobbings

This recently published book is an informal guide to Intermediate Olympiads, not only for potential candidates, but for anyone wishing to tackle more challenging problems. The discussions of sample questions aim to show how to attack a problem which may be quite unlike anything seen before.

6. *Introduction to Combinatorics*, Gerry Leversha and Dominic Rowland

The subject of combinatorics provides a rich source of material for mathematics competitions. At one level it can be thought of as a sort of extreme 'counting–how' do we enumerate the number of ways of different ways of doing something? However, the subject is broader than that. It addresses situations which involve organising things so as to satisfy certain 'criteria–placing' tiles on a chessboard, seating people in a circle, chopping up a cube; and then asks whether or not a certain outcome is possible. This accessible text aims to give the enthusiastic student plenty of tips on how to tackle questions of this nature. For ages 16+.

7. *First Steps for Problem Solvers*, Mary Teresa Fyfe and Andrew Jobbings

This book is a guide to pupils aged 11-13 who are attempting problems in competitions such as the Junior Mathematical Olympiad, which are administered by the UKMT and similar organisations. Written with the pupil in mind, the book covers all of the section B questions set in the Junior Mathematical Olympiad papers over sixteen years of the competition. For ages 11-13.

The *EXCURSIONS IN MATHEMATICS* series consists of monographs which focus on a particular topic of interest and investigate it in some detail, using a wide range of ideas and techniques. They are aimed at high school students, undergraduates, and others who are prepared to pursue a subject in some depth, but do not require specialised knowledge.

1. *The Backbone of Pascal's Triangle*, Martin Griffiths

Everything covered in this book is connected to the sequence of numbers: 2, 6, 20, 70, 252, 924, 3432, ... Some readers might recognize this list straight away, while others will not have seen it before. Either way, students and teachers alike may well be astounded at both the variety and the depth of mathematical ideas that it can lead to.

2. *A Prime Puzzle*, Martin Griffiths

The prime numbers 2, 3, 5, 7, ... are the building blocks of our number system. Under certain conditions, any arithmetic progression of positive integers contains infinitely many primes, as proved by Gustave Dirichlet. This book seeks to provide a complete proof which is accessible to school students possessing post-16 mathematical knowledge. All the techniques needed are carefully developed and explained.

The *PATHWAYS* series aims to provide classroom teaching material for use in secondary school. Each title develops a subject in more depth and detail than is normally required by public examinations or national curricula.

1. *Crossing the Bridge*, Gerry Leversha

This book provides a course on geometry for use in the classroom, re-emphasising some traditional features of geometrical education. The bulk of the text is devoted to carefully constructed exercises for classroom discussion or individual study. It is suitable for students aged 13 and upwards.

2. *The Geometry of the Triangle*, Gerry Leversha

The basic geometry of the triangle is widely known, but readers of this book will find that there are many more delights to discover. The book is full of stimulating results and careful exposition, and thus forms a trustworthy guide. Recommended for ages 16+.

The *PROBLEMS* series consists of collections of high-quality and original problems of Olympiad standard.

1. *New Problems in Euclidean Geometry*, David Monk

This book should appeal to anyone aged 16+ who enjoys solving the kind of challenging and attractive geometry problems that have virtually vanished from the school curriculum, but which still play a central role in national and international mathematics competitions. It is a treasure trove of wonderful geometrical problems, with hints for their solutions.

We also sell:

1. *The First 25 Years of the Superbrain*, Diarmuid Early & Des MacHale

This is an extraordinary collection of mathematical problems laced with some puzzles. This book will be of interest to those preparing for senior Olympiad examinations, to teachers of mathematics, and to all those who enjoy solving problems in mathematics.

2. *The Algebra of Geometry*, Christopher J Bradley

In the 19th century, the algebra of the plane was part of the armoury of every serious mathematician. In recent times the major fronts of research mathematics have moved elsewhere. However, those skills and methods are alive and well, and can be found in this book. The Algebra of Geometry deserves a place on the shelf of every enthusiast for Euclidean Geometry, amateur or professional, and is certainly valuable reading for students wishing to compete in senior Mathematical Olympiads. For age 16+ mathematicians.

3. The UKMT is the European agent for a large number of books published by the Art of Problem Solving (http://www.artofproblemsolving.com/).

To find out more about these publications and to order copies, please go to the UKMT website at www.publications.ukmt.org.uk.

In addition to the books above, UKMT continues to publish its termly Newsletter, giving the latest news from the Trust, mathematical articles, examples from Challenge papers and occasional posters for the classroom wall. This is sent free to all schools participating in the UKMT Maths Challenges.